Airplane Design

Part II: Preliminary Configuration Design and Integration of the Propulsion System

Dr. Jan Roskam
Ackers Distinguished Professor of Aerospace Engineering
The University of Kansas, Lawrence

2004

1440 Wakarusa Drive, Suite 500 • Lawrence, Kansas 66049, U.S.A.

PUBLISHED BY
Design, Analysis and Research Corporation (*DARcorporation*)
1440 Wakarusa Drive, Suite 500
Lawrence, Kansas 66049
U.S.A.
Phone: (785) 832-0434
Fax: (785) 832-0524
e-mail: info@darcorp.com
http://www.darcorp.com

Library of Congress Catalog Card Number: 97-68580

ISBN 1-884885-43-8

In all countries, sold and distributed by
Design, Analysis and Research Corporation
1440 Wakarusa Drive, Suite 500
Lawrence, Kansas 66049
U.S.A.

Printed in the United States of America
First Printing, 1985
Second Printing, 1989
Third Printing, 1997
Fourth Printing, 2004

TABLE OF CONTENTS

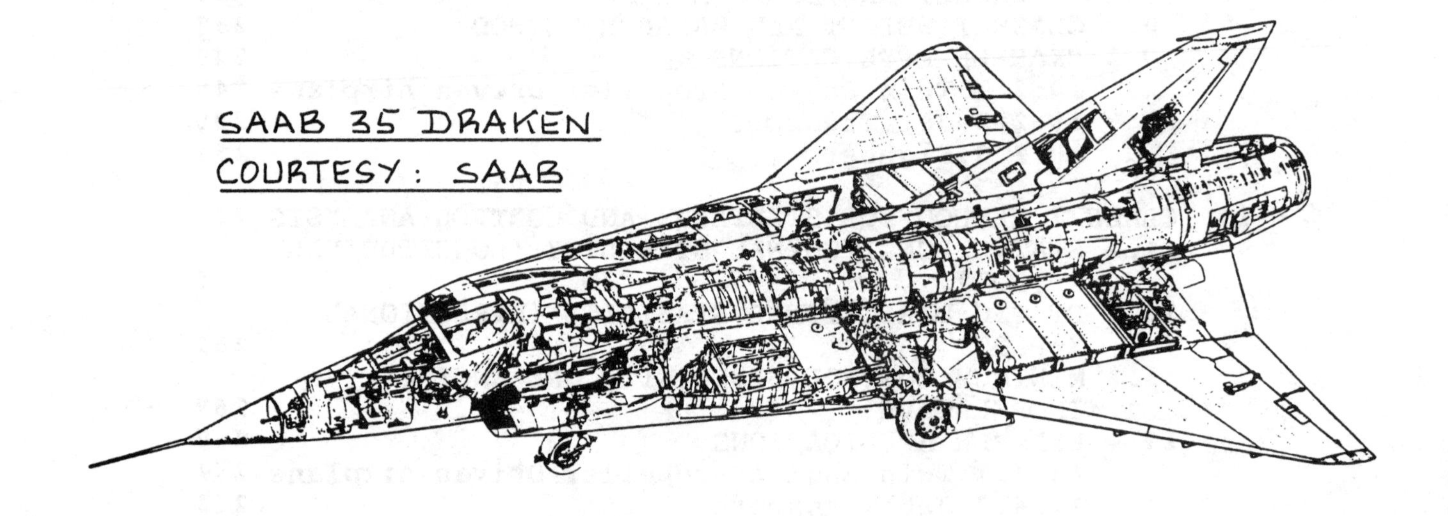
SAAB 35 DRAKEN
COURTESY: SAAB

TABLE OF SYMBOLS

Symbol	Definition	Dimension
A	Wing aspect ratio	-----
b	Wing span	ft
b_a	Aileron span	ft
b_f	Flap span	ft
b_t	Tire width	ft
c	Wing chord	ft
c'	Wing chord with t.e. flaps down	ft
c''	Wing chord with l.e. flaps down	ft
$\bar{c}$	Wing mean geometric chord	ft
c_f	Flap chord	ft
c_f (second use)	Equivalent skin friction coefficient	-----
C_D	Drag coefficient	-----
C_{D_0}	Zero lift drag coefficient	-----
c_l	Section lift coefficient	-----
c_{l_α}	Section liftcurve slope	1/rad
$c_{l_{\alpha_f}}$	Section liftcurve slope with flaps down	1/rad
$c_{l_{\delta_f}}$	Derivative of section lift coefficient with flap deflection	1/rad
C_L	Lift coefficient	-----
C_m	Pitching moment coeff.	-----
D	Drag	lbs
D_p	Propeller diameter	ft
D_t	Tire diameter	ft
d_f, D_f	fuselage diameter	ft

Symbol	Definition	Unit
e	Oswald's efficiency factor	-----
E	Endurance	hours
f	equivalent parasite area	ft^2
FAR	Federal Air Regulation	-----
g	acceleration of gravity	ft/sec^2
h	altitude	ft
i_w	wing incidence angle	deg
k_Λ	Sweep angle corr. factor	-----
k_f	Corr. factor for split flaps	--
k_λ	Taper ratio corr. factor	-----
K'	Corr. factor for plain flaps	--
L	Lift	lbs
L/D	Lift-to-drag ratio	-----
l_f	fuselage length	ft
l_{fc}	fuselage cone length	ft
l_m	Dist. c.g. to main gear	ft
l_n	Dist. c.g. to nose gear	ft
M	Mach number	-----
n	Load factor	-----
nm	Nautical mile (6,076 ft)	nm
n_p	number of propeller blades	----
n_s	Number of struts	-----
N	No. of engines, Yaw. mom.	-----
P	Power, Horse-power (1hp = 550 ft.lbs/sec)	hp
P_{bl}	Blade power loading	hp/ft^2
P_{ef}	Probability of engine failure	-
P_n	Load on nosewheel strut	lbs
P_m	Load on main gear strut	lbs
$\bar{q}$	dynamic pressure	psf

Symbol	Description	Units
R	Range	nm or m
R_n	Reynold's number	-----
S	Wing area	ft^2
SHP	Shaft horsepower	hp
S_{wet}	Wetted area	ft^2
S_{wf}	Flapped wing area	-----
t	time	sec, min, hr
t/c	thickness ratio	-----
T	Thrust	lbs
V	True airspeed	mph, fps, kts
$\bar{V}$	Volume coefficient	-----
W	Weight	lbs
X	T(hrust) or P(ower)	lbs or hp
$\bar{X}_{ac}$	Distance from l.e. $\bar{c}$ to aerodynamic center	
x,y,z	Distance from reference to a component c.g.	ft
x_v, x_h, x_c	Dist. from c.g. to a.c. of a surface	ft
y_t	Engine-out moment arm	ft

Greek Symbols
=============

Symbol	Description	Units
α	Angle of attack	-----
β	Sideslip angle	-----
δ	Control surface defl.	-----
λ	Taper ratio	-----
Λ	Sweep angle	-----
π	Product, or 3.142	-----
Γ	Dihedral angle	-----
σ	Air density ratio	-----
θ_{fc}	Fuselage cone angle	deg.
ϕ	Lateral ground clearance angle	
θ	Longitudinal ground clearance angle	
θ_{lof}	Lift-off angle	
ε	Downwash angle	-----
ε_t	Twist angle	-----
η	Spanwise station, fr. span	----
ψ	Lateral tip-over angle	deg.

Subscripts

a	aileron	ME	Manufacturer's empty
A	Approach	mc	Minimum control speed
abs	absolute	OE	Operating empty
c	canard	PL	Payload
cat	catapult	RC	Rate-of-climb
cl	climb	r	root, or rudder
cr	cruise	res	reserve (fuel)
crew	crew	reqd	required
crit	critical	s	stall
c/2	semi chord	TO	Take-off
c/4	quarter chord	t	tip
des	design	te	trailing edge
dry	without fluids or afterburner	tent	tentative
		tfo	trapped fuel and oil
e	elevator	used	used (fuel)
E	Empty	v	vertical tail
f	flaps	w	wing
ff	fuel fraction (see M_{ff})	wet	wetted
		wf	wing-fuselage
F	Mission fuel		
h	altitude		
h	horizontal tail		
le	leading edge		
max	maximum		
L	Landing		

Acronyms

AEO	All engines operating	LCC	Life cycle cost
APU	Auxiliary power unit	p.d.	preliminary design
B.L.	Buttock line	RFP	Request for proposal
c.g.	center of gravity	ROI	Return on investment
DOC	Direct operating cost	R.S.	Rear spar
FOD	Foreign object damage	sls	Sealevel standard
F.S.	Fus.sta., Front spar	TBP	Turboprop
OEI	One engine inoperat.	W.L.	Waterline
OWE	Oper. weight empty		

ACKNOWLEDGEMENT

Writing a book on airplane design is impossible without the supply of a large amount of data. The author is grateful to the following companies for supplying the raw data, manuals, sketches and drawings which made the book what it is:

Beech Aircraft Corporation
Boeing Commercial Airplane Company
Canadair
Cessna Aircraft Company
DeHavilland Aircraft Company of Canada
Gates Learjet Corporation
Lockheed Aircraft Corporation
McDonnell Douglas Corporation
Rinaldo Piaggio S.p.A.
Royal Netherlands Aircraft Factory, Fokker
SIAI Marchetti S.p.A.

A significant amount of airplane design information has been accumulated by the author over many years from the following magazines:

Interavia (Swiss, monthly)
Flight International (British, weekly)
Business and Commercial Aviation (USA, monthly)
Aviation Week and Space Technology (USA, weekly)
Journal of Aircraft (USA, AIAA, monthly)

The author wishes to acknowledge the important role played by these magazines in his own development as an aeronautical engineer. Aeronautical engineering students and graduates should read these magazines regularly.

Most of the threeviews in this part of the book were prepared by Mr. G.Tukker of Molenaarsgraaf, The Netherlands. The author wishes to thank Mr. Tukker for his patience and for his painstaking attention to detail.

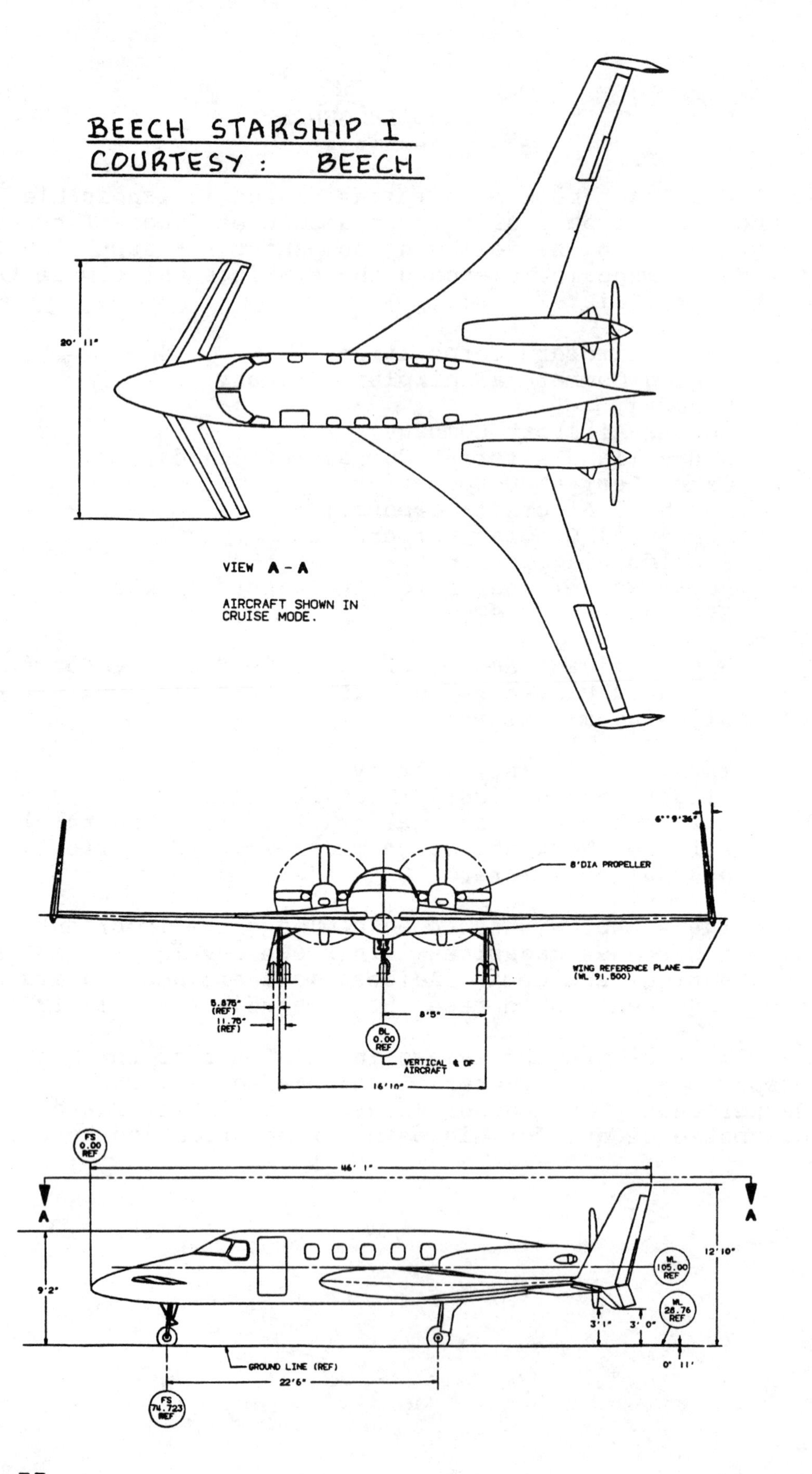
BEECH STARSHIP I
COURTESY : BEECH
20' 11"
VIEW A - A
AIRCRAFT SHOWN IN
CRUISE MODE.
8'DIA PROPELLER
WING REFERENCE PLANE
(WL 91.500)
8'5"
BL
0.00
REF
VERTICAL ℄ OF
AIRCRAFT
16'10"
FS
0.00
REF
46' 1"
A
A
12'10"
9'2"
WL
105.00
REF
WL
28.76
REF
3'1"
3' 0"
0" 11"
GROUND LINE (REF)
22'6"
FS
74.723
REF

1. INTRODUCTION

The purpose of this series of books on Airplane Design is to familiarize aerospace engineering students with the design methodology and design decision making involved in the process of designing airplanes.

The series of books is organized as follows:

PART I: PRELIMINARY SIZING OF AIRPLANES
PART II: PRELIMINARY CONFIGURATION DESIGN AND INTEGRATION OF THE PROPULSION SYSTEM
PART III: LAYOUT DESIGN OF COCKPIT, FUSELAGE, WING AND EMPENNAGE: CUTAWAYS AND INBOARD PROFILES
PART IV: LAYOUT DESIGN OF LANDING GEAR AND SYSTEMS
PART V: COMPONENT WEIGHT ESTIMATION
PART VI: PRELIMINARY CALCULATION OF AERODYNAMIC, THRUST AND POWER CHARACTERISTICS
PART VII: DETERMINATION OF STABILITY, CONTROL AND PERFORMANCE CHARACTERISTICS: FAR AND MILITARY REQUIREMENTS
PART VIII: AIRPLANE COST ESTIMATION: DESIGN, DEVELOPMENT, MANUFACTURING AND OPERATING

The purpose of PART II is to present a systematic approach to the problem of configuration design, including the integration of the propulsion system.

Configuration design amounts to making the following decisions:

1. Selection of the overall configuration:

   * Conventional (that means tail aft)
   * Flying wing (that means no horizontal tail and no canard)
   * Tandem wing
   * Canard
   * Three Surface
   * Joined Wing

2. Selection of the fuselage layout:

   * Arrangement of crew, passengers, baggage, fuel, cargo and other payloads
   * Cockpit or flightdeck layout
   * Cabin layout
   * Window, door and emergency exit layout

* Check of fuel, baggage and cargo volume
* Weapons and stores arrangement
* Access for loading and unloading
* Access for maintenance and for servicing

In the case of a flying wing design all these items must be arranged to fit in the wing.

3. Selection of propulsion system type(s):

   * Piston/propeller with or without supercharging
   * Turbo/propeller or prop-fan
   * Propfan or unducted fan
   * Turbojet or turbofan
   * Ramjet or rocket
   * Rotary/diesel
   * Electric (solar, microwave, lithium fuel cell)

4. Selection of the number of engines and/or propellers

5. Integration of the propulsion system:

   * Propellers: pusher or tractor
   * Engines buried in the fuselage or in the wing
   * Engines in nacelles on the fuselage or on the wing
   * Disposition of engines and nacelles

6. Selection of planform design parameters for the wing and for the empennage (tails and/or canard:

   * Size (i.e. area) of wing
   * Aspect ratio
   * Sweep angle (fixed or variable)
   * Thickness ratio
   * Airfoil type
   * Taper ratio
   * Control surface size and disposition
   * Incidence angle (fixed or variable)
   * Dihedral angle

7. Selection of type, size and disposition of high lift devices:

   * Mechanical or powered (blown) flaps
   * Trailing edge and/or leading edge devices

8. Selection of landing gear type and disposition:

   * Fixed or retractable
   * Tail dragger, tricycle or tandem
   * Number of struts and tires
   * Wheel location up and down
   * Feasibility of gear retraction

9. Selection of major systems to be employed by the airplane:

   * Flight control system, primary and secondary
   * Auxiliary power unit (APU)
   * Fuel system
   * Hydraulic System
   * Pneumatic system
   * Electrical system
   * Oxygen system
   * Environmental control system (this includes the cabin pressurization system)
   * Anti-icing and de-icing system
   * Spray system (i.e. for agricultural airplanes)
   * Navigation and guidance system
   * Fire control system

10. Selection of structural arrangement, type of structure and manufacturing breakdown:

   * Metallic, composite or mixture
   * Arrangement of primary structure of major airplane components
   * Attachment structure for landing gear
   * Manufacturing and assembly sequence

11. Determination of the cost of research, development, manufacturing and operation:

   * Assessment of profit potential (civil)
   * Assessment of mission effectiveness = (availability)x(survivability)x(accuracy) for military airplanes
   * Assessment of life cycle cost (civil and military)

Decisions 1-11 are <u>not</u> listed in an implied order of importance.

<u>IMPORTANT NOTES:</u>

<u>1.) Configuration design is a non-unique and iterative process</u>

2.) During the early phases of configuration design 90 percent of the life cycle cost of an airplane gets locked in

There are many different methodologies which can lead to a satisfactory design. It is quite possible that more than one and sometimes radically different configurations can be found to satisfy a given mission specification. Classical illustrations of this fact are the Boeing B47 and the AVRO Vulcan jet bombers. These airplanes while differing radically in their configurations were designed to very similar mission specifications. Figure 1.1 shows threeviews of these airplanes. The tabulated data in Figure 1.1 serve to illustrate the differences in geometry and the similarity in performance between these two airplanes.

Chapter 2 provides a step-by-step guide through the process of configuration design.

Configuration design as presented in Chapter 2 is broken down into two preliminary design (p.d.) sequences:

1. p.d. sequence I which involves 16 design steps.

The objective of p.d. sequence I is to decide on the feasibility of a given configuration with a minimum amount of engineering work.

2. p.d. sequence II which involves 30 design steps.

The objective of p.d. sequence II is to arrive at a reasonably detailed layout of a given configuration so that its mission capabilities can be compared to those of other competing concepts with confidence.

During each p.d. sequence estimates must be made for drag, for stability and control, for weight and balance and for other factors involved in making the 11 decisions listed before. The depth to which these estimates are made should match the depth required in each p.d. sequence.

Engineering methods used in conjunction with p.d. sequence I are referred to as Class I methods. These methods have limited accuracy but require only a small amount of engineering manhours. This part (Part II) concentrates on the so-called Class I methods only.

Engineering methods used in conjunction with p.d.

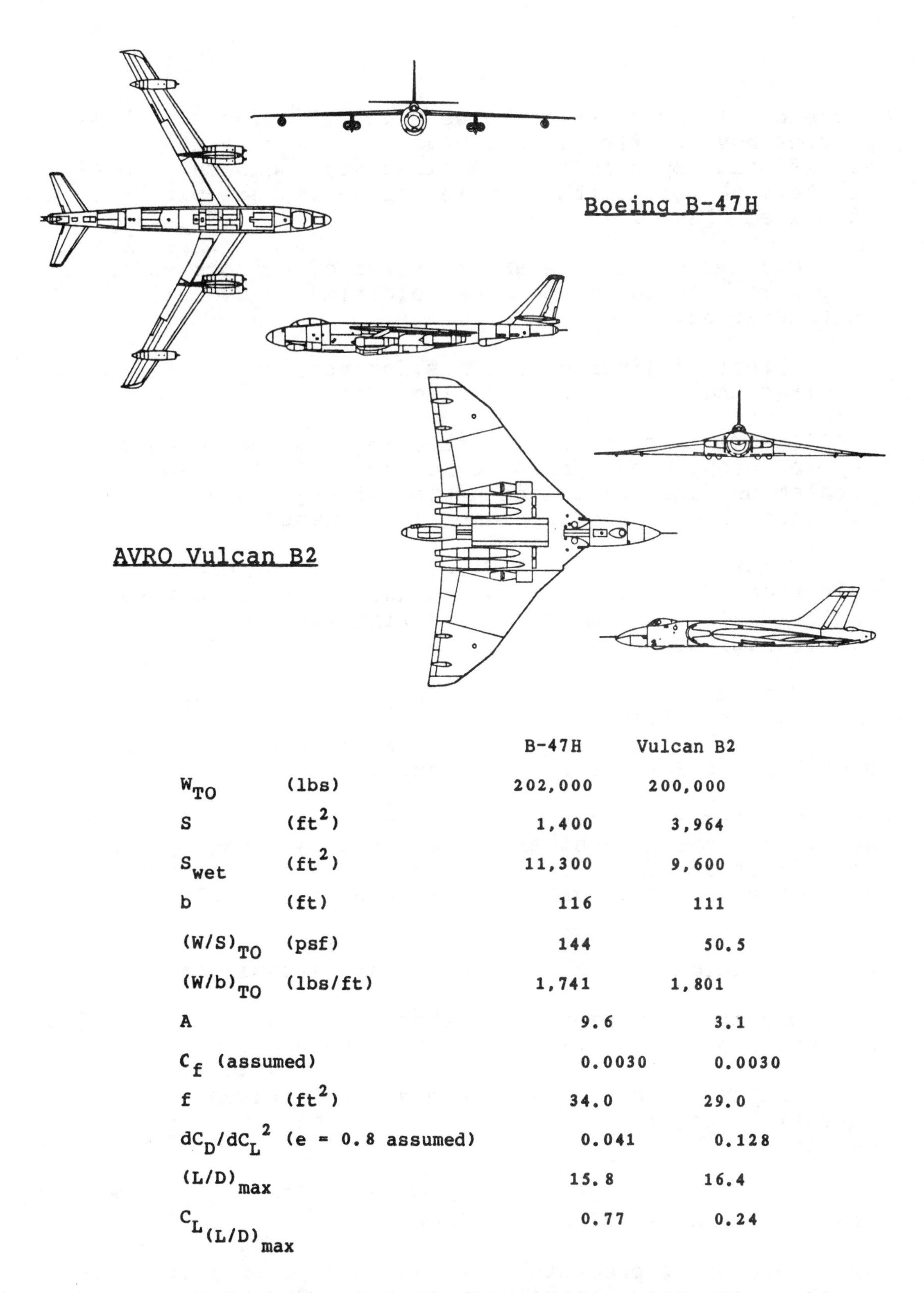

		B-47H	Vulcan B2
W_{TO}	(lbs)	202,000	200,000
S	(ft^2)	1,400	3,964
S_{wet}	(ft^2)	11,300	9,600
b	(ft)	116	111
$(W/S)_{TO}$	(psf)	144	50.5
$(W/b)_{TO}$	(lbs/ft)	1,741	1,801
A		9.6	3.1
C_f (assumed)		0.0030	0.0030
f	(ft^2)	34.0	29.0
$dC_D/dC_L{}^2$	($e = 0.8$ assumed)	0.041	0.128
$(L/D)_{max}$		15.8	16.4
$C_{L_{(L/D)_{max}}}$		0.77	0.24

Figure 1.1 Example of Radically Different Configurations with Similar Mission Performance

sequence II are referred to as Class II methods. These methods have fairly good accuracy but require a significant expenditure of engineering manhours. Parts III through VIII of this series of books deal with the so-called Class II methods.

Chapter 3 presents a discussion of factors which play a role in the process of selecting an overall configuration.

Chapter 4 gives guidelines for the design of the fuselage and the cockpit or flightdeck.

Chapter 5 provides a methodology for deciding on the type of propulsion system to be used. In addition, the problem of deciding on the number of engines and their disposition over the airplane is discussed.

Chapter 6 presents a discussion of the problem of selection of planform design parameters for the wing. Included also is a method for sizing wing mounted lateral control surfaces.

Chapter 7 contains a method for determining the maximum clean lift coefficient capability of an airplane. A rapid method for preliminary sizing of the required high lift devices is also presented.

Chapter 8 contains a step-by-step procedure for selecting empennage sizes (areas) and empennage planform geometries and disposition. Included also is a method for sizing longitudinal and directional control surfaces.

Chapter 9 presents a method for landing gear sizing and for deciding on the landing gear disposition.

Chapter 10 presents a method for checking the weight and balance characteristics of an airplane.

Chapter 11 contains a method for determining the essential stability and control characteristics of a new design.

Chapter 12 presents a rapid method for estimating the drag polar(s) of an airplane.

Chapter 13 presents three example Class I threeviews which result from the work outlined in Chapters 2 - 12. Tables with geometric characteristics for these example threeviews are also presented.

2. STEP-BY-STEP GUIDE TO CONFIGURATION DESIGN

The purpose of this chapter is to provide a step-by step guide through the process of airplane configuration design.

Figure 2.1 shows a schematic of the preliminary design (p.d.) process. As can be seen from Figure 2.1, the p.d. process is broken down into the following parts:

1.) Preliminary sizing

2.) Preliminary configuration layout and integration of the propulsion system

It will be assumed here, that the preliminary sizing part of this p.d. process has been completed. Part I (Ref.1) presents a systematic methodology for the preliminary sizing of airplanes. The preliminary sizing started by assuming that a mission specification for the airplane to be designed is available. Example mission specifications were given in Part I (Ref.1) as Tables 2.17 through 2.19.

As a result of the preliminary sizing of Part I, the following data are available for the airplane:

Weights: Take-off weight, W_{TO}

Operating weight empty, W_E

Payload weight, W_{PL}

Mission fuel weight, W_F

Wing area: S

Wing aspect ratio: A

Take-off power: P_{TO} or take-off thrust, T_{TO}

Required lift coefficients: clean, $C_{L_{max}}$

take-off, $C_{L_{max_{TO}}}$

landing, $C_{L_{max_L}}$

These data are the 'input' data for the airplane

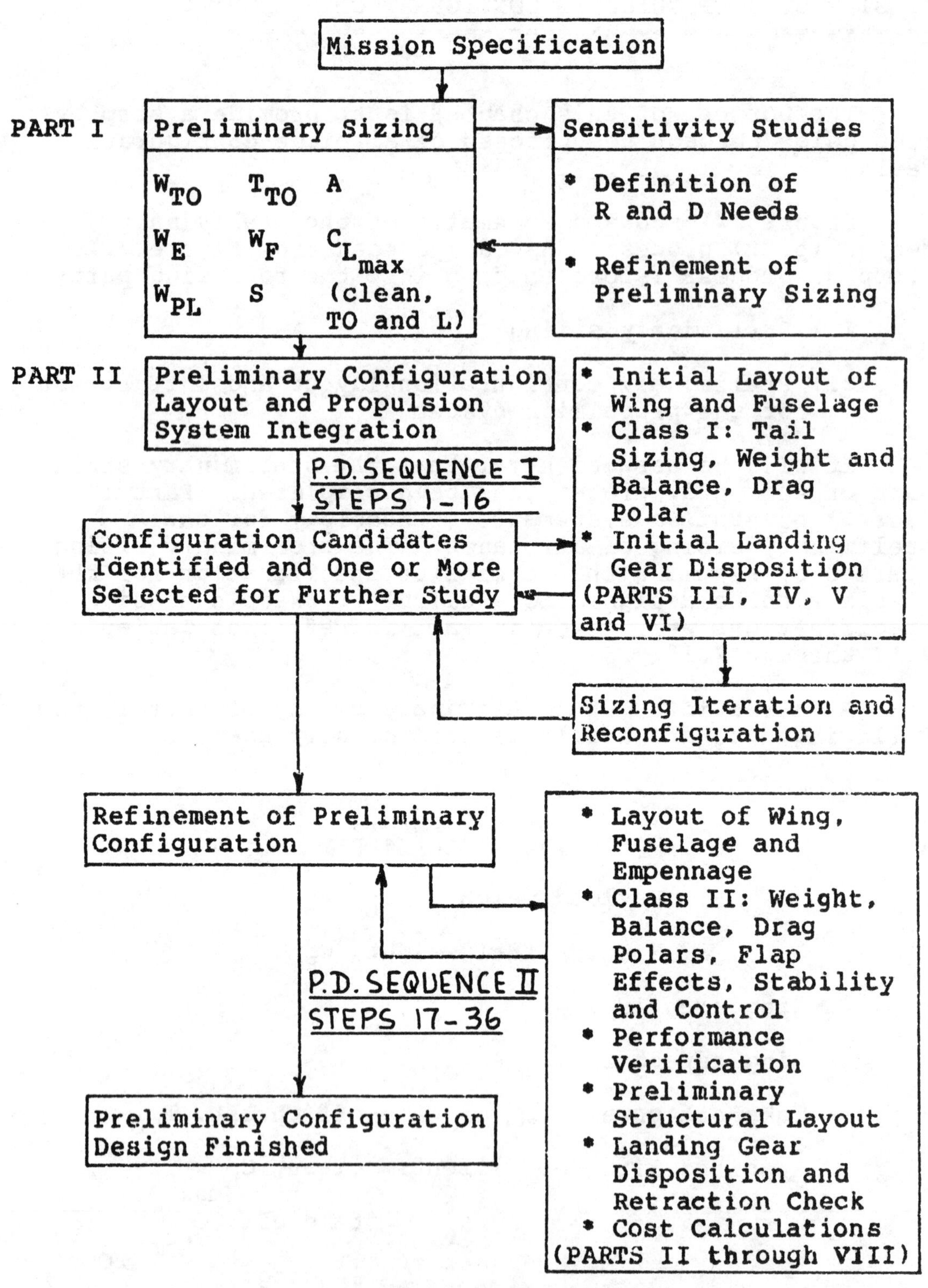

Figure 2.1 The Preliminary Design Process as Covered in Parts I Through VIII of Airplane Design

configuration design process. This process includes overall layout design as well as the integration of the propulsion system.

Figure 2.1 divides the process of preliminary configuration layout and propulsion system integration into two iterative p.d. sequences:

1.) Preliminary Design Sequence I:

The objective here is to arrive at a decision about the feasibility of a certain configuration with a minimum amount of engineering work. Engineering methods employed in this first p.d. sequence are preliminary in nature: they are referred to as Class I methods. Chapters 3 - 13 in this book concentrate on these Class I methods.

Section 2.1 presents an outline of the work which needs to be done during p.d. sequence I. The outline of work is presented in the form of a step-by-step guide: Steps 1 - 16. After completing these steps, it should be evident to the designer, whether or not the proposed configuration is workable. If indeed it is, then there is reason to proceed with the second p.d. sequence:

2.) Preliminary Design Sequence II:

The objective here is to arrive at a realistic, reasonably detailed layout of an airplane configuration. The feasibility of this configuration was already determined in p.d. sequence I. The goal now is to 'fine tune' this configuration. That means to determine whether or not the configuration indeed meets all requirements laid down in its mission specification.

Engineering methods employed during p.d. sequence II are referred to as Class II methods. As the reader will see, these class II methods require considerably more engineering manhours. However, they also are more accurate. Parts III - VIII (Refs 2-7) concentrate on these Class II methods.

Section 2.2 presents an outline of the work which needs to be done during p.d. sequence II. The outline of work is presented in the form of a step-by-step guide: Steps 17 - 36. After completing these steps it will be evident to the designer whether or not the proposed design can meet all requirements of the mission specification.

The end result of p.d. sequence II is sometimes referred to as a 'point' or 'baseline' design. This point design should now be compared with other competing concepts. Depending on the outcome of this comparison, further studies may be called for. In particular studies involving the optimization of the point design in terms of a number of cost criteria may be required. Typical cost criteria can be: (L/D), (nm/lbs), (fuel burn per seat mile), DOC, ROI, and LCC. Methods for cost determination and optimization are the subject of Part VIII (Ref.7).

ADVICE TO STUDENTS:

1.) Students in their first semester of a course on airplane design are urged to follow the design guide of Sections 2.1 and 2.2 as closely as possible. The author has seen many students waste a large amount of calendar time by aimlessly floundering about while trying to come up with a satisfactory configuration.

2.) In the process of going through Steps 1 - 36 a sizable number of engineering calculations will have to be made. These calculations should be recorded in a professional manner, so that other people can follow them without undue effort. All engineering calculations should be:

a) neatly and logically organized according to subject. A table of contents should be provided.
b) dated, with the name of the originator appearing on each page.
c) cross-referenced throughout so that it is obvious where input numbers come from.
d) assumptions made must be carefully stated and identified as such.
e) page numbered

3.) Don't carry more significant figures in any calculations than are justified by the accuracy of the methods used. In preliminary design it is generally not justified to carry more than three significant figures. Round off all computer outputs accordingly!

2.1 PRELIMINARY DESIGN SEQUENCE I

Step 1: Carefully review the mission specification and prepare a list of those items which have a major impact on the design.

Examples of items which can have a major impact on the design are:

a) very short and soft field requirements
b) hot and high field requirements
c) water based or amphibious requirements
d) requirements for carrying large vehicles
e) requirements for extreme range or endurance
f) requirements for large search radars

Make it a habit to review the mission specification at each step in the p.d. sequences. Not doing so will result in a design which is only partially responsive to the mission specification.

Step 2: Perform a comparative study of airplanes with similar mission performance.

This can usually be accomplished by referring to one or more issues of Ref. 8: Jane's All the World Aircraft. A collection of data on five to ten similar airplanes should be included in this comparative study. Results of this study should include:

1. A discussion of major differences in mission capability and configuration.

2. A tabulated comparison of significant airplane sizing parameters and planform design parameters.

3. A critical discussion of the configurations of these airplanes, as seen from their threeviews in Ref. 8.

THE OBJECTIVE IS: FAMILIARIZE YOURSELF WITH THE COMPETITION AND WITH WORK DONE BY OTHERS!

Step 3: Select the type of configuration to be designed.

Chapter 3, Section 3.1 contains a discussion of existing configurations for twelve categories of airplanes. A discussion of 'unusual' configurations is included in Section 3.2. An outline of configuration possibilities is presented in Section 3.3.

In selecting a configuration type, the required characteristics of the propulsion system, including its disposition, should be kept in mind. Step 5 deals with the propulsion system more specifically.

Section 3.4 presents a step-by-step procedure for selecting a configuration.

For a student who is just getting started in the study of airplane design it is important to:

<u>MAKE A DECISION TO GO WITH A CERTAIN TYPE OF CONFIGURATION AND MOVE ON</u>

At this point in the p.d. process, many airframe manufacturers follow the so-called red, white and blue team approach. Different design teams are assigned the task to evolve and study different types of configurations. The idea is to find the most suitable configuration for the mission task at hand.

<u>Step 4:</u> Prepare a preliminary (scaled) drawing of the fuselage and cockpit layout.

Chapter 4 contains a step-by-step guide for preparing fuselage and cockpit layouts.

<u>Step 5:</u> Decide which type of propulsion system is to be used and how the propulsion system will be arranged.

This step has a major impact on the design. Selection of engine type(s), number of engines and overall engine arrangement will affect the layout of the fuselage (sometimes the cockpit), the wing and/or other components of the airplane.

The reader is reminded of the fact that the total required thrust or power level (at take-off) is already known: this was determined during the preliminary sizing work outlined in Part I (Ref.1).

Chapter 5 contains a step-by-step outline of the process used in deciding on the type, the number and the disposition of the engines.

<u>Step 6:</u> Decide which wing planform design parameters are to be used. Also decide on the size and location of wing mounted lateral controls.

The reader is reminded of the fact that wing area, S

and wing aspect ratio, A are already known: these were determined during the preliminary sizing work outlined in Part I (Ref. 1).

The following additional parameters must now be selected:

*Wing taper ratio, λ_w

*Wing sweep angle, Λ_w

*Wing thickness ratio, $(t/c)_w$

*Wing airfoil(s)

*Wing incidence angle, i_w

*Wing dihedral angle, Γ_w

If the mission calls for a variable geometry wing (such as variable sweep), the effect of this on the planform must also be determined.

Another result of the preliminary sizing process was the numerical determination of the required maximum lift coefficients: clean, take-off and landing. The planform parameters of the wing must be compatible with the required maximum lift coefficients. As will be seen in Step 7, the maximum lift coefficient requirements may limit the available choice of wing planform parameters.

Chapter 6 contains a step-by-step procedure for determining the wing planform geometry as well as the size and the disposition of wing mounted lateral controls.

<u>Step 7:</u> Decide on the type, the size and the disposition of high lift devices.

The reader is again reminded of the fact that numerical values for the required maximum lift coefficients (clean and flaps down) are already known. These were the result of the preliminary sizing process described in Part I (Ref.1).

Chapter 7 contains a step-by-step methodology for defining the required high lift devices.

Step 8: Decide on the layout of the empennage: size, planform geometry and disposition. Also select the size and location of longitudinal and directional controls.

The word 'empennage' is used here to indicate tails, canards and other additional stabilizing or control surfaces to be used in the configuration.

From Step 3 it is known whether the overall configuration is:

a) conventional (i.e. tail aft)
b) flying wing (i.e. no horizontal tail and no canard)
c) tandem wing
d) canard
e) three surface
f) joined wing

In either case it will now be necessary to decide on the following empennage design parameters:

*Area and location,
*Aspect ratio,
*Taper ratio,
*Sweep angle,
*Thickness ratio
*Airfoil(s)
*Incidence angle
*Dihedral angle

In addition, the preliminary size and disposition of the longitudinal and directional controls need to be selected.

Chapter 8 contains a step-by-step method for arriving at these design decisions.

Step 9: Decide which type of landing gear is to be used. Also: decide on the landing gear disposition and determine the required number and size of tires.

The following questions need to be answered:

1. What type of landing gear is required?

2. How many and what size tires are required?

3. How are the landing gear wheels to be arranged?

4. Is the space designated for the retracted landing gear sufficient?

5. Does the landing gear retraction cause the gear to interfere with other airplane components or airplane structure?

6. Do the landing gear attachment points require major additional structural provisions?

WARNING: Students should not underestimate the importance of preliminary landing gear design. The answers to questions 1-6 may well determine the ultimate feasibility of the proposed configuration.

Questions 4 and 5 are mute in the case of fixed landing gears.

Chapter 9 contains a step-by-step procedure for making these landing gear design decisions.

Step 10: Prepare a scaled preliminary arrangement drawing of the proposed configuration and perform a Class I weight and balance analysis.

Chapter 10 provides a step-by-step method for performing a Class I weight and balance analysis. Examples of the required preliminary arrangement drawings are also presented.

Step 11: Perform a Class I stability and control analysis of the proposed configuration.

Chapter 11 contains a step-by-step method for performing a Class I stability and control analysis.

Step 12: Perform a Class I drag polar analysis.

Chapter 12 presents a step-by-step method for computing Class I drag polars.

Step 13: Analyze the results of Steps 10 and 11.

By inspecting the results obtained under Steps 10 and 11, it is possible to draw one or more of the following conclusions:

1. The weight and balance results (Step 10) as well as the stability and control results (Step 11) are satisfactory:

   Proceed to Step 14.

2. The results of Step 10 show that the airplane has a 'tip-over' problem. This means that the c.g. is incorrectly located relative to the landing gear.

   Try making minor adjustments to wing and landing gear locations and see if the problem can be solved that way. If it can, make the change(s) and go on to Step 14. If the problem cannot be solved with minor adjustments, consider a change in the configuration. That may imply going back to Step 2.

3. The airplane has too much travel between forward and aft c.g.

   The suggestions made under 2. apply here also.

   This problem tends to disappear if the payload c.g., the fuel c.g. and the OWE c.g. are close together. Try to achieve this.

   Sometimes the problem can be solved by relocation of a particularly 'heavy' component.

4. The results of Step 11 show that the airplane has too much or too little longitudinal and/or directional stability, or that a V_{mc} problem exists.

   Make the required adjustments to tail or canard sizes and when necessary redo Steps 10 and 12.

   Proceed to Step 14.

Chapters 10 and 11 provide the information needed to arrive at one or more of these four conclusions.

<u>Step 14:</u> From the drag polars of Step 12, compute those L/D values which correspond to the mission phases and to the sizing requirements considered in the prelimininary sizing process of Part I (Ref.1).

14.1) Tabulate the new and the old L/D values.

14.2) Determine the impact of any changes in L/D on W_{TO}, W_E and W_F. This can be done using

the results of the sensitivity analyses carried out during the preliminary sizing process described in Part I (Ref.1).

The following cases should be considered:

1. Weight changes are less than 5 percent.
2. Weight changes are more than 5 percent but less than 15 percent.
3. Weight changes are more than 15 percent.

Case 1. Resizing of the airplane is not necessary. Proceed to Step 15.

Case 2. Resize the airplane using the results of the sensitivity analyses carried out during the preliminary sizing process described in Part I (Ref.1).

Go back to Step 3.

Case 3. Resize the airplane with the methods of Part I.

Go back to Step 3.

While working on Steps 13 and 14 the discovery may be made that the configuration choice made in Step 3 was a bad one. Don't be discouraged. This is precisely the reason for p.d. sequence I: to weed out the bad ideas from the good ones.

From the work done up to this point it is possible to distill clues for any configuration changes which need to be made.

<u>Step 15:</u> Prepare a dimensioned threeview which reflects all the changes which were made as a result of the iterations involved in Steps 10 through 14.

On the threeview or as an addendum to the threeview, include a tabulation af all essential dimensional and dimensionless design parameters. Chapter 13 shows examples of such tabulations.

Step 16: Prepare a report which documents the results obtained during p.d. sequence I. Include recommendations for change, for further study or for research and development work which needs to be carried out.

At this point the first preliminary design sequence is complete. The second preliminary design sequence can now be started. Section 2.2 presents an outline of work to be done during p.d. sequence II: Steps 17 - 36.

2.2 PRELIMINARY DESIGN SEQUENCE II

This p.d. sequence starts with the threeview of Step 15 and with the report of Step 16.

The reader will quickly discover, that the amount of work to be done in p.d. sequence II is considerable. For that reason, p.d. sequence II is usually carried out by a team of engineers. Such a team may number anywhere from 3-15 engineers depending on the complexity of the airplane.

Step 17: List the major systems needed in the airplane. Also: prepare 'ghost' views indicating the general system arrangements and their location in the airframe.

Part IV (Ref.4) addresses this problem. There are two reasons for identifying the required airplane systems at this point:

1. Airplane systems have a significant impact on empty weight. In Step 21 a detailed weight estimate must be made.

2. To determine any obvious conflicts which would arise by having two or more systems occupy the same space in the airplane. The so-called 'ghost' views help identify such conflicts early in the design.

Step 18: Size the landing gear tires and struts using Class II methods. Also: verify the validity of the proposed landing gear disposition and of the proposed retraction scheme.

Part IV contains the Class II landing gear sizing methods as well as detailed examples of landing gear design practice.

Prepare drawings showing that the landing gear can be retracted into the designated volume. These drawings should include a so-called 'stick-diagram' of the retraction kinematics to be employed. The force-stroke diagram for the retraction actuator should be determined and its feasibility verified.

Part IV (Ref.4) addresses these problems.

<u>Step 19:</u> Prepare an initial structural arrangement drawing.

A step-by-step method by which a structural arrangement can be put together is contained in Part III (Ref.2).

There are two reasons for preparing the structural arrangement at this point:

1. The structural arrangement has a major impact on the Class II weight predictions of Step 21.

2. The structural arrangement will influence the manufacturing breakdown of Step 34 and in turn the cost estimates of Step 36.

<u>Important Note:</u> Frequently it is possible to achieve a synergistic effect by cleverly combining major structural components to take advantage of mutually supporting functions. Whenever structural synergism can be achieved, the empty weight of the proposed airplane will be reduced.

<u>Step 20:</u> Construct a V-n diagram.

Part V (Ref.3) addresses the problem of how to construct a V-n diagram for a given type airplane.

<u>Step 21:</u> Perform a Class II weight and balance analysis. This includes the calculation of moments and product(s) of inertia.

Part V (Ref.3) addresses this problem.

<u>Step 22:</u> Analyze the results of Step 21. This step is similar to Step 13, points 1-3.

<u>Step 23:</u> Redraw the threeview obtained at the end of p.d. sequence I, as required.

Step 24: Perform a Class II stability and control analysis using the threeview of Step 23.

As part of the Class II stability and control analysis, the following items need to be considered:

1. Trim diagram (power-on and power-off)
2. Take-off rotation
3. Minimum control speed with engine out including the effect of bank angle
4. Roll performance
5. Crosswind control during final approach and on the runway
6. Open loop dynamic handling
7. Gain sizing of any required SAS-loops
8. For airplanes with reversible flight control systems the slopes $\partial F/\partial V$ (stick-force versus speed) and $\partial F/\partial n$ (stick-force versus load factor) need to be determined and checked against the certification base
9. Actuator size and rate requirements

The necessary Class II stability and control analysis methods are presented in Part VII (Ref.6).

The important outcome of the Class II stability and control analysis is that 'final' sizes of stabilizing and control surfaces are established. If necessary, the threeview of Step 23 should be adjusted. Any other required iterations should also be performed. An example of a required iteration would be the case where the tail sizes change by more than 10 percent in area and/or in weight, in going from Class I to Class II results. Both drag (thrust and fuel) and weight may be significantly affected, requiring another iteration in the design.

For airplanes which lack inherent static and/or dynamic stability, the Class II analysis should also result in the preliminary definition of any required stability augmentation system and its required gains. This includes the initial determination of actuator size and rate requirements. Part VII contains a methodology for arriving at a preliminary definition of the SAS and of the required actuator performance.

Step 25: Recompute the drag polars using Class II methods.

In recomputing the drag polars the tail and surface

sizes of Step 23 should be used.

Class II drag polar methods, also called component build-up methods are presented in Part VI (Ref.5).

Step 26: Compute the installed power and/or thrust characteristics of the propulsion system.

Nota bene: Account for all essential installation losses as well as for losses caused by the operation of all 'flight essential' airplane systems.

Methods for computing installed power and/or thrust characteristics are presented in Part VI(Ref.5).

Step 27: List all performance requirements which the airplane must meet. This includes FAR as well as mission requirements. Identify those requirements found to be critical in the preliminary sizing of the airplane.

Step 28: Compute the critical performance capabilities of the airplane and compare them with the requirements of Step 27.

All calculations of critical performance capabilities must be carried out with the Class II drag polars of Step 25 and with the Class II installed engine characteristics of Step 26.

The Class II performance methods of Part VII (Ref.6) must be used in this case. Depending on the results of these performance calculations further design iterations may be needed.

Step 29: Iterate through Steps 17 - 28 as needed and adjust the configuration.

The reader will now appreciate why configuration design was referred to as a non-unique, iterative process in the introduction (Chapter 1).

Step 30: Finalize the threeview and tabulate the essential airplane geometry.

Examples of threeviews and of geometric tabulations are presented in Part III (Ref.2).

Step 31: Finalize the inboard profile(s).

Examples are shown in Part III (Ref.2).

Step 32: Prepare a preliminary layout drawing for all essential airplane systems, in particular the primary and secondary flight control systems.

Part IV contains examples of layout drawings for various airplane systems.

Check for any conflicts and go through the 'WHAT IF' safety and maintenance checklist given in Part IV (Ref.3).

It is of particular importance to insure that no undue fire hazards and no obstacles to crash survivability have been 'built in'.

Step 33: Finalize the structural arrangement.

Step 19 asked for an initial structural arrangement. As a result of any modifications imposed by the work done in Steps 20-32 this initial structural arrangement may have to be modified.

Step 34: Prepare a preliminary manufacturing breakdown.

Part III (Ref.3) addresses the problem of deciding on manufacturing breakdowns.

Step 35: Make a study of maintenance and accessibility requirements.

As part of this study the following schematics are needed:

1. A schematic showing all essential access requirements for inspection and for maintenance. Compatibility with the structural arrangement should be ensured.

2. For transports and for military airplanes, a schematic demonstrating the accessibility of standard service, loading and unloading vehicles is required.

3. Prepare a schematic showing that the engine(s) and the APU can be easily inspected and removed.

Part IV contains useful hints with regard to maintenance requirements of various airplane systems.

Step 36: Perform a preliminary cost analysis for the airplane.

This generally includes an estimation of the following cost items:

1. Design and development cost
2. Manufacturing cost
3. Operating cost

Part VIII (Ref.7) presents methods for estimating these cost items.

On the basis of these estimates a judgement can be made as to whether or not the proposed airplane will allow the manufacturer as well as the operator to make a profit.

In the case of a military airplane, the cost analysis should include a comparison of the military utility or the 'bang-per-buck' obtainable with the proposed new airplane as compared to alternate solutions. A rationale for the selected design in view of expected enemy threats must be included.

At this point it often makes sense to study the possible benefits of design optimization relative to cost criteria. Typical of such cost criteria are: DOC, ROI and LCC. Part VIII (Ref.7) addresses this problem also.

A final report documenting the results obtained during p.d. sequence II should be prepared. This rounds off all p.d. sequence II work.

IMPORTANT COMMENT:

Experience has shown that the decisions made during preliminary configuration design 'lock in' 90 percent of the life-cycle-cost (LCC) of the airplane.

This is of staggering importance, because the total investment made in the airplane at the end of the preliminary design phase is negligible when compared even with the total full scale development cost.

Clearly, it is penny-wise and dollar-foolish not to invest heavily in supportive research work during the early design work on a new airplane.

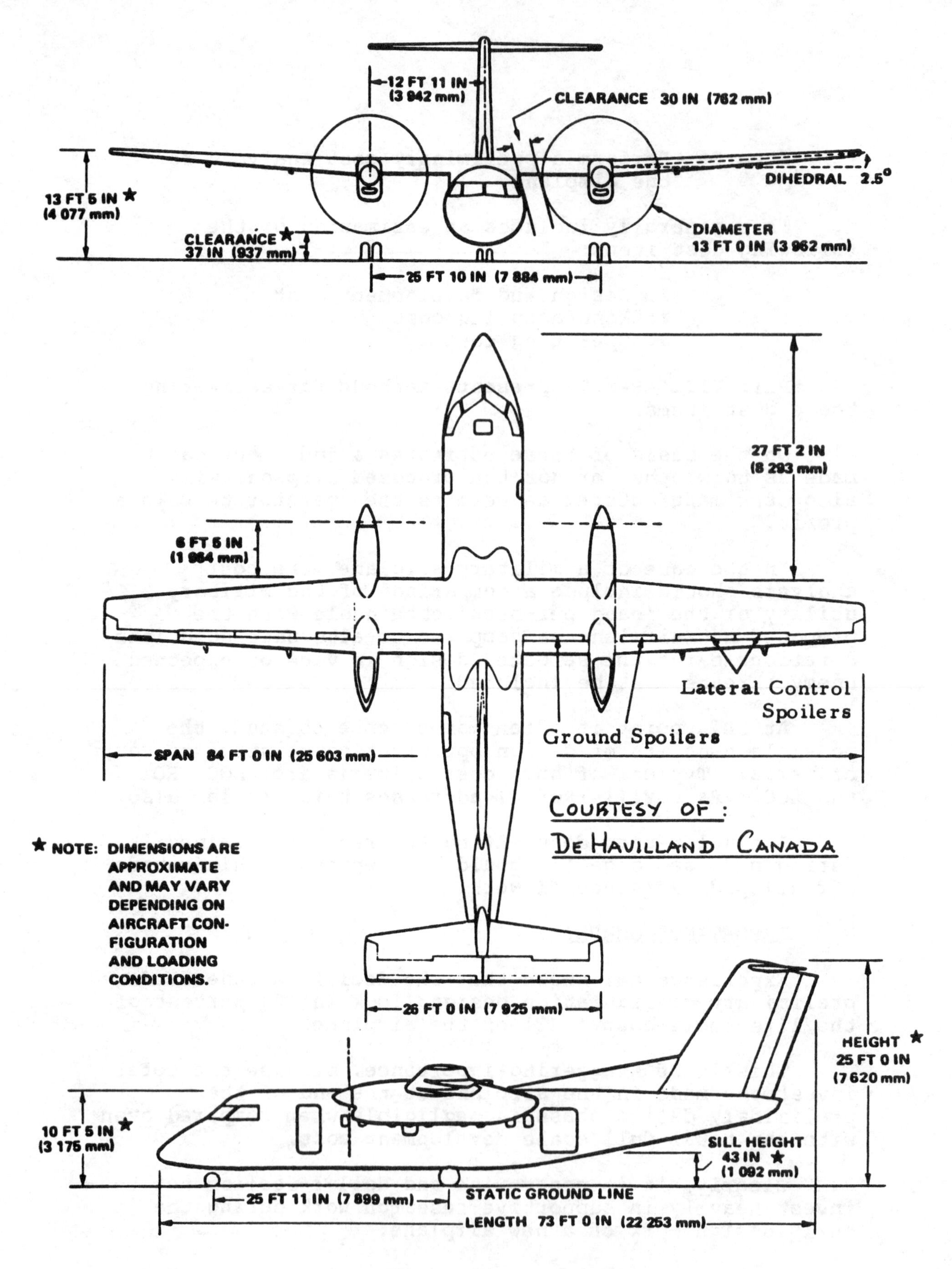

DASH 8 General Arrangement

3. SELECTION OF THE OVERALL CONFIGURATION

In addition to a large number of technical considerations, configuration design is also influenced by marketing, emotional and styling considerations. Only technical considerations are discussed in this chapter.

The following technical considerations play a role in the selection of the overall configuration:

1. It is nearly always desirable to place the fuel c.g., the payload c.g. and the empty weight c.g. at the same longitudinal location. Doing this limits c.g. travel. Limiting c.g. travel results in a configuration with less wetted area due to less need for trim control power.

    This consideration has a major influence on the relative placement of those airplane components, which primarily affect the overall c.g. location.

2. The critical Mach number of the wing of a subsonic airplane should be selected such that the airplane does not cruise too far into the drag rise.

    This requirement means that wing sweep angle, airfoil type and airfoil thickness ratio must be choosen in such a way as to avoid excessive drag rise at cruise Mach numbers.

3. The critical Mach number of the wing should always be lower than the critical Mach number of stabilizing or control surfaces.

    This requirement means that the thickness ratio, sweep angle and aspect ratio of stabilizing and of control surfaces must be selected to yield critical Mach numbers greater than that of the wing.

4. The integration of major components such as: nacelle on wing, nacelle on fuselage, wing on fuselage and so on needs to be done so that interference drag is minimized.

    Ideally this means that any connecting, intersecting items should intersect at as close as possible to 90 degrees. If it is not possible to do this, extensive fairings are needed to avoid interference drag penalties.

At high subsonic speeds it is frequently found necessary to apply local area ruling to reduce subsonic wave drag. Subsonic area ruling is discussed in Part VI (Ref.5).

5. In fighter aircraft with requirements for supersonic cruise performance or supersonic maneuvering performance the wave drag becomes an essential design consideration.

To minimize supersonic wave drag the configuration must be arranged such that the shape of the cross-sectional area distribution (arranged as an equivalent body of revolution) is smooth. Ideally this should approximate the so-called Sears-Haack shape. Supersonic area ruling is discussed in Part VI (Ref.5).

6. Major intersecting structural components should be arranged to avoid duplication of special heavy structure.

Low weight airplane structures come about only by judiciously combining multiple functions into major structural elements. This is referred to as structural synergism.

For example: in a high wing transport with fuselage mounted main landing gear, it is desirable to attach the landing gear to the same fuselage frames which are used to attach the wing. This is referred to as structural synergism.

7. In deciding on the location of the major airplane components:

<u>THINK LIGHT, THINK SIMPLE, THINK ACCESSIBILITY, THINK MAINTAINABILITY AND THINK COST.</u>

Remember that above certain cost levels no airplanes will be sold. Another way of putting this is: <u>Your job depends on it!</u>

Configurations are often selected as an outgrowth of an existing configuration. This is particularly true in the large airplane companies. Examples are: 707, 727, 737 and 757. These airplanes all use the same fuselage cross section. The same is true for the DC-9 and MD-80 and -82 series.

When a new configuration evolves, it is often the result of a large number of trade studies done by different teams trying to come up with the most economical solution to some mission requirement. In the large companies two or more teams may be working toward the same mission objective, each folowing a different configuration approach. It may be safely assumed, that the companies would not do this, if configurations could be selected on a direct rational basis.

It is not yet possible to present straightforward, unique procedures by which an airplane configuration can be selected so that it 'best' satisfies customer requirements. There are too many variables involved in this process, most of which defy mathematical modelling.

For the beginning design student it is difficult to get started on the selection of a configuration. To assist the student in that process, a number of existing configurations will be presented in the form of airplane threeviews for twelve different airplane categories. These configurations are discussed in Section 3.1.

Section 3.2 presents a discussion of what are called unusual configurations.

Section 3.3 provides an outline of configuration possibilities. This section should be consulted before 'freezing' a configuration.

A step-by-step process for selecting a configuration is presented in Section 3.4.

Section 3.5 contains three example applications.

3.1 EXAMPLES OF EXISTING CONFIGURATIONS

The purpose of this section is to review a number of existing configurations. The review is presented for the following airplane categories.

3.1.1 Homebuilts
3.1.2 Single engine propeller driven airplanes
3.1.3 Twin engine propeller driven airplanes
3.1.4 Agricultural airplanes
3.1.5 Business jets
3.1.6 Regional turbopropeller driven airplanes
3.1.7 Jet transports
3.1.8 Military trainers
3.1.9 Fighters
3.1.10 Military patrol, bomb and transport airplanes
3.1.11 Flying boats, amphibious and float airplanes
3.1.12 Supersonic cruise airplanes

The reader is encouraged to also consult Jane's All the World's Aircraft (Ref. 8) for further information on these and other airplane configurations. Jane's has been published annually since 1909 and contains a wealth of data. The author believes that a historical perspective is vitally important to any aeronautical engineer. An easy way to acquire such a perspective is to study earlier versions of Jane's. In addition to reading Jane's, the author recommends that students of airplane design read the books listed under 'historical references' in Section 14.2.

CAUTION: In the following discussions the author presents a number of pros and cons for various configuration aspects. After reading the remainder of this section the reader should keep the following points in mind:

1. In airplane configuration design there are no absolute pros and cons, only relative pros and cons.

2. During configuration design many pros and cons are traded against each other and a compromise is struck.

3. Unless one has been involved in the decision making process leading to a given configuration, it is very hard to know how the pros and cons were compromised.

4. In discussing pros and cons it is almost impossible not to reflect a certain amount of personal biasses. Therefore: reader beware!

3.1.1 Homebuilts

Figures 3.1-3.3 illustrate twelve fairly typical homebuilt configurations. The following observations are offered:

1. These airplanes range from simple, basic, low performance machines (such as the Sizer Sapphire of Fig.3.2b) to rather sophisticated high performance machines (such as the Sequoia Model 300 of Fig.3.1c).

2. Except for the tandem wing Piel C.P.500 (Fig.3.3d) all of the homebuilts shown have rather conventional configurations.

3. To some homebuilders the ability to store the airplane at home is a necessity. This sometimes leads to the incorporation of wing-fold mechanisms. Examples are shown in Figures 3.1a, 3.2a and 3.3a.

4. There seems to be no preference amongst homebuilders for tri-cycle or for tail-dragging landing gear designs. Both types are widely used. However: note the preference for fixed landing gears (cost and simplicity!).

5. The homebuilts shown have tractor, piston-propeller type of propulsion. The Coot of Fig.3.3a is the only exception. It is also the only amphibious layout shown.

6. Observe that except for the airplanes of Figures 3.2b, 3.2d and 3.3d all wings are of the cantilever type.

7. Of interest is the wide variety in wing planforms, ranging from bi-plane to mono-plane and from straight untapered to elliptical. Cost and hours spent in construction are important considerations to the homebuilder. If a homebuilder wants an efficient, elliptical wing, he will have to spend the time required to build such a wing.

8. It is interesting to note the preference for low wing designs. This is probably caused by the desire to attach the landing gear to the wing and to keep the gear as short (and thus light) as possible.

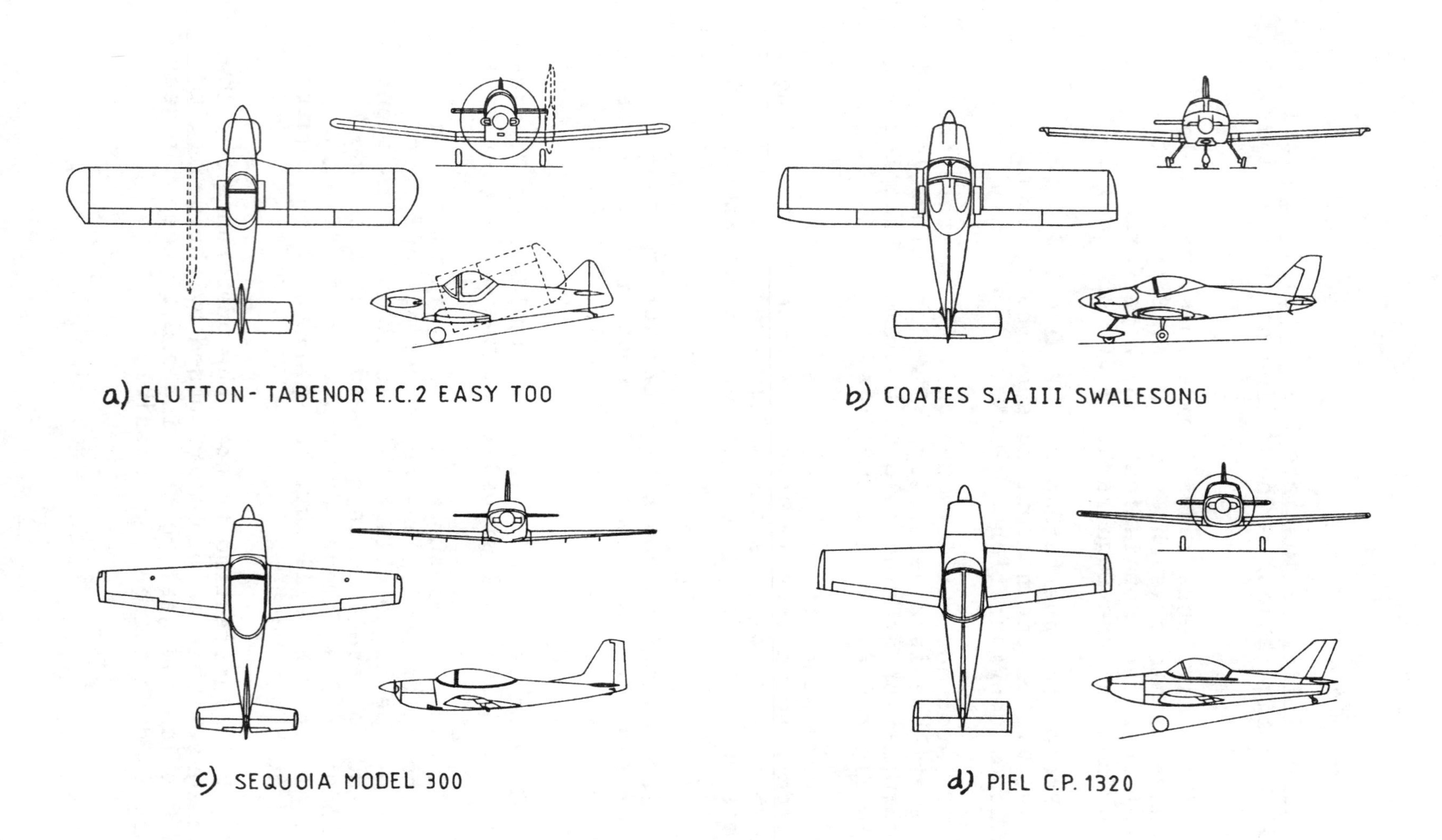

Figure 3.1 Homebuilt Propeller Driven Airplanes

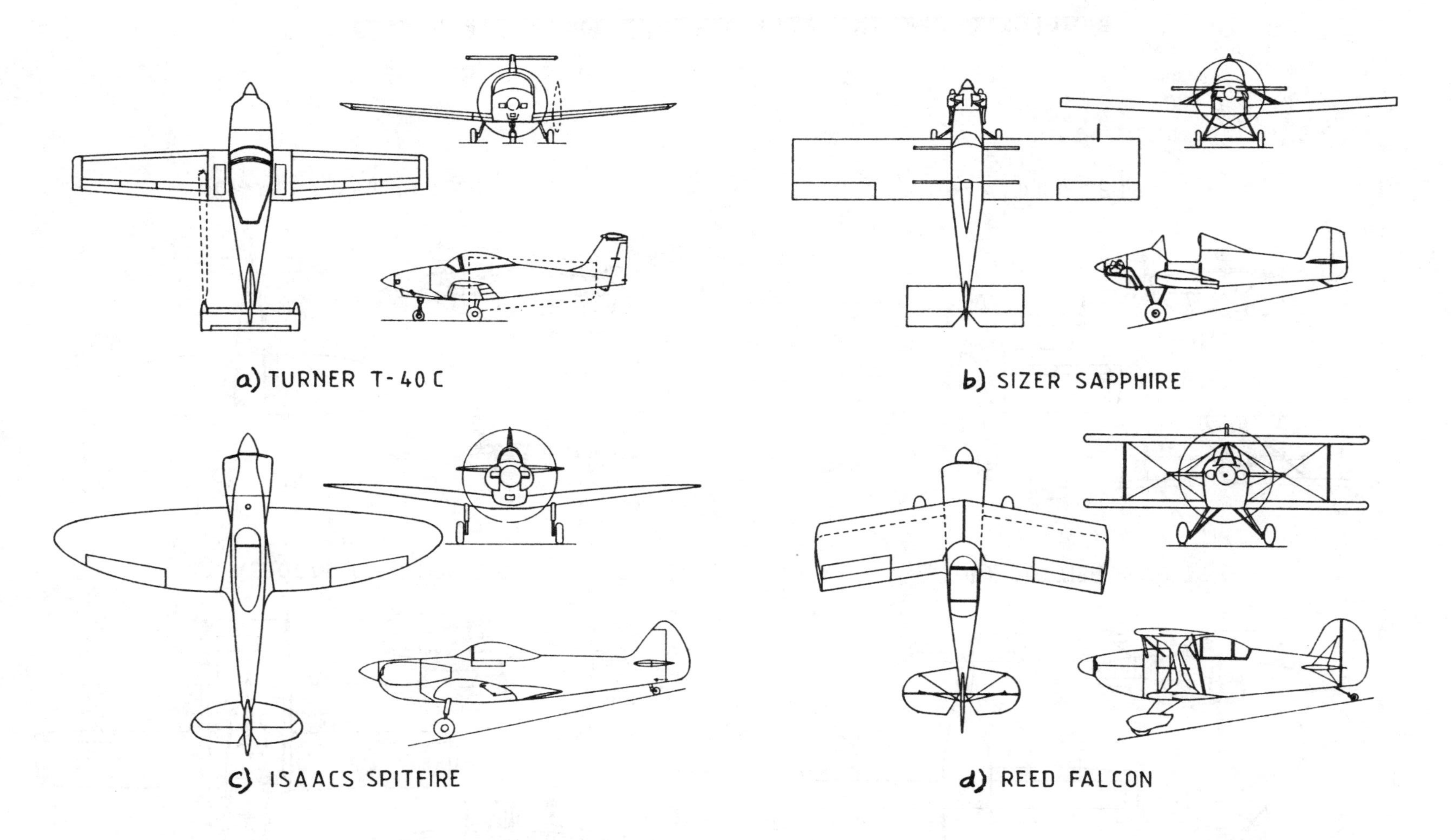

Figure 3.2 Homebuilt Propeller Driven Airplanes

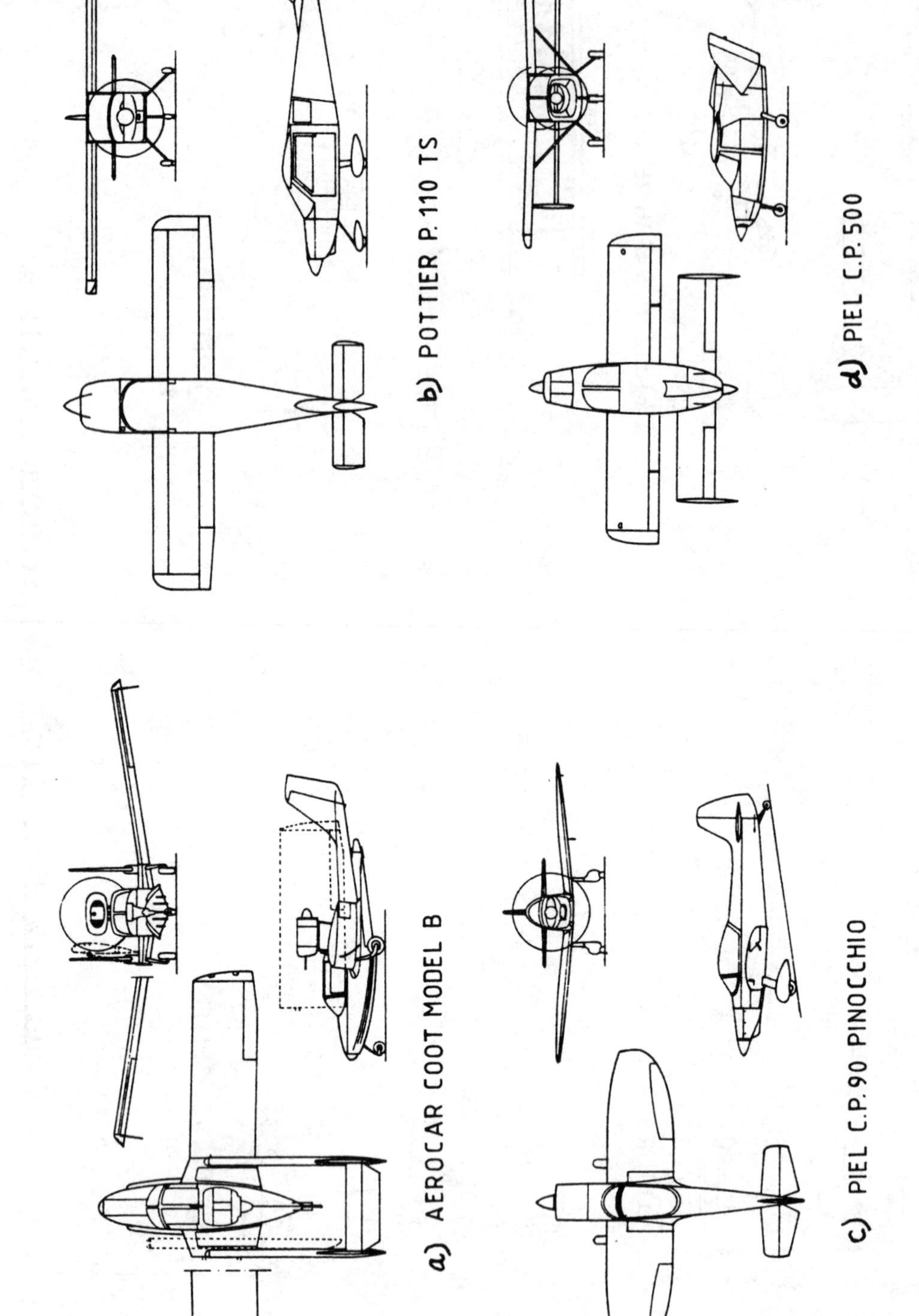

Figure 3.3 Homebuilt Propeller Driven Airplanes

3.1.2 Single Engine Propeller Driven Airplanes

Figures 3.4-3.6 show twelve typical configurations for airplanes in this category. The following observations are offered:

1. Nine of these airplanes have low wings, three have high wings. Except for the Cessna's of Fig.3.5 which have externally braced wings, all employ cantilever wings.

2. All configurations are of the tractor type, except for the Pöschel P-300 Equator of Figure 3.5.

3. Observe the vertical placement of the horizontal tail on these airplanes: three have T-tails, while nine have the horizontal tail placed roughly at the root of the vertical tail. T-tail airplanes in this category share some problems which need to be weighed before deciding to incorporate a T-tail:

a) because of the height of the T-tail, they are difficult to inspect without a ladder.
b) having the horizontal tail away from the propeller slipstream makes rotation during take-off more difficult. That results in longer take-off runs. Note that the Pöschel P-300 gets around that problem by having the propeller installed at the T-tail junction.

4. Also observe the longitudinal placement of the horizontal tails on these airplanes. On several, the horizontal tail is placed aft of the rudder hinge line. This is done to keep the rudder away from the separated horizontal tail wake, when the airplane has stalled and may be entering a spin. Keeping the rudder away from this wake allows for easier recovery from a spin. This does not imply however, that the other types cannot be recovered from a spin.

5. Only four of these airplanes have retractable landing gear. A retractable gear reduces cruise drag but increases cost: both acquisition cost and maintenance cost. In this type of airplane a retractable gear also tempts the pilot to forget lowering the gear before landing.

6. Except for one airplane, all have swept aft vertical tails. For low sweep angles, this improves the product of tail moment arm and tail lift curve slope. This in turn improves vertical tail effectiveness. Vertical tails are also swept for reasons of styling.

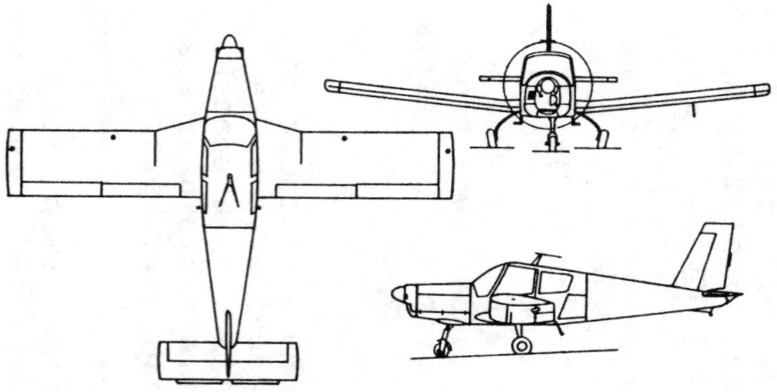

a) ZLIN 43

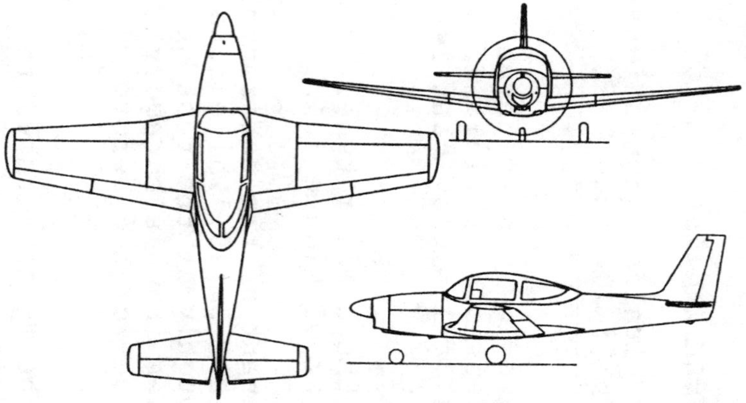

b) INTERCEPTOR 400

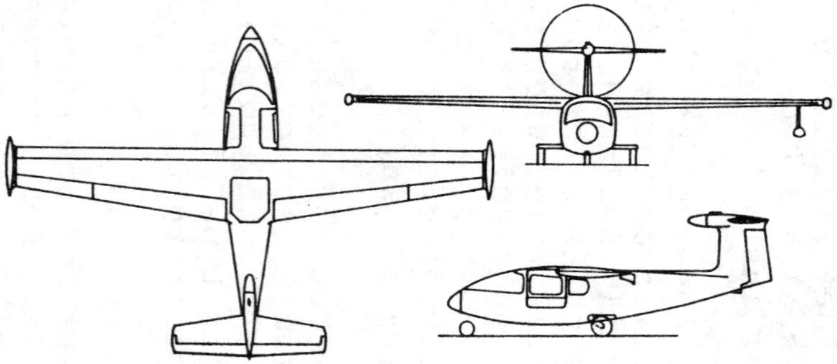

c) PÖSCHEL P-300 EQUATOR

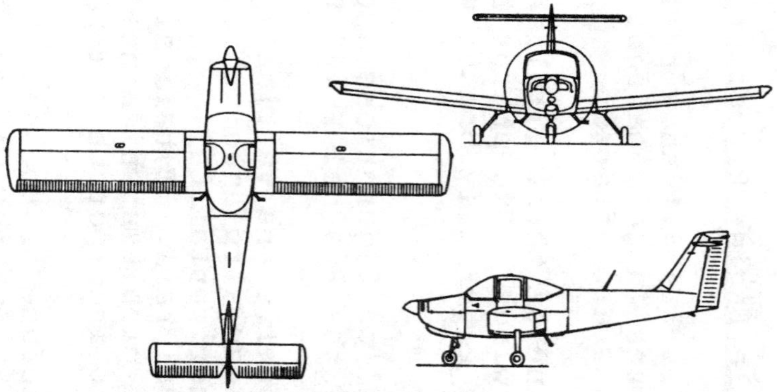

d) PIPER TOMAHAWK II

Figure 3.4 Single Engine Propeller Driven Airplanes

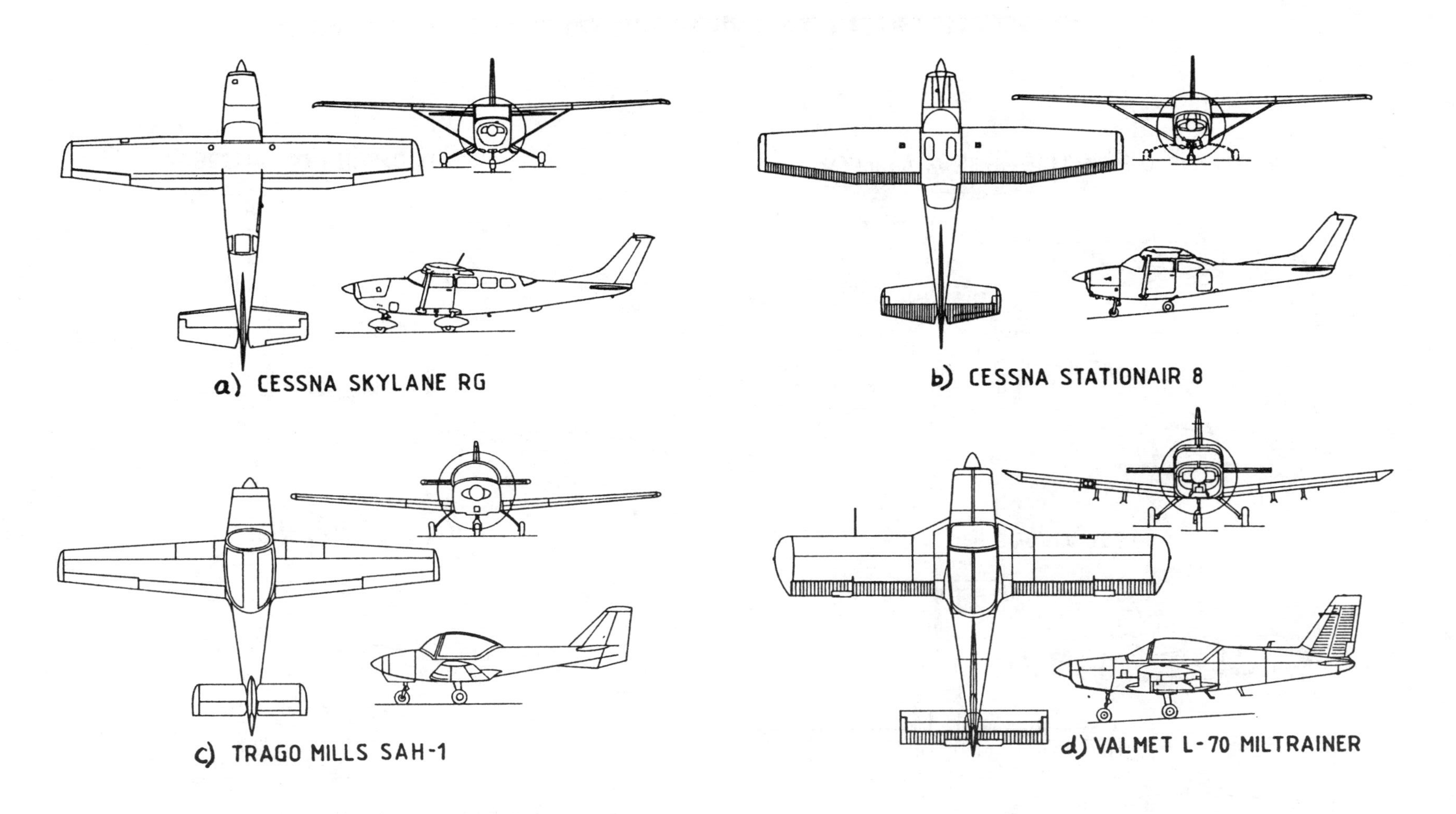

Figure 3.5 Single Engine Propeller Driven Airplanes

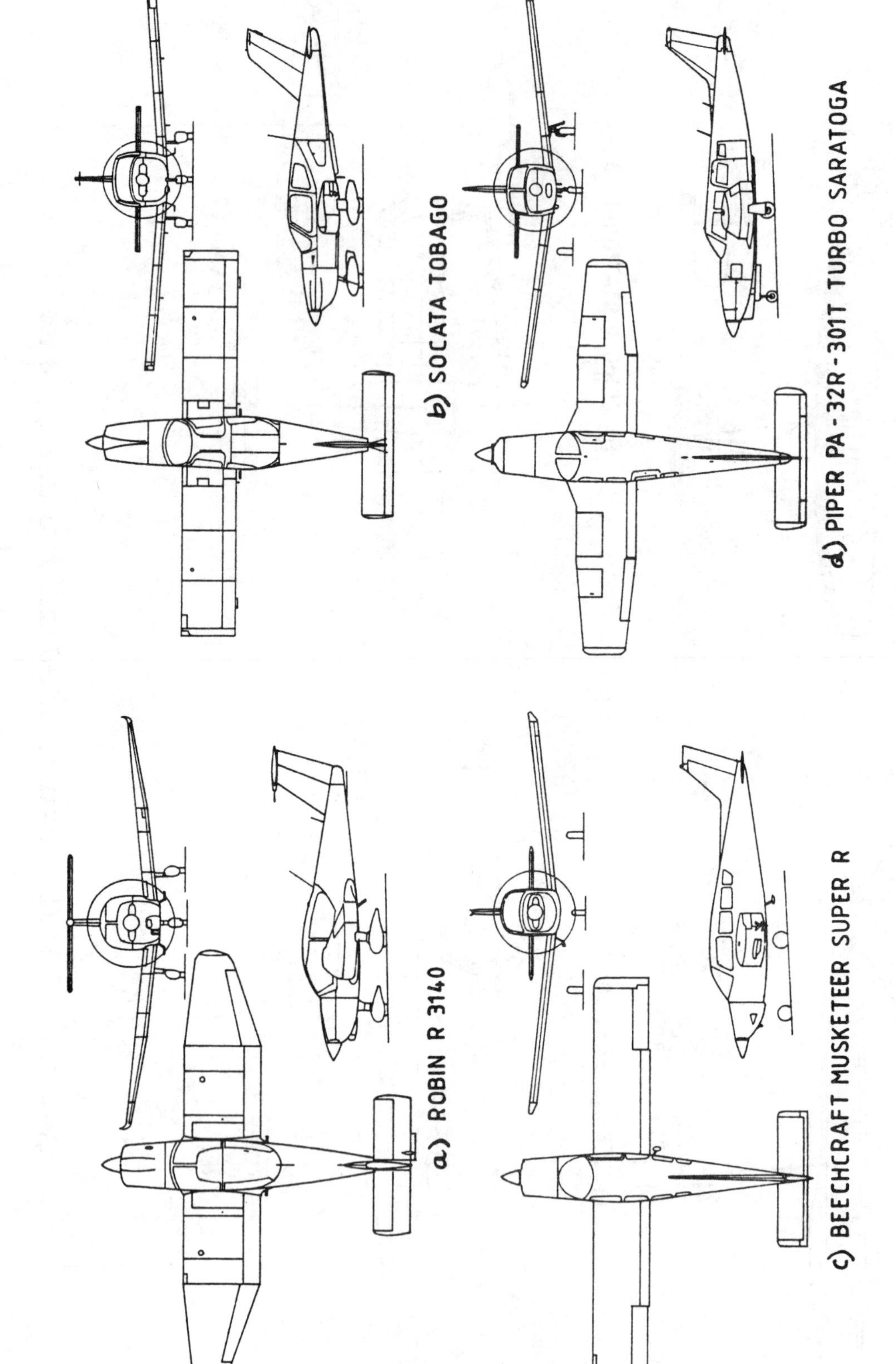

Figure 3.6 Single Engine Propeller Driven Airplanes

3.1.3 Twin Engine Propeller Driven Airplanes

Figures 3.7-3.9 show twelve examples of twin engine propeller driven airplanes. The following observations are offered:

1. Note that some of these were listed in Part I (Ref.1) as regional propeller driven airplanes. This is an indication that any categorization of airplanes is an arbitrary one. At the 'high' weight end of twins and at the 'low' weight end of the 'regionals' there is a considerable overlap.

2. Note that four of the twins are high wing airplanes while the other eight have low wings.

3. The only pure pusher configuration is the Piaggio P166. The Cessna 336 is a pusher-tractor combination. This is also referred to as 'centerline' thrust. Clearly in an engine out situation, this type will be much easier to control. Engine-out control problems are a major design consideration in conventional twins.

4. Observe the horizontal tail locations in Figures 3.7-3.9. Several twins have the horizontal tail directly in the propeller slipstream. The effect of that is to make controllability a function of engine power. There can be advantages to that. However, particularly for twins with low power loadings (that means very powerful engines), propeller slipstream can cause significant tail fatigue problems.

5. Another factor which has to be weighed before deciding on horizontal tail location is controllability in a 'go-around' situation. In a low power approach, with the airplane trimmed for that flight situation, the sudden application of power can result in a large increase in control force required from the pilot. A physically not so strong pilot may have problems with longitudinal control in that case. By keeping the tail away from the slipstream, this problem is diminished. An interim solution sometimes is to give the horizontal tail enough geometric dihedral.

6. Note that nine of the twins have retractable landing gears. Most twins retract the gear into the wings. This is not the lightest solution! However, from a weight and balance viewpoint there sometimes is no choice.

7. Except for the Islander of Fig.3.9a all twins have single wheel main gears.

8. Several of the twins are seen to have 'sharp-edged' dorsal fins. These help to increase directional stability as well as to eliminate 'rudder-lock'.

9. Observe the widely differing nacelle/wing integration methods in use. There is no unanimity about the nacelle/wing shape with the lowest interference effects. One problem with low wing twins is the fact that propeller/ground clearance may dictate the nacelle location.

10. Several twins have the outboard aileron stations inboard relative to the wing tip. This comes about when additional wing span is added to a 'growth' version of an airplane. In that case it is often found that the tooling expense associated with extending the ailerons outboard is not worth it. This is particularly true if the airplane does not need the additional lateral control power.

11. A potential disadvantage of a twin boom pusher configuration such as the Cessna 336 (Fig.3.9c) is that failure of an aft propeller blade can result in structural failure of one of the tailbooms.

12. The gull wing of the Piaggio P166-DL3 of Fig.3.7b came about because this airplane was derived from an amphibious airplane. Gull wings are often used in amphibious airplanes to keep the propeller out of the water spray from the hull. An advantage of the gull wing is that it provides a low interference intersection with the fuselage. A disadvantage is the structural discontinuity which adds weight to the wing.

13. Note that many twins have baggage space in the rear of the nacelles.

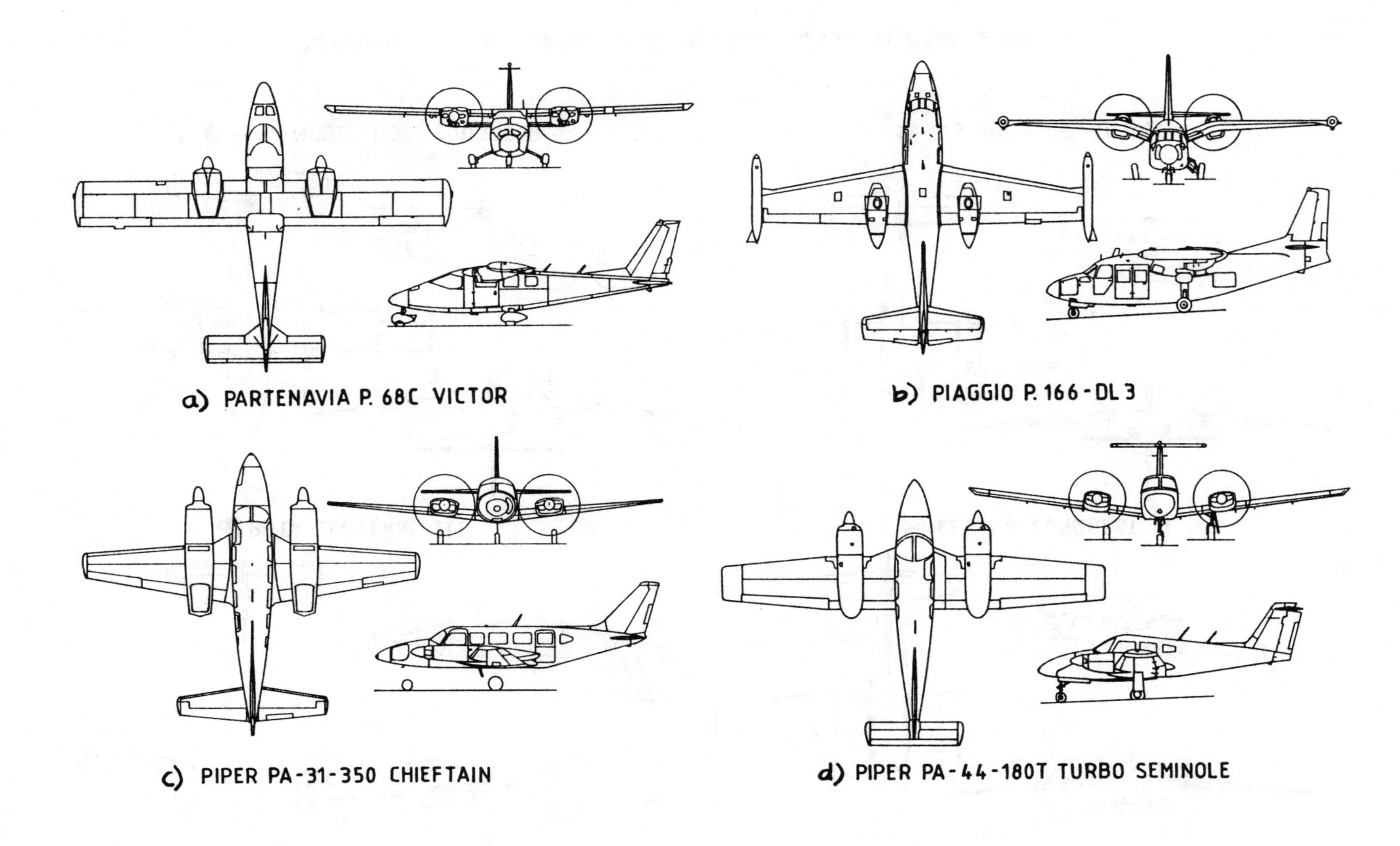

Figure 3.7 Twin Engine Propeller Driven Airplanes

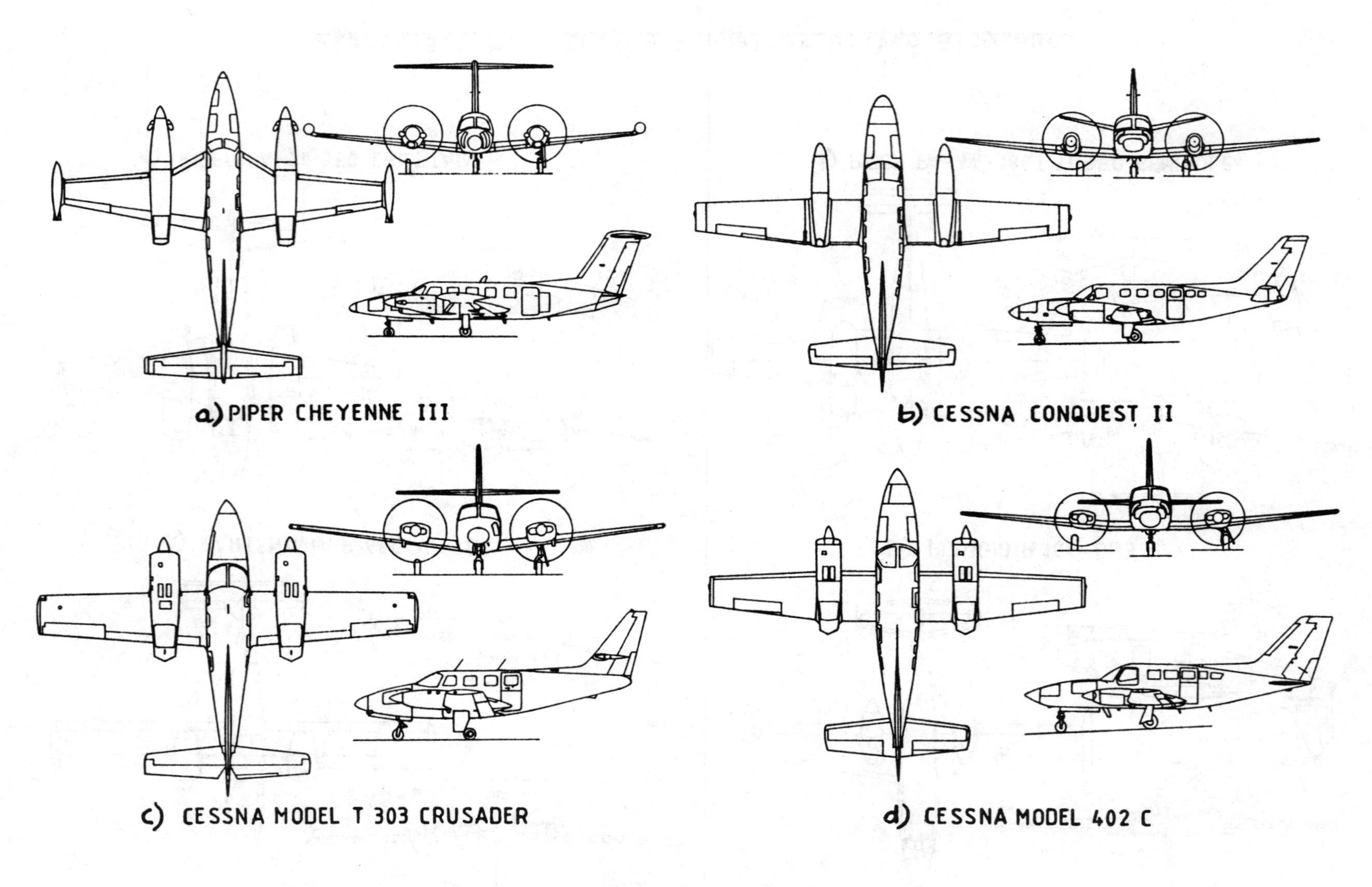

Figure 3.8 Twin Engine Propeller Driven Airplanes

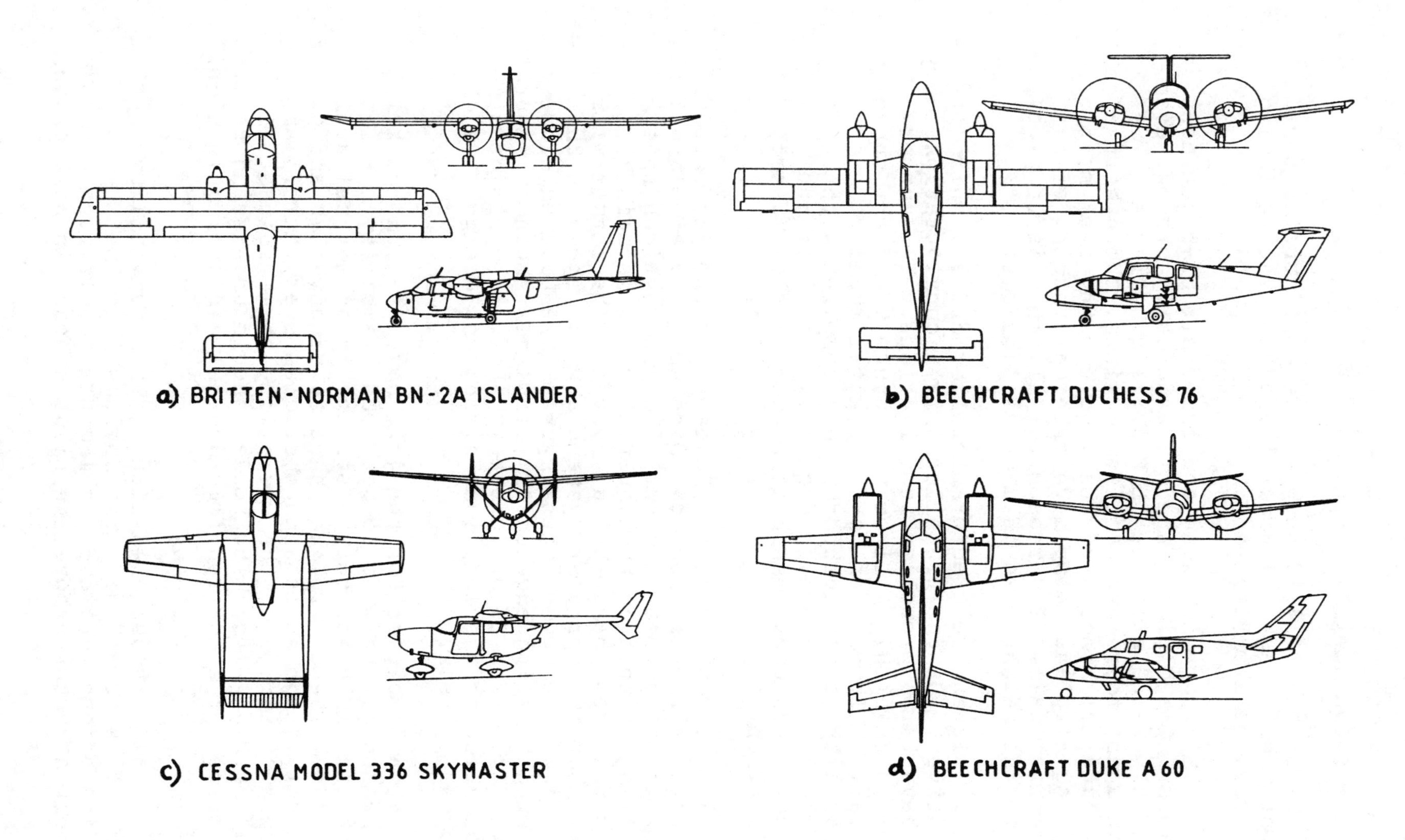

Figure 3.9 Twin Engine Propeller Driven Airplanes

3.1.4 Agricultural Airplanes

Figures 3.10-3.12 show twelve configurations of recently built agricultural airplanes. The following observations are offered:

1. Nine are low wing and three are bi-plane configurations. The biplanes are all externally braced, even the jet powered airplane of Fig.3.11c. Of the monoplanes, four have cantilever wings, the others also have external bracing on the wing. Note, that most of these ag-airplanes also have external bracing of the horizontal tail. The reason for all this is to keep the structural weight down as much as possible.

2. Eleven are tractor-propeller driven, while one is jet driven. Of the propeller driven configurations only two have turbo-propeller installations. The author predicts that this will be the future trend for these airplanes. The reason is the greater inherent reliability of the turboprop when compared with the piston engine. The high acquisition cost of the turboprop has been responsible for its slow market penetration.

3. All configurations, except for the jet, suffer to some extent from a classical problem of ag-airplanes: the propeller slipstream and the wing tip vortices have a 'swirling' effect on the material which is being deposited from the spray bar system. The reader will note, that the spraybar systems are not shown in the threeviews. However, these systems are mounted close to the wing trailing edge on all airplanes shown in Figures 3.10-3.13. Part IV of this text (Ref. 3) contains some information on the location, sizing and design of such spraybar systems.

4. All, except for the jet, have 'raised' cockpits. The reason for this is to get good visibility. Pilot visibility is absolutely essential in an agricultural airplane. These airplanes have to maneuver in and out of some very tough spots with obstacles everywhere. An extreme variation on the visibility theme is the HAL HA-31 of Fig.3.10b. The reader should understand that the price for so-called '360-degree' visibility is high drag.

5. All are designed with crash survivability in mind. This is not directly obvious from the configurations. However, all contain some form of support structure above the pilot's head, in case of an

inverted crash. The jet of Fig.3.11c seems to have a problem in terms of pilot survivability in case of a head-on collision with an obstacle.

6. Except for two, all are configured as 'taildraggers'. Most ag operators feel, that because they operate from some very rough fields, the weight penalty associated with a nose gear is not worth the improvement in ground handling.

7. The 'hoppers' in most ag-planes are mounted ahead of the pilot. The concensus is that this improves crash survivability. On the other hand, in case of a leaky hopper, the pilot can be exposed to chemicals. On the IA 53 (Fig.3.11a) and on the HAL HA-31(Fig.3.10b), the hoppers are mounted beneath the pilot. On the WSK-Mielec M-15(Fig.3.11c) the hoppers are mounted in the fuselage behind the pilot and in the wing-strut containers. On the Antonov An-2M (which was not specifically designed for ag-duties), shown in Fig.3.10a, the hoppers are mounted in the cabin behind the cockpit.

A method used in a number of ag airplanes to positively evacuate chemicals from the cockpit is to apply a slight amount of pressurization with suitably installed escape vents. Such a 'directed' leakage path can keep most of the undesirable compounds away from the human operator.

8. Bird-proof windshields, wire cutters and wire deflectors are necessary features in all ag-planes. The birdproof windshields imply some weight penalty, particularly when the windshield is large. Wire cutters are usually mounted ahead of the windscreen. Wire deflectors generally run from the top of the canopy or cockpit roof to the top of the vertical tail.

9. Note that most ag-planes have non-retractable landing gears. Several arguments can be made against a retractable landing gear in the case of an ag-airplane:

a.) complexity and maintenance
b.) pilots tend to forget lowering the landing gear
c.) the drag advantage is small in an airplane which has very large drag increments due to bracing, spray-bar and raised windshield.

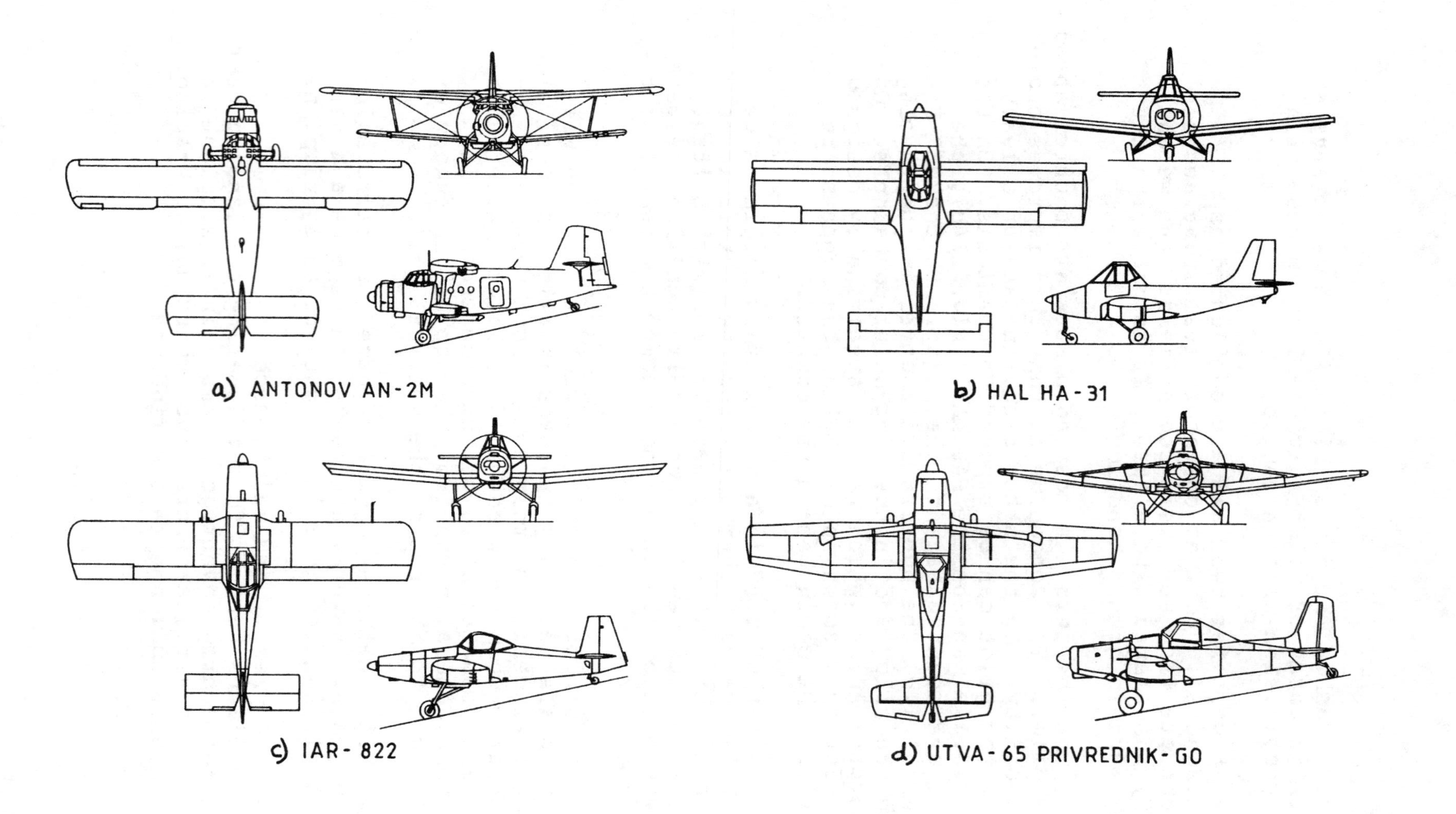

Figure 3.10 Agricultural Airplanes

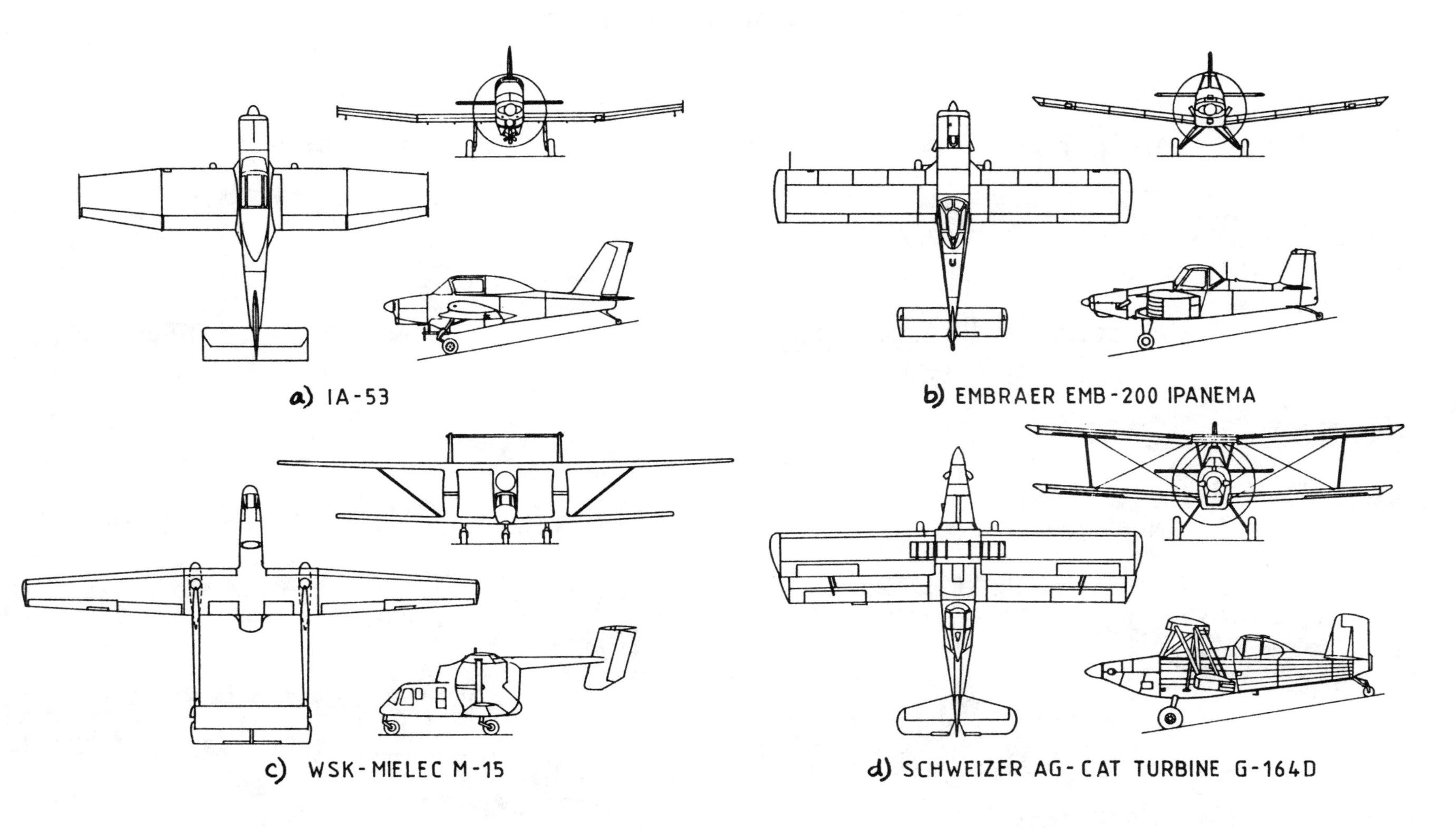

Figure 3.11 Agricultural Airplanes

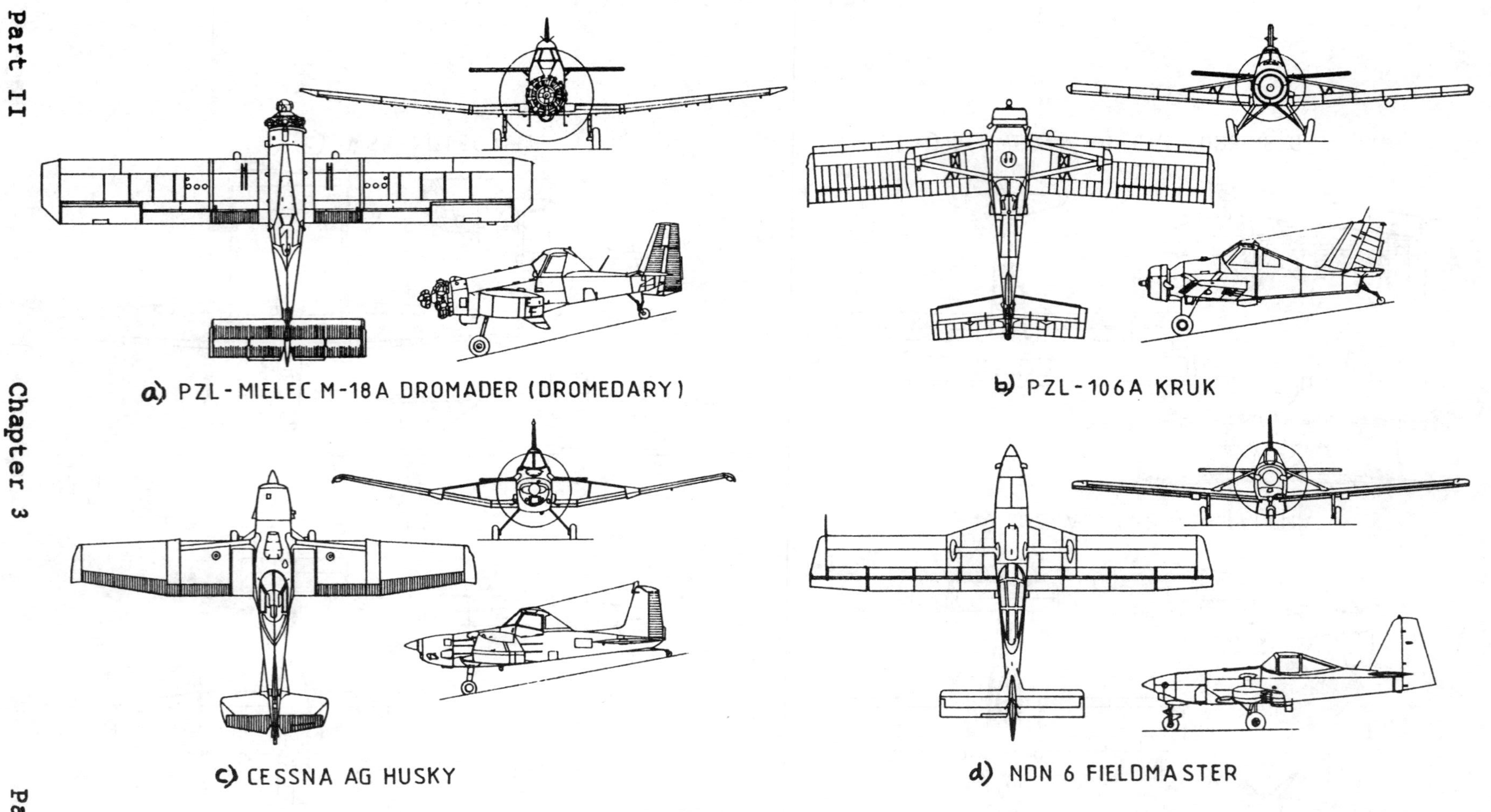

Figure 3.12 Agricultural Airplanes

3.1.5 Business Jets

Figures 3.13-3.15 present twelve configurations of business jets. The following observations are offered:

1. Ten of the twelve are twins, one is a tri-jet (Fig.3.13d) and one has four jet engines (Fig.3.13a)

2. All have the engines installed in nacelles on the rear fuselage. This configuration was pioneered by the French on the Sud Caravelle jet transport. The middle engine of the Falcon 50 is an exception, it is installed like the center engine on the Boeing 727.

3. The early business jets had severe problems with fuel volume. This is evidenced by the use of tiptanks and slipper tanks as seen in Figs. 3.13a, 3.13b, 3.14b and 3.15c. The reason for this was the very high specific fuel consumption of the early jet engines.

4. Business jets were among the first airplane types to use winglets for lower induced drag. Examples are shown in Figs. 3.13c and 3.14c.

5. Designers of several recent business jets have opted for a so-called supercritical wing. This provides improved dragrise behavior. Examples are shown in Figs. 3.13c, 3.14a, 3.15a and 3.15d.

6. All business jets retract the landing gear into the wing or into the wing/fuselage intersection.

7. Except for the Westwind (Fig.3.15c) all business jets have a low wing configuration. It is observed that the Westwind was originally developed from the propeller driven Aero Commander which had a mid wing configuration.

8. Observe that only four of the business jets have T-tail configurations. The rest have cruciform or low tail arrangements.

9. All landing gears are of the tricycle type. Single and double wheels are used.

10. Observe that three of the business jets have essentially no sweep angle. This implies a thin wing at high speed (Learjet of Fig.3.13b) or a thick wing at somewhat lower speed (Citation of Fig.3.14c).

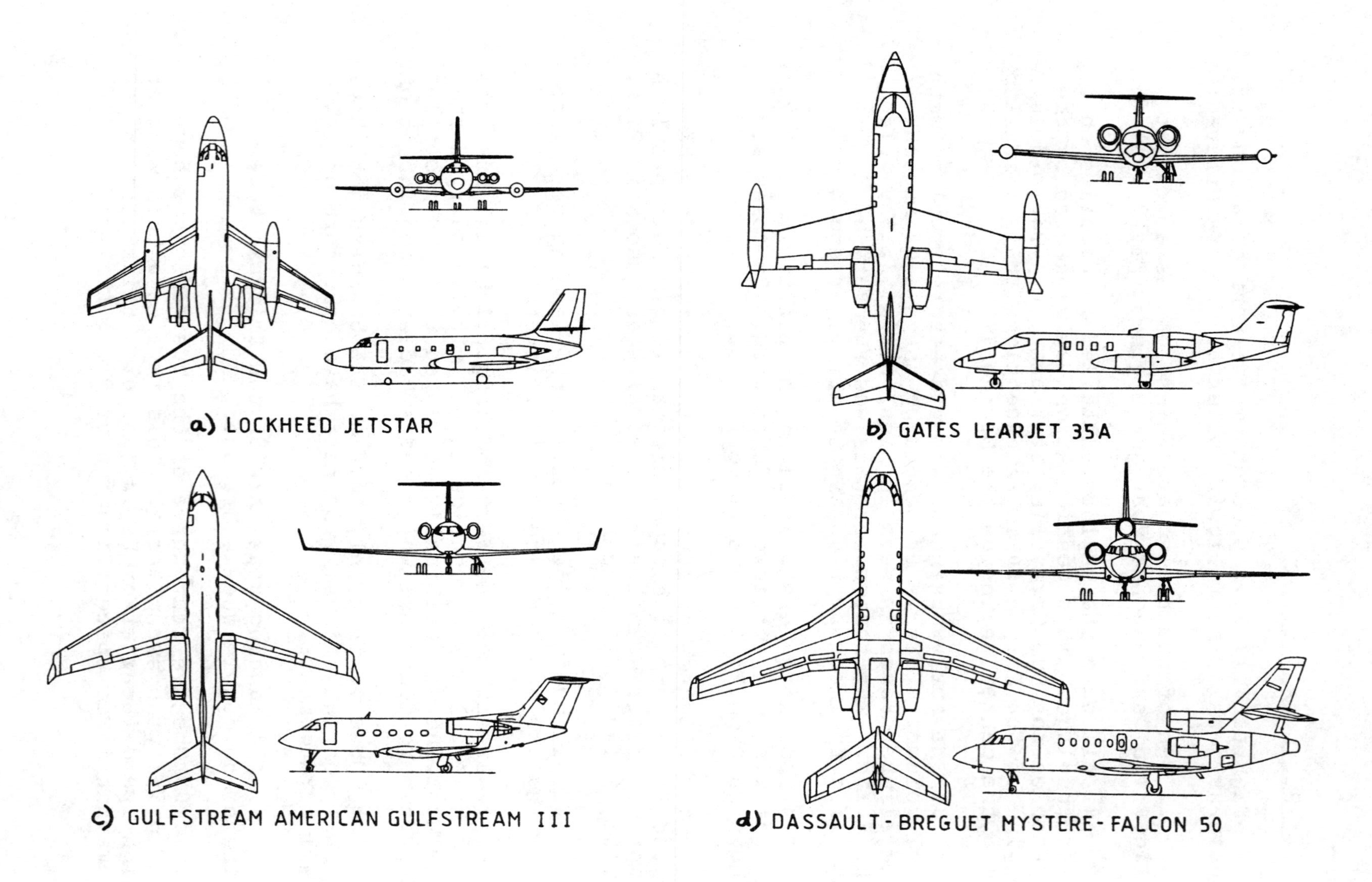

Figure 3.13 Business Jets

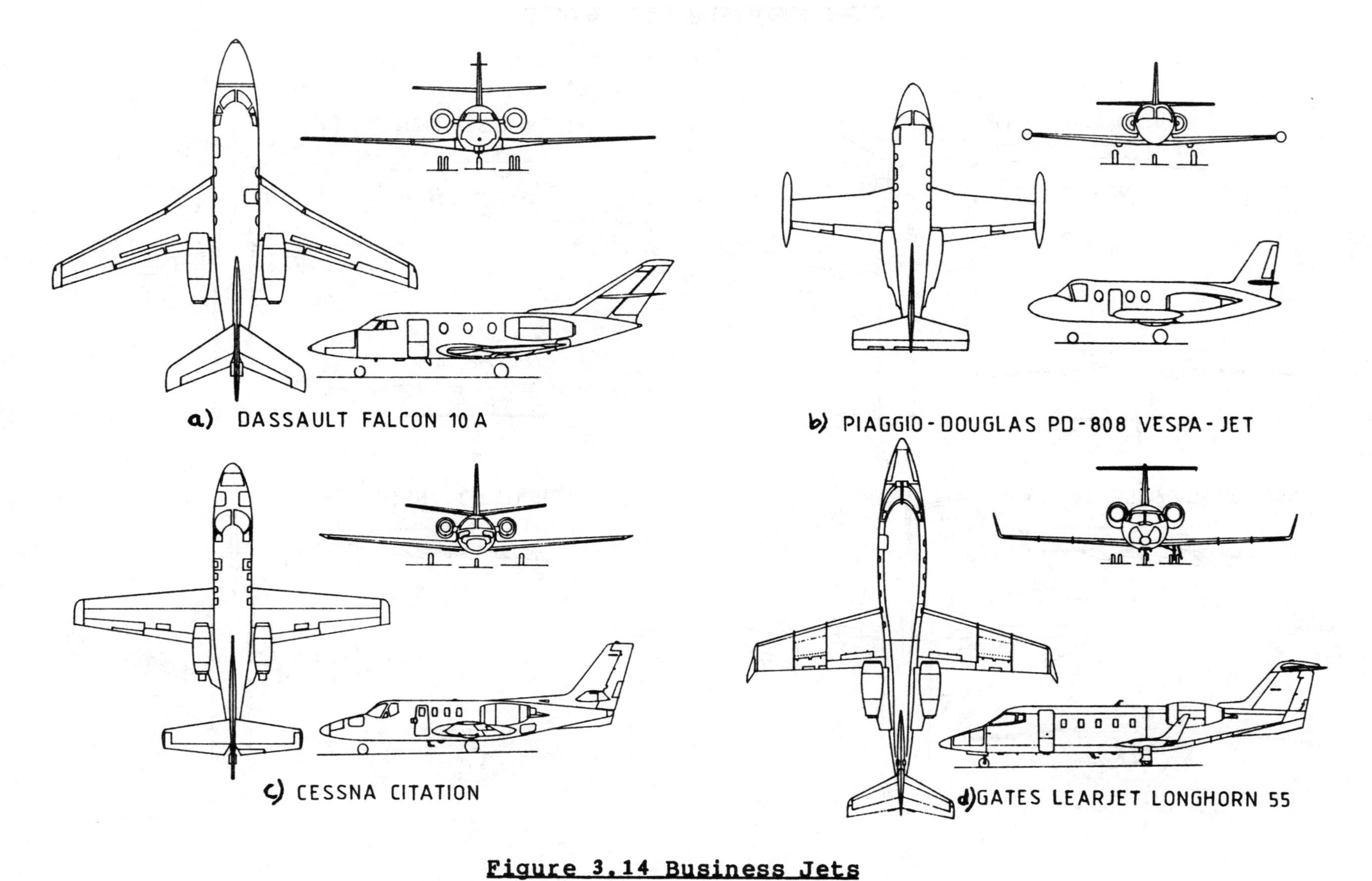

Figure 3.14 Business Jets

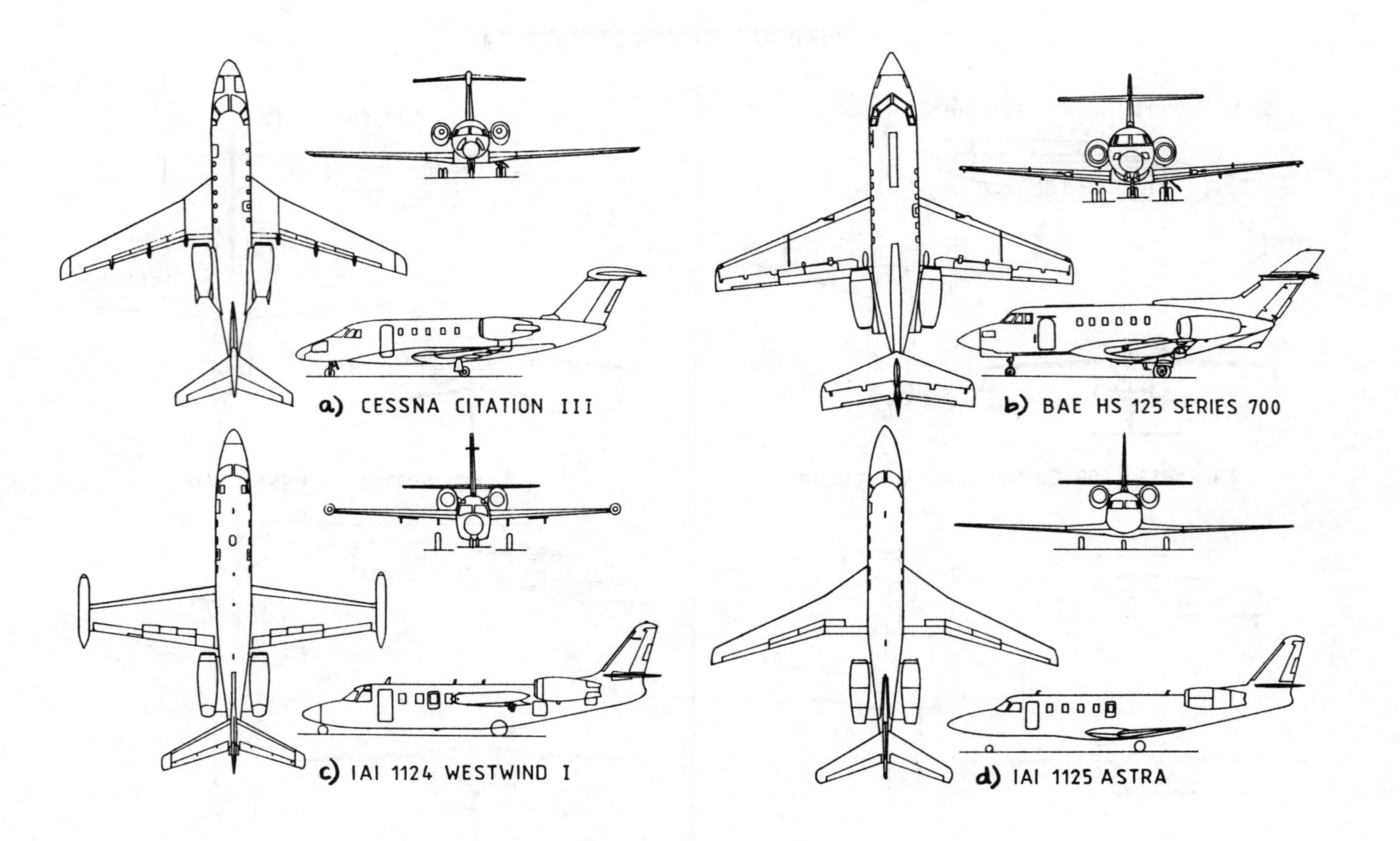

Figure 3.15 Business Jets

3.1.6 Regional Turbopropeller Driven Airplanes

Figures 3.16-3.18 show twelve configurations of regional turbopropeller driven airplanes. The following observations are offered:

1. Five are high wing and seven are low wing configurations.

2. Only one (the Shorts 330 of Fig.3.18d) has external bracing, all others are of cantilever construction. For cruise type vehicles, the drag penalty associated with external bracing is usually not acceptable, despite the weight advantage. Note that several of the configurations have wings with very large aspect ratios: A = 12.7 for the BAe 748 of Fig.3.18c is the highest.

3. Four have T-tail empennages, one a twin vertical tail empennage while the others have conventional horizontal and vertical tails. The position of the horizontal tail relative to the slipstream of the propeller is important from a handling quality point of view and from a tail fatigue point of view. The comments made for the twins in sub-section 3.1.4 apply here as well. Note that the Beech 1900 has an extra horizontal stabilizing surface as well as 'taillets'.

4. All have the nacelles installed in the wings. Note also that all are of the tractor configuration.

Wing-nacelle integration is important from an interference drag and from an induced drag point of view. Propeller distance to the ground and associated landing gear length all play a role in deciding how to integrate a nacelle into a wing. The fact, that significant differences exist between the twelve designs are indicative of the fact that nacelle integration continues to be a significant design problem.

5. Most retract the landing gear into a nacelle. Two of the high wing airplanes use a 'blister' fairing on the fuselage for gear retraction. The Jetstream retracts the gear into the wing itself. Landing gear retraction is an important design aspect of these airplanes. Blister fairings tend to be very draggy. On the other hand, they lead to short gear legs and thus save weight. Retracting a gear into the wing is potentially a bad idea: major cut-outs in the primary structure are usually the result. This leads to a substantial weight increase for the wing structure.

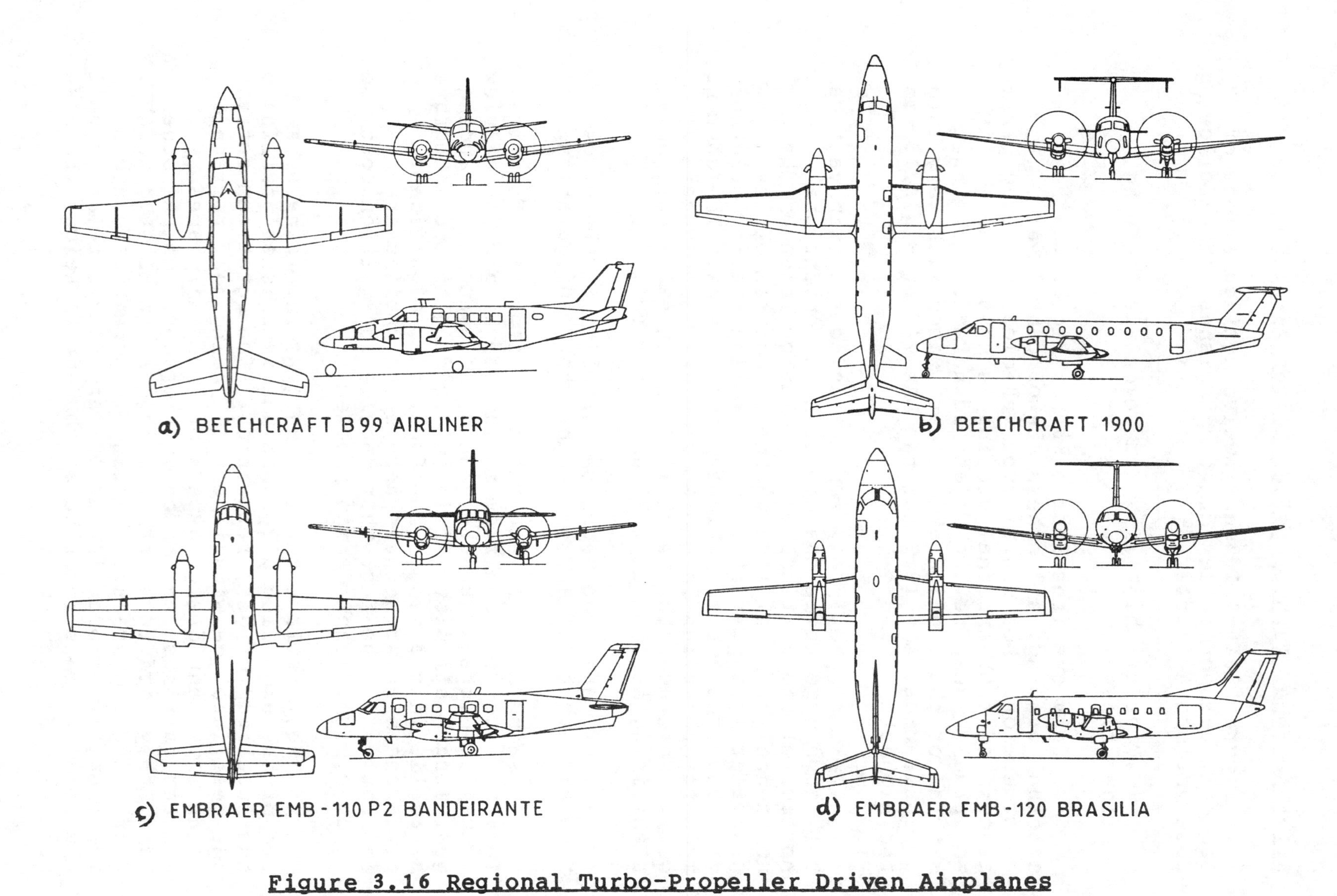

Figure 3.16 Regional Turbo-Propeller Driven Airplanes

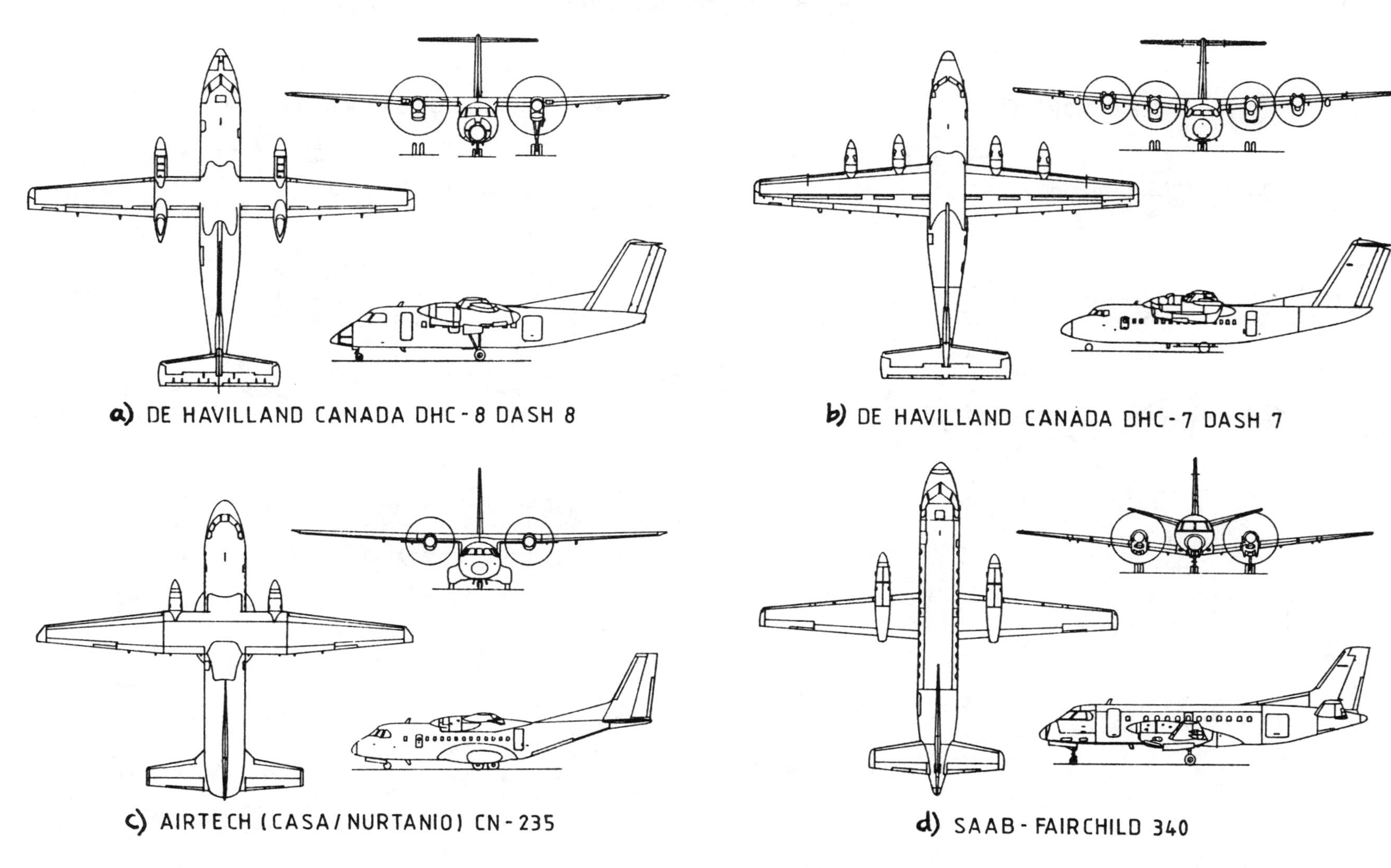

Figure 3.17 Regional Turbo-Propeller Driven Airplanes

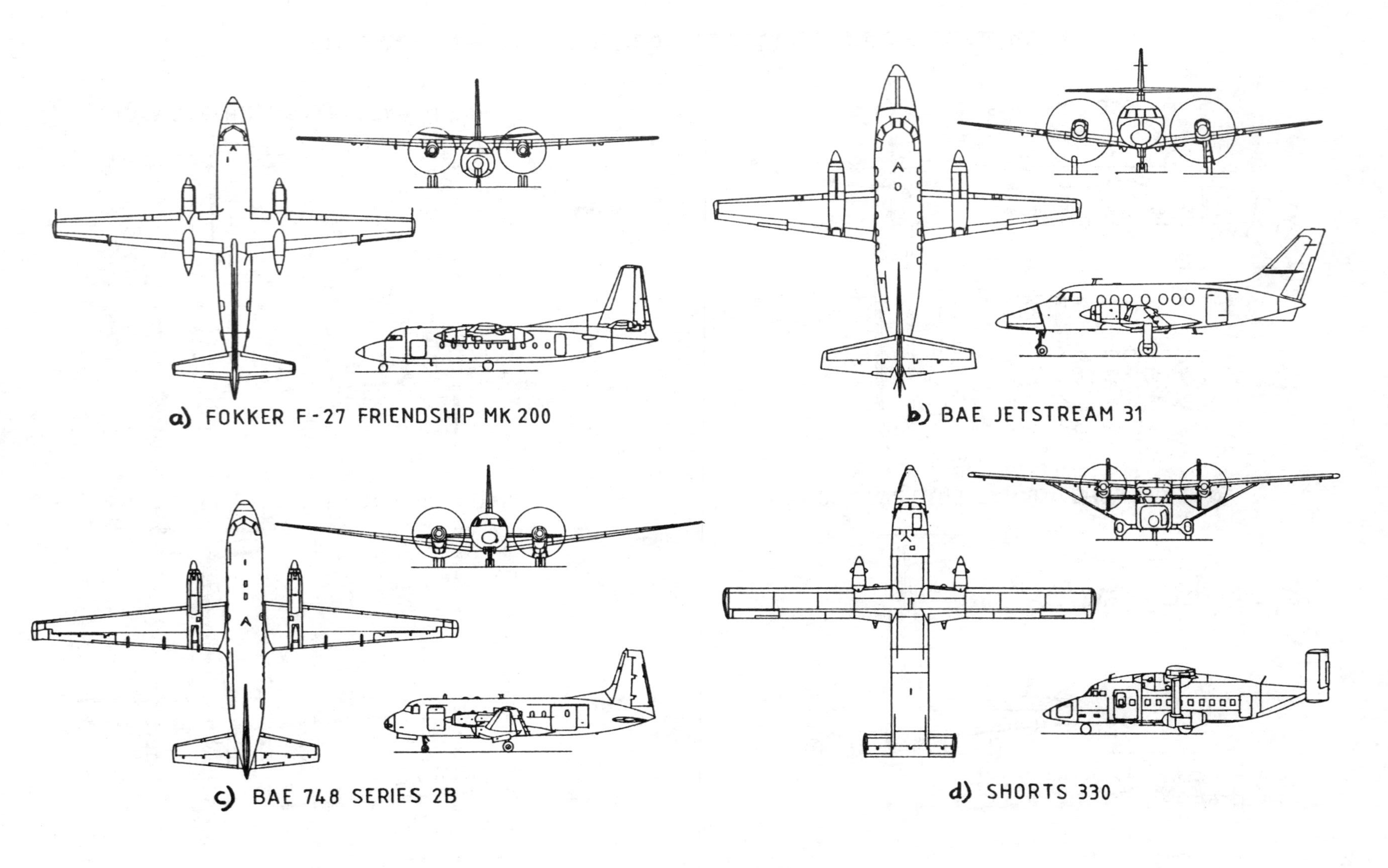

Figure 3.18 Regional Turbo-Propeller Driven Airplanes

3.1.7 Jet Transports

Figures 3.19-3.21 present twelve configurations of jet transports. The following observations are offered:

1. Except for the BAe 146 of Fig.3.21d, all jet transports have a low wing configuration.

2. All have the engines installed in nacelles on the rear fuselage or under the wing. The Tristar of Fig.3.20a has its center engine buried in the fuselage with an inlet in the form of an S-duct. Jet engines podded below the wing were pioneered by Boeing on the B47 bomber and before that by Arado in Germany during WWII. Jet engines on fuselage mounted nacelles were pioneered by the French on the Sud Caravelle.

Not shown in Figs. 3.19-3.21 are jet engines buried in the wing. These were pioneered by the British and used on many jet bombers and transports. Examples are the DH Comet, the HP Victor, The AVRO Vulcan (Fig.1.1) and the Vickers Valiant. The BAe Nimrod of Fig.3.28b which was derived from the Comet also sports this type of engine arrangement.

3. Note that except for the BAe 146 all jet transports retract the landing gear into the wing/fuselage intersection. The fuselage mounted gear of the BAe 146 is a very clean installation (aerodynamically speaking). However it does limit lateral stability on the ground due to the small distance between the main gears.

4. Many jet transports follow the Boeing wing/fuselage arrangement with a wing glove and a wing yehudi. The glove/yehudi arrangement (pioneered on the 707) provides for favorable drag, a thick wingroot and a way to get the landing gear retracted without interfering with either the inboard flaps or the rear spars. It also offers very good lateral stability on the ground.

5. Most jet transports use a tricycle landing gear layout. The Boeing 747 uses four main gear struts, while the DC 10-30 uses three main gear struts.

6. Observe that three jet transports use T-tails, the remainder using low horizontal tails.

7. For in-flight speedbrakes, ten of the jet transports use wing mounted spoilers. However, the Fokker F-28 and the BAe 146 (Figs. 3.21c and d) use rear fuselage mounted clamshell doors.

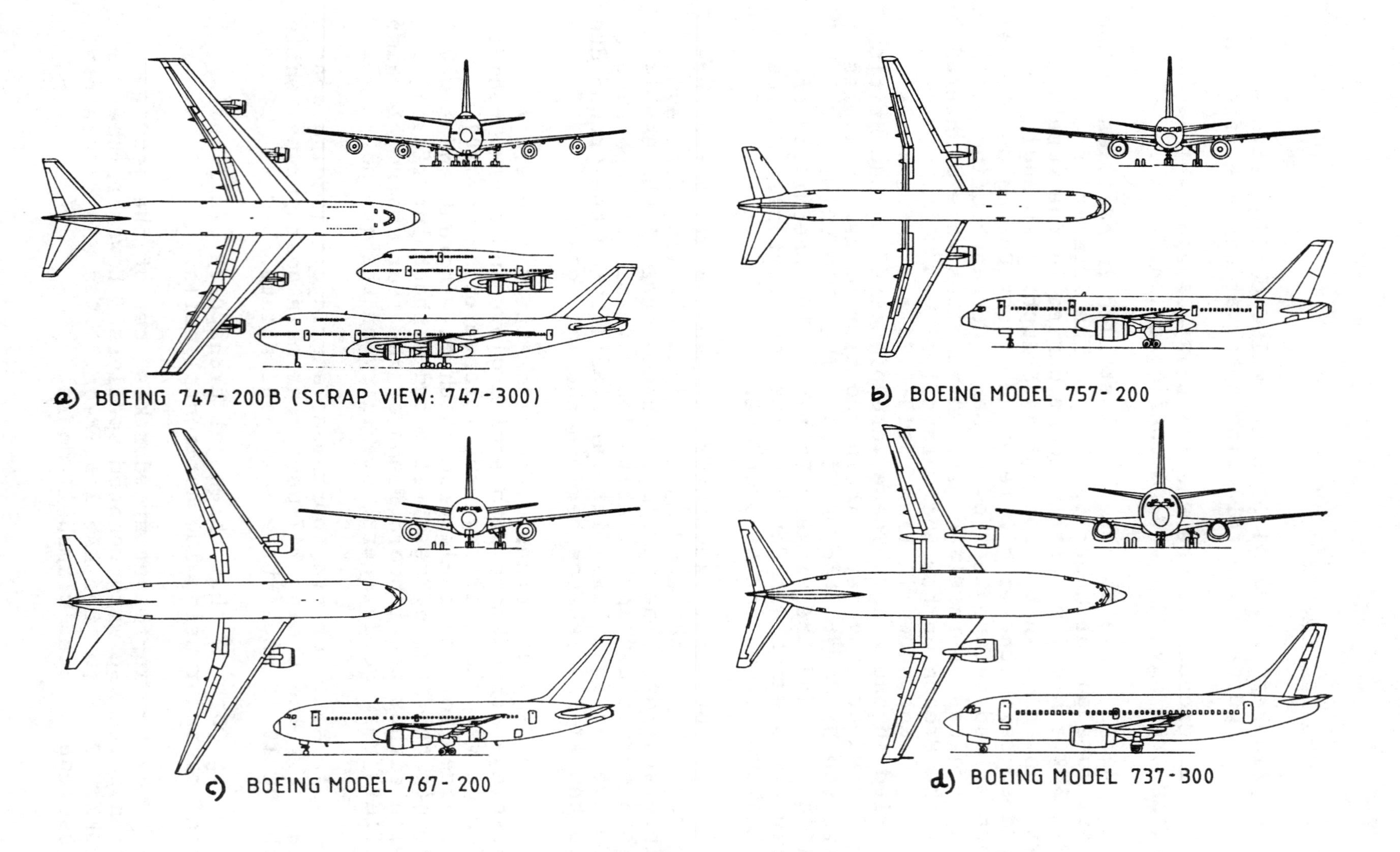

Figure 3.19 Jet Transports

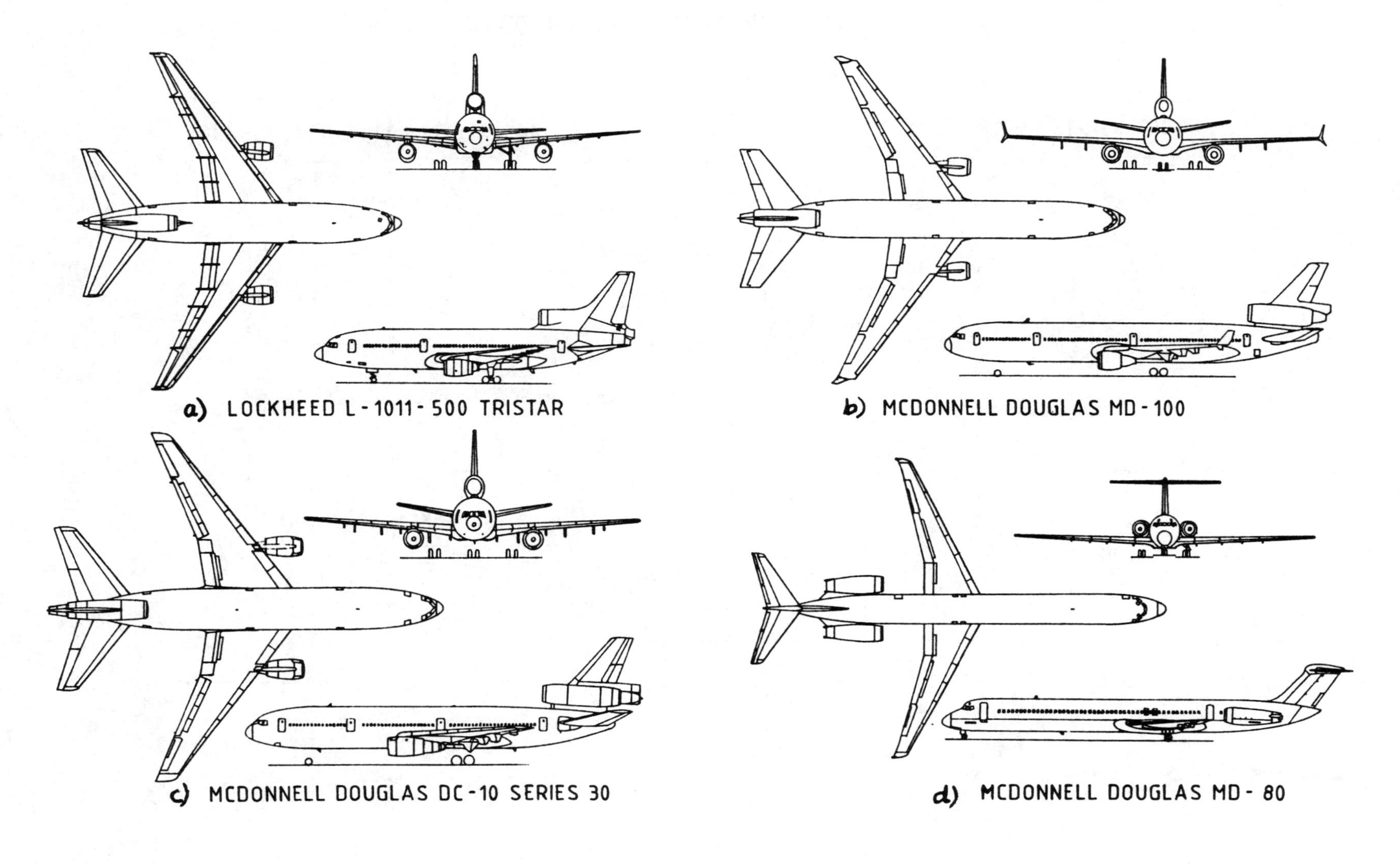

Figure 3.20 Jet Transports

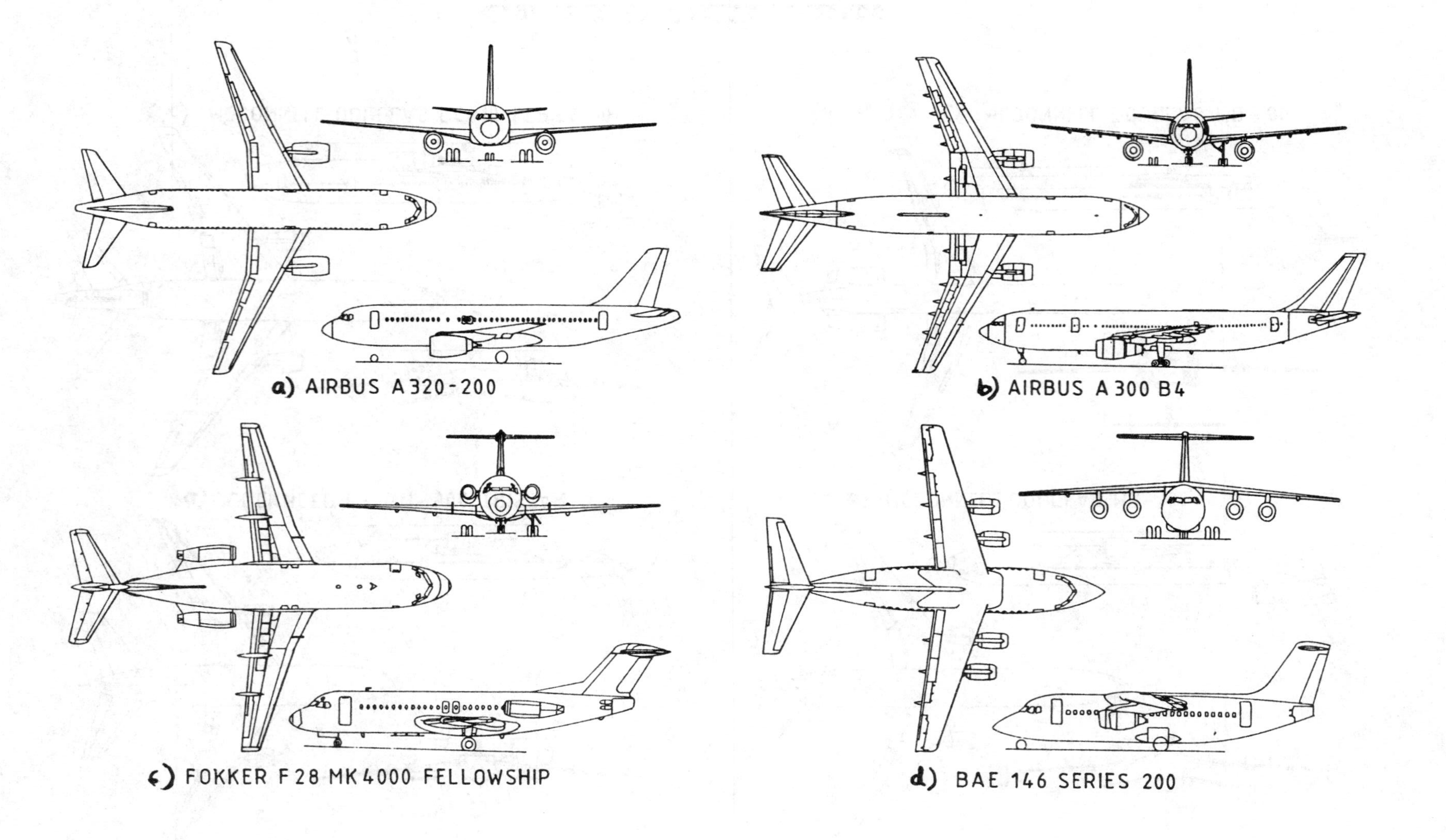

Figure 3.21 Jet Transports

3.1.8 Military Trainers

Figure 3.22 shows four propeller driven military trainers. Figures 3.23 and 3.24 present eight jet driven military trainers. The following observations are offered:

1. The propeller driven trainers are primarily used for initial or basic training. The jet driven trainers are used for advanced training.

2. All are capable of being equipped with gun and bomb racks.

3. Note the RFB Fantrainer of Fig.3.22d. It uses a ducted fan (5 blades) with the fan shaft and duct structure used as an integral part of the fuselage. The forward sweep angle on the wing was selected for reasons of weight and balance, not for aerodynamic reasons. The Fantrainer is the only pusher, the others are tractors.

4. Observe the extensive use of strakes and fins on most trainers. These were probably added during flight test as 'aerodynamic afterthoughts' to fix stall and/or spin problems.

5. Note that two of the eight jet trainers have high wings, the rest have low wings.

6. All jet trainers shown use buried engines in the fuselage. A major drag problem with all these configurations is to fair the relatively large inlets into the wing root or into the fuselage with a minimum of flow distortion. With the single engine configurations, another design problem is the bifurcated s-ducts leading to the engine. These ducts are very critical to the successful operation of the engine and require a lot of detail design attention early on.

7. Observe that the inboard part of the engine inlets are located a good distance away from the fuselage. The reason is to prevent 'tired' boundary layers from getting into the inlet duct.

8. All trainers use the tricycle landing gear layout.

9. The tail configurations range from one T-tail to several cruciform and low tail layouts. The T-46A of Fig.3.23b uses a twin vertical tail, an unusual feature for this type of airplane.

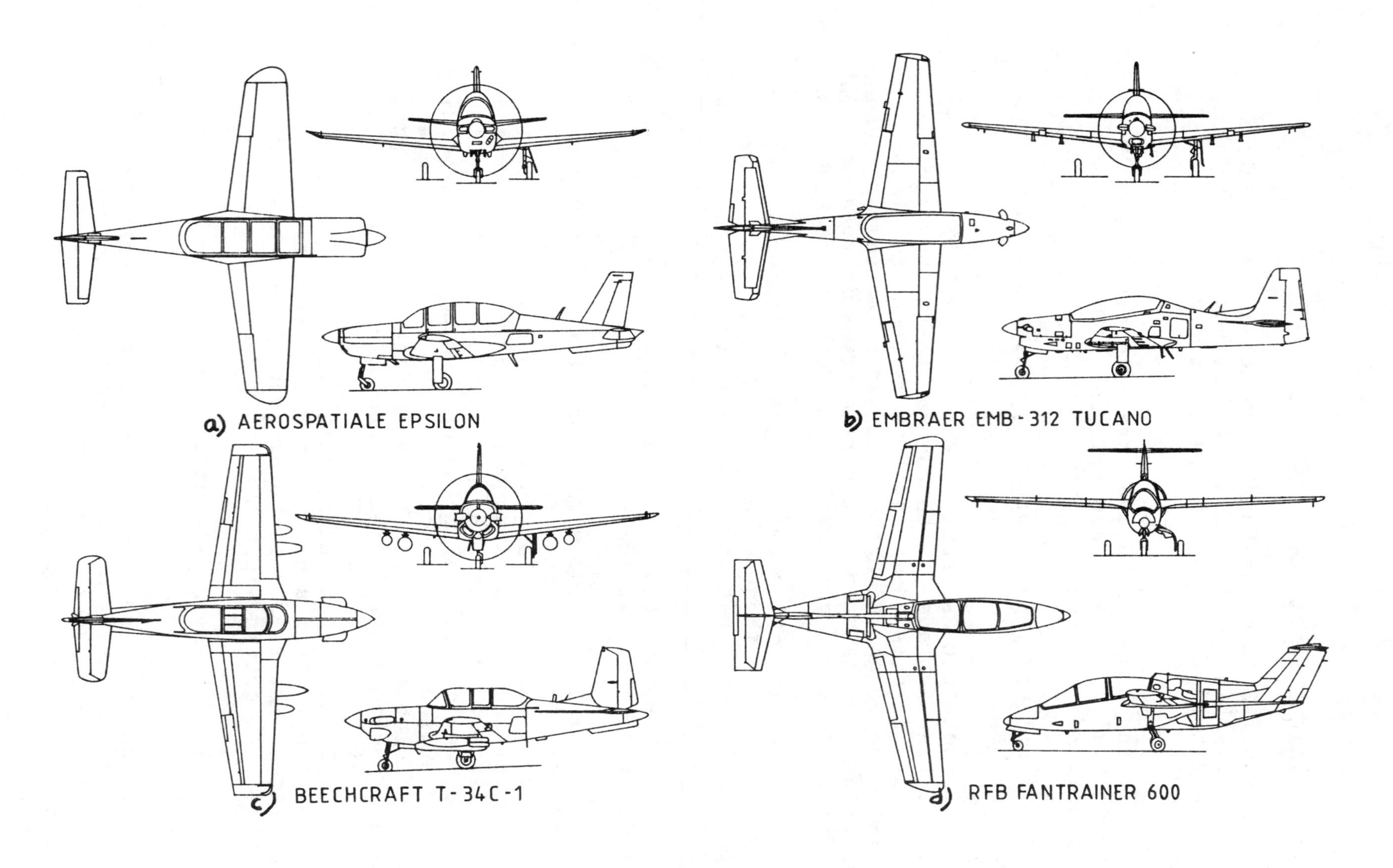

Figure 3.22 Military Trainers

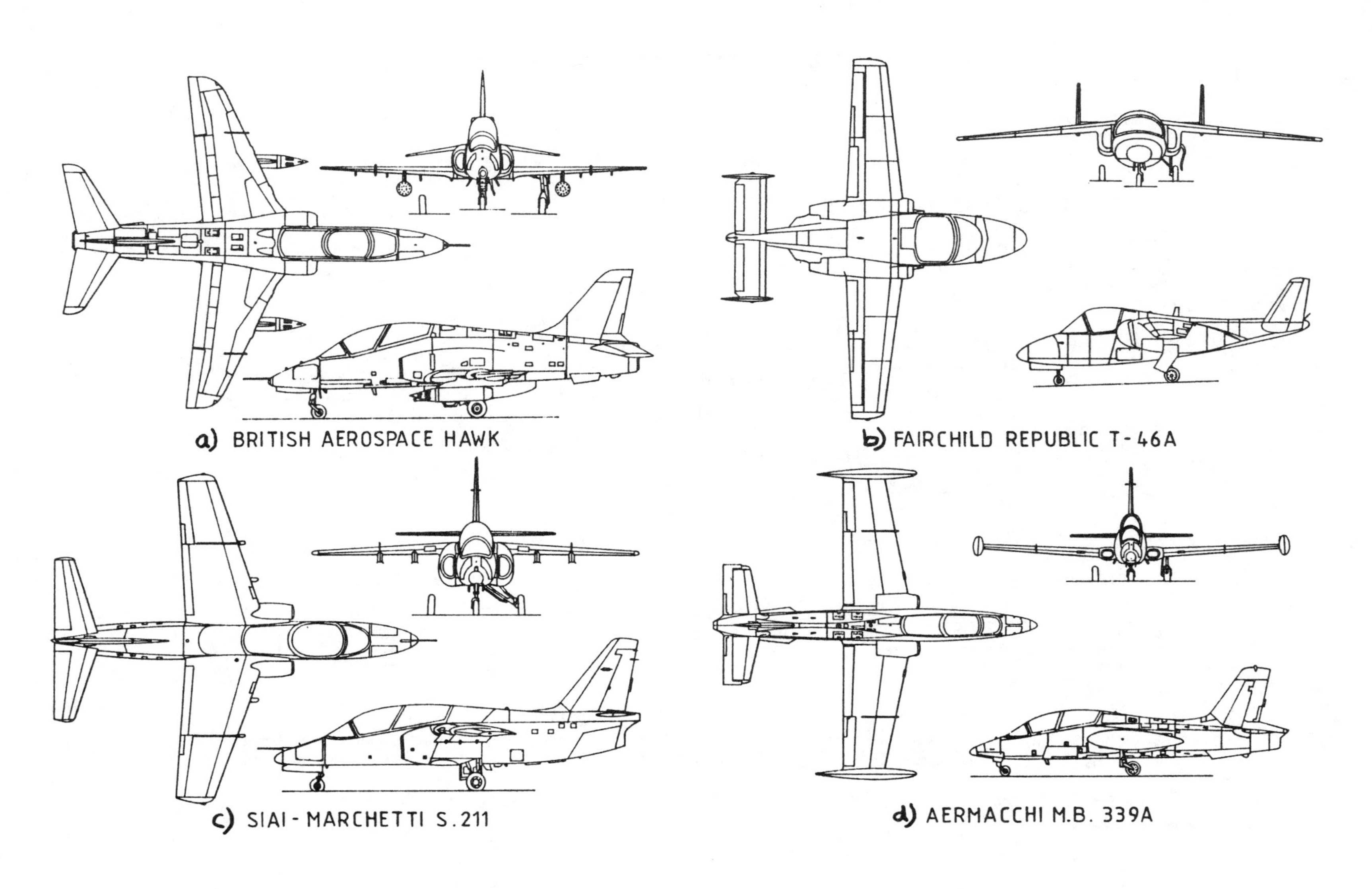

Figure 3.23 Military Trainers

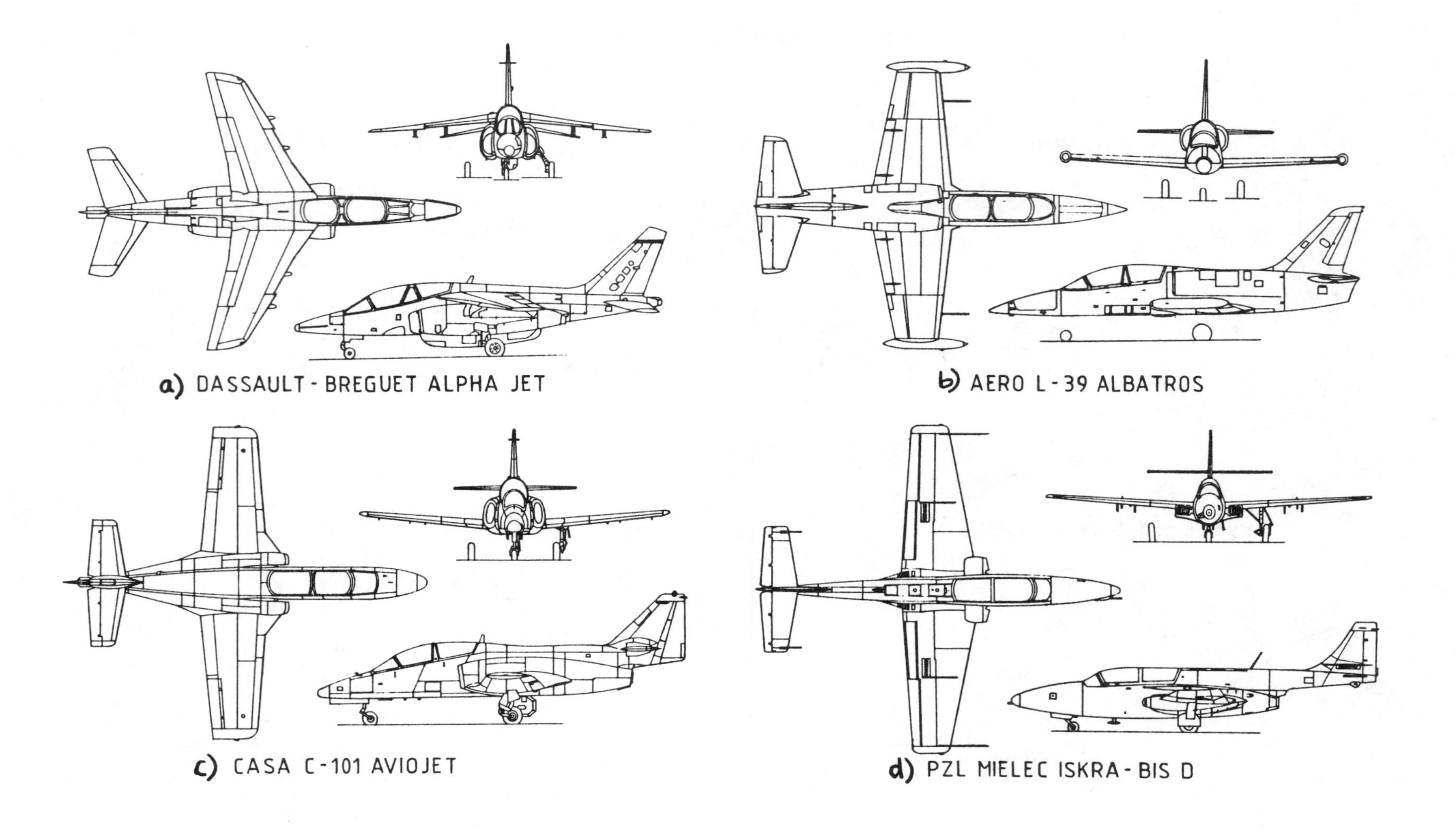

Figure 3.24 Military Trainers

3.1.9 Fighters

Figures 3.25-3.27 present twelve fighter configurations. The following observations are offered:

1. Except for the Pucara of Fig.3.26c all fighters are jet driven. Unless there is a requirement for high dash speeds, the turboprop offers a cost and a take-off performance advantage over jets.

2. Note that six of the fighters are singles and six are twins.

3. All fighters shown have a tri-cycle landing gear. Note the tandem wheel arrangement on the Viggen of Fig.3.27d. That arrangement was selected to allow the gear to be retracted into the thin wing.

4. Observe that most of the fighters shown employ only one wheel per main strut. However four of them have two nosewheel tires.

5. Two of the fighters shown use a variable sweep wing. This is a very expensive feature (in terms of weight and cost) and is justified only in cases where supersonic range, subsonic range and low speed performance are all critical to the mission of the airplane.

6. Note the preference for conventional configurations. The Mirage IIIE of Fig.3.26c employs a delta wing configuration. This is a very efficient form if the dominating mission requirement is for rapid acceleration to supersonic attack or cruise. The blended wing-body of the GD F-16XL (Fig.3.25c) is a modern variation on the delta theme.

7. The coupled canard/delta planform (Fig.3.27c) of the Viggen was pioneered by SAAB (Sweden). By proper relative arrangement of the canard above and forward of the wing it is possible to achieve very favorable interference between the canard lifting vortex and the flow over the following delta wing.

8. A major design problem with a high speed, highly maneuverable fighter is the achievement of sufficient directional stability at high angles of attack. Vortices shed from the forebody tend to interfere with the vertical tail. This leads some designers to use two large vertical tails. Figures 3.25a and 3.27b are typical examples.

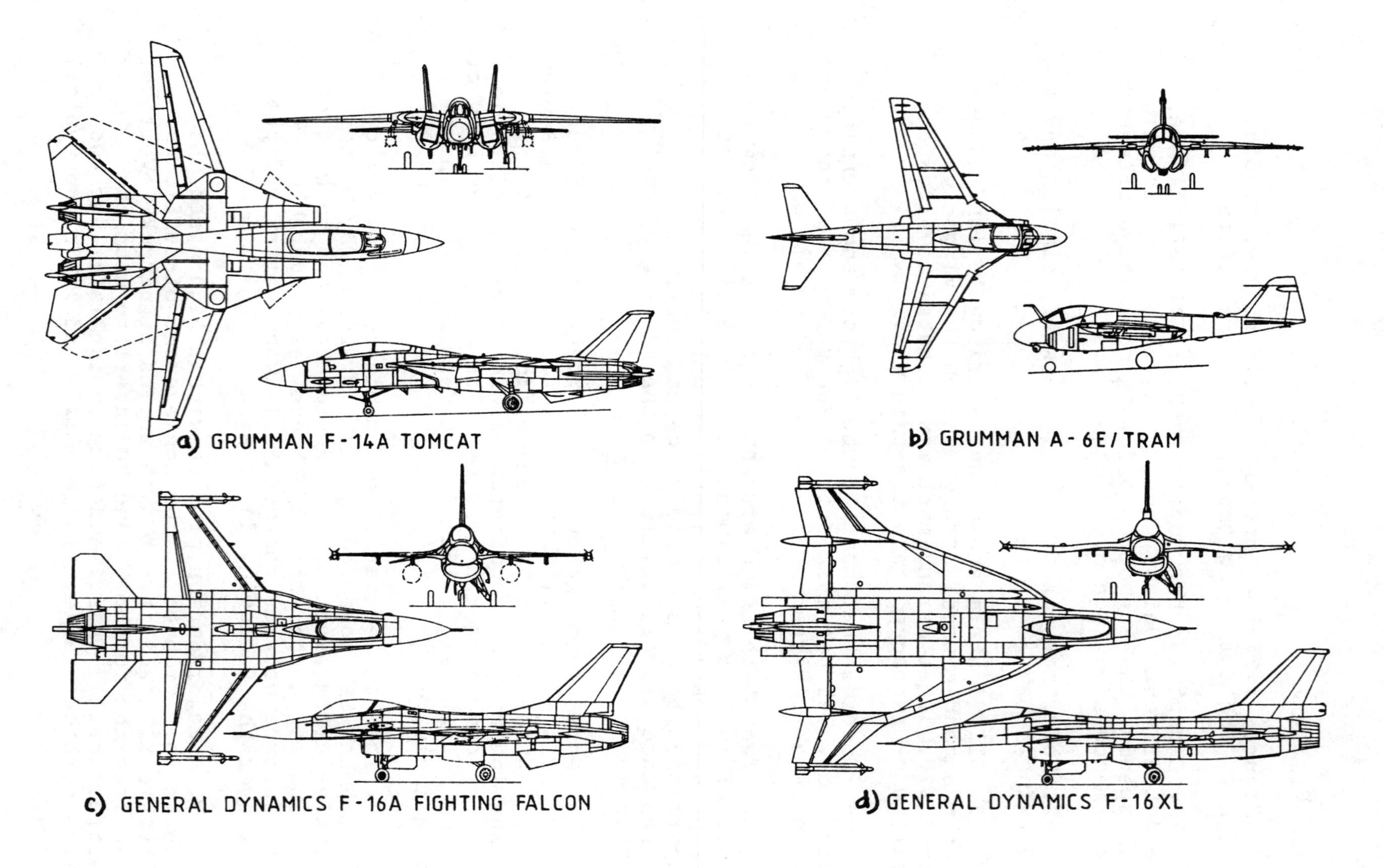

Figure 3.25 Fighters

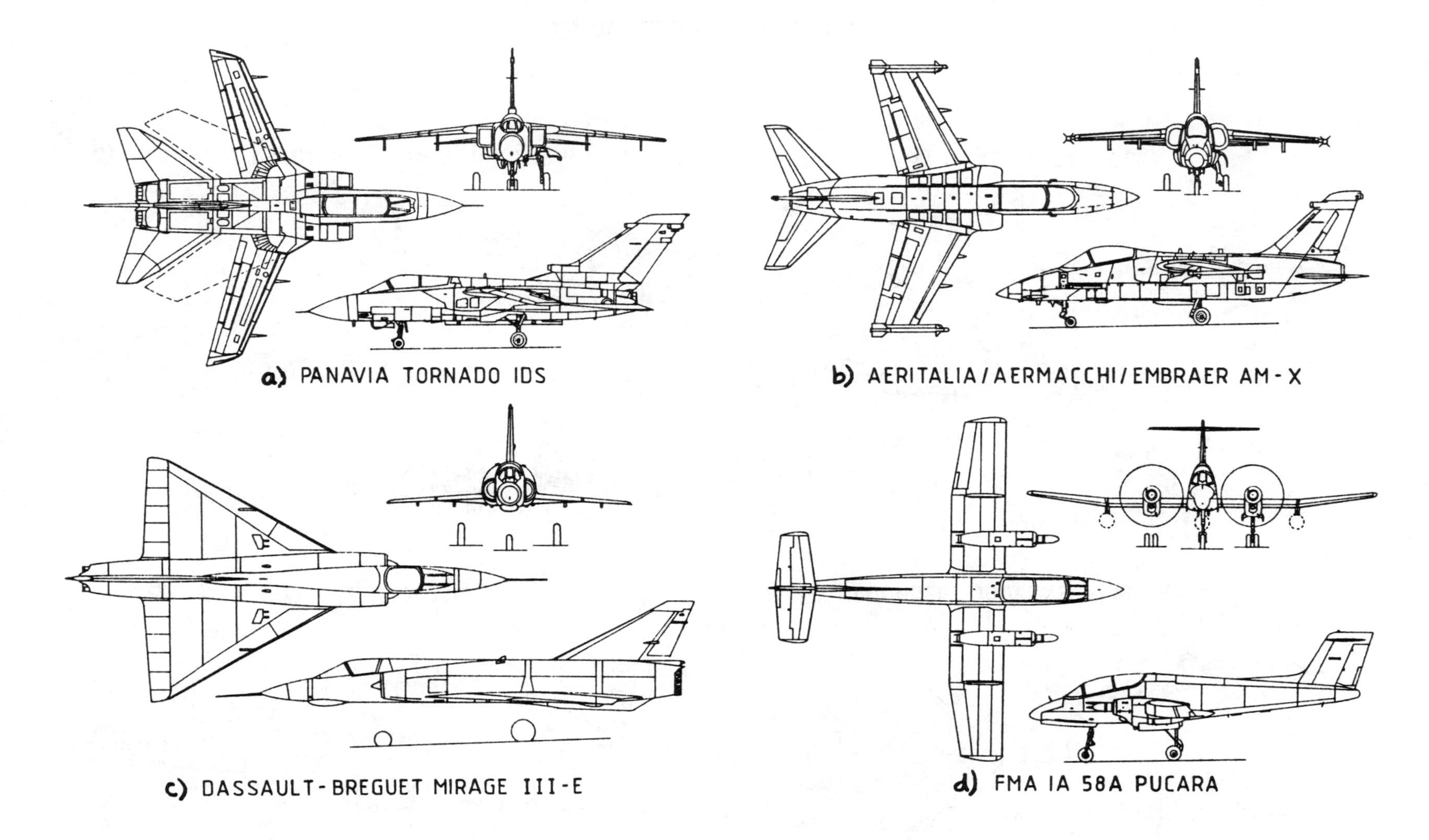

Figure 3.26 Fighters

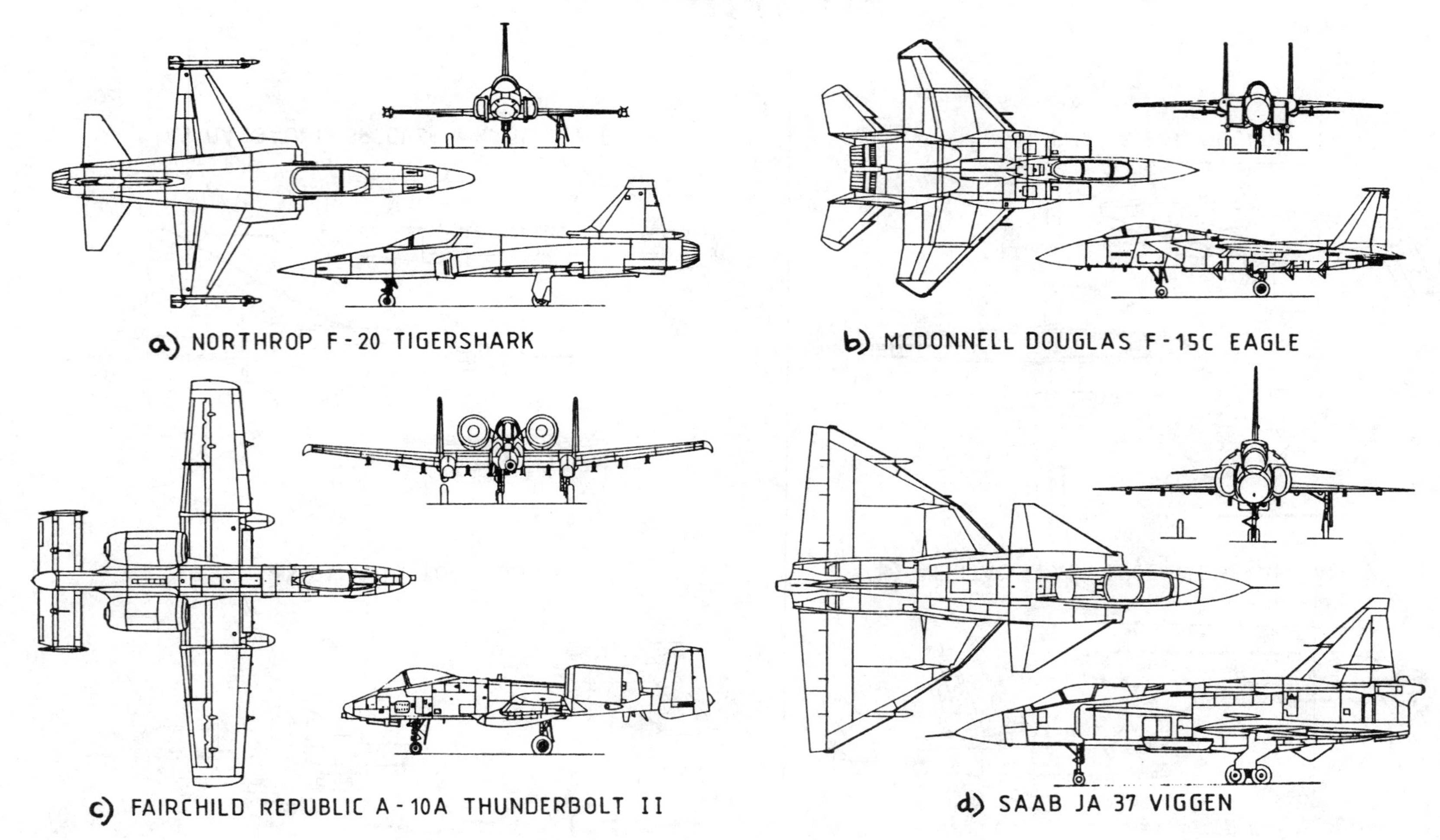

Figure 3.27 Fighters

3.1.10 Military Patrol, Bomb and Transport Airplanes

Figures 3.28-3.30 present twelve configurations for airplanes in this category. The following observations are offered:

1. The B52H of Fig.3.28a is a long range bomber designed around a long bomb bay. This forced the high wing layout and the tandem landing gear. Because of the tandem gear layout, rotation during take-off is not possible: the airplane 'flies off'. This in turn results in longer take-off distances. It also forces a rather large wing incidence angle. In turn this causes the airplane to cruise 'nose down' which is not the best attitude from a drag viewpoint. The point of these comments is: a seemingly innocent and logical mission requirement such as a long bomb bay can dominate the configuration design of an airplane.

2. Note thet the transports of Figures 3.28c, d, 3.29b, d and 3.30a all have high wing layouts with body mounted landing gears. This configuration feature is forced by the requirement to load and unload heavy equipment without external help.

3. The tanker/transports of Figures 3.29b and d and the patrol airplane of Fig.3.28b were developed from civil transports. That is the main reason for their low wing configurations.

4. Note that the configurations are conventional.

5. Note the large search radars in Fig.3.30c and 3.30d. These radars are designed for 'look-up' as well as 'look-down' capability. The fuselage and the empennage of both airplanes hinder the look-down' capability to some extent. The empennage of the Hawkeye is made of composites for that reason.

6. All jets in this category have significant wing sweep while the turboprops do not. The reason is the difference in design cruise speed.

7. Note the four vertical tails on the Hawkeye. This is a carrier based airplane with commensurate restrictions on length, width and height. In turn this leads to 'short-coupled' configurations. When a large radome is added, directional stability suffers, leading to the requirement for more vertical tail area. Since the height is also restricted, one solution is to put on more vertical tails.

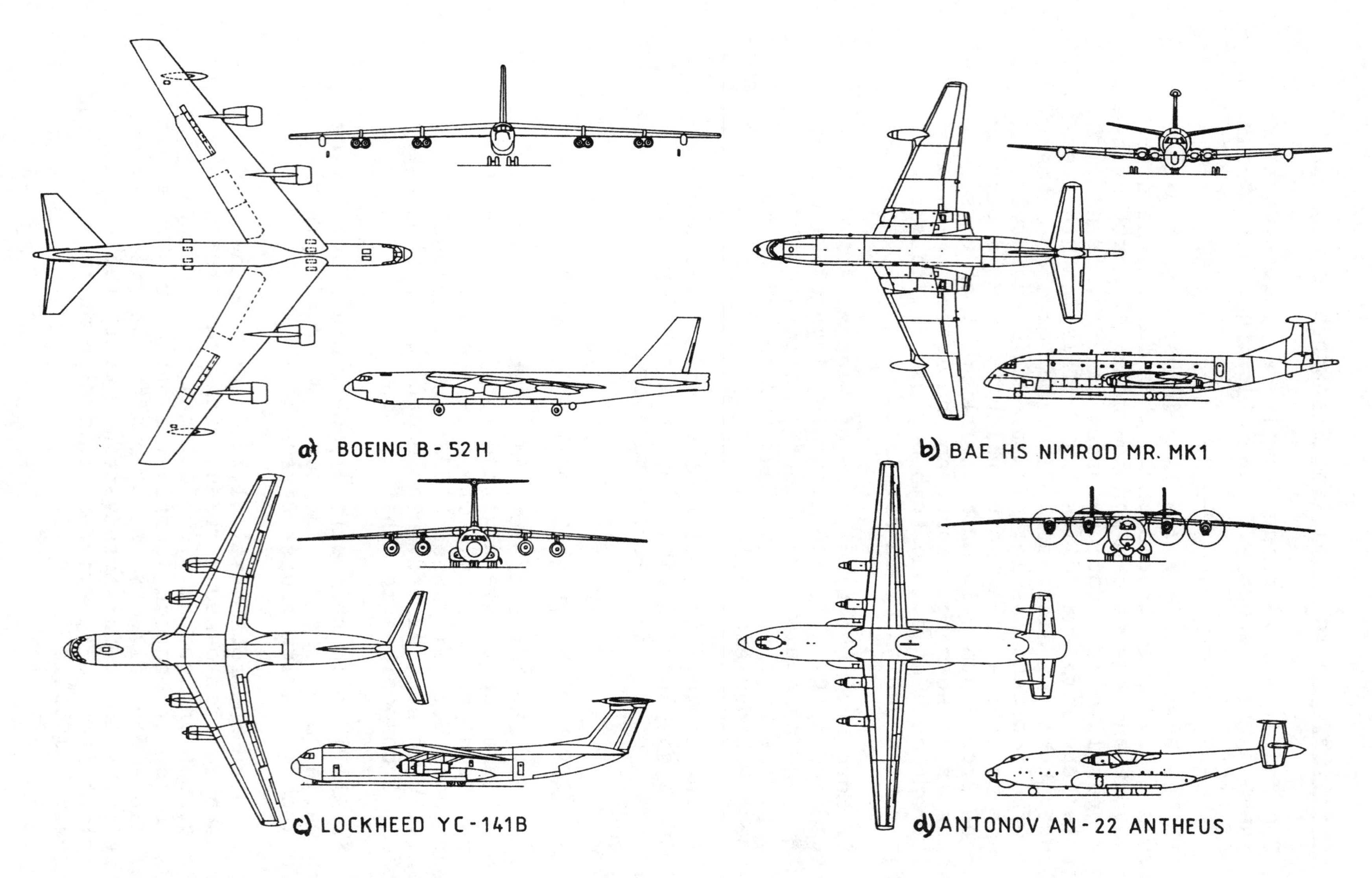

Figure 3.28 Military Patrol, Bomb and Transport Airplanes

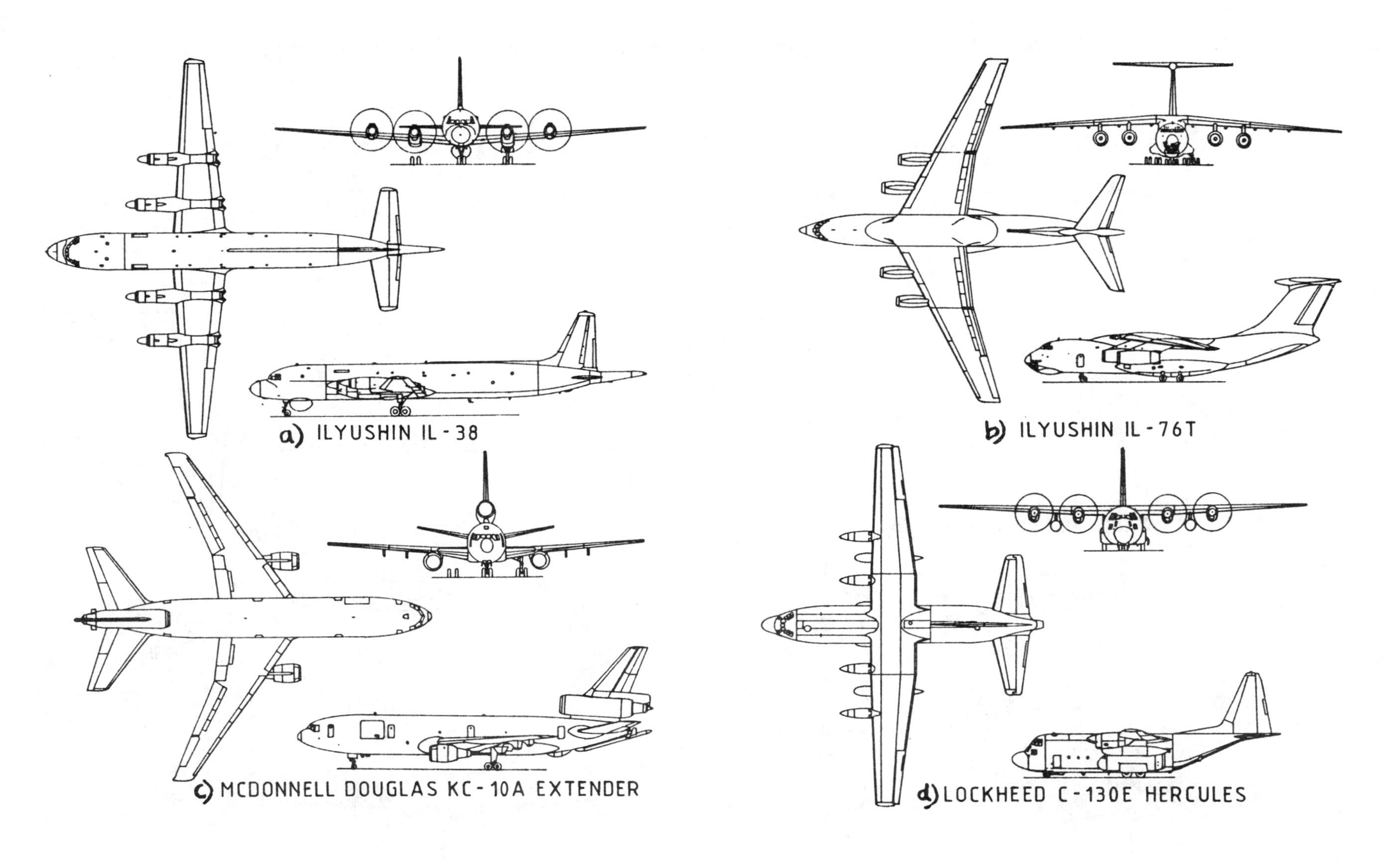

Figure 3.29 Military Patrol, Bomb and Transport Airplanes

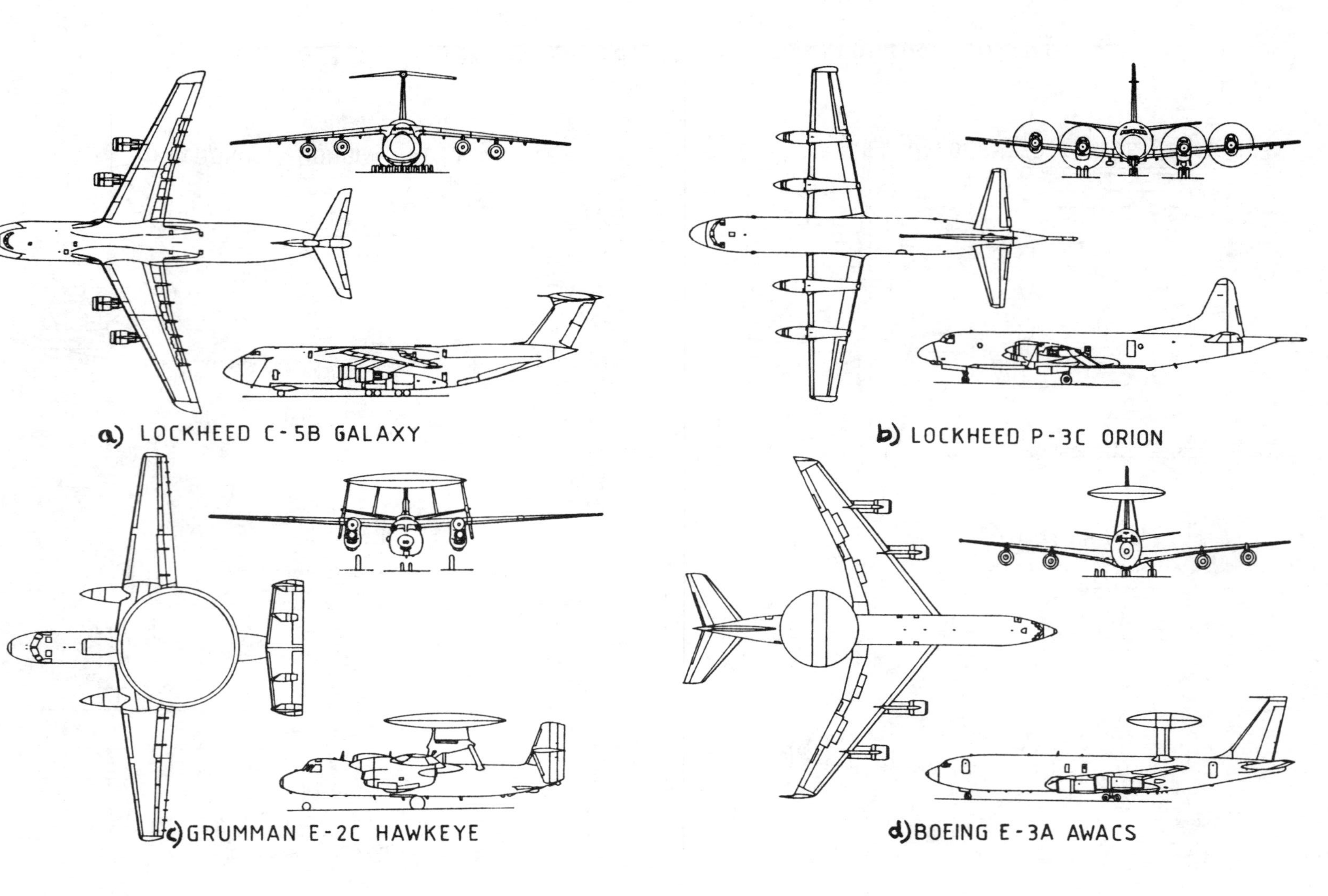

Figure 3.30 Military Patrol, Bomb and Transport Airplanes

3.1.11 Flying Boats, Amphibious and Float Airplanes

Figures 3.31-33 present twelve configurations in the flying boat and amphibious category. The following observations are offered:

1. These airplanes are dominated by the requirement for a large, hydrodynamically shaped hull. This requirement results in much larger wetted area and profile drag than is the case in land based airplanes. On the other hand it gives these airplanes a unique capability: landing and take-off from water.

2. The airplanes in Figures 3.31-3.32c are 'modern era' types, the others date from just before and during WWII. Observe the preference for conventional configurations.

3. A major design problem with water based airplanes is to keep the water spray from the hull away from engine components: salt water does not agree very well with most metals.

4. A consequence of item 3 is that the thrust lines in some flying boats end up rather high above the c.g. This has significant consequences to the flying characteristics of these airplanes in going from power-on to power-off.

5. Note that turboprops are used in most modern flying boats.

6. The Martin Seamaster of Fig.3.32b was an attempt to develop a very high speed flying boat for the USNavy. Ref.22 in Section 14.2 gives the reasons for its failure.

7. The huge, ten-engine, turboprop Princess of Fig.3.32c was an attempt just after WWII to capture the transatlantic passenger market. It failed because of the introduction of passenger jets such as the 707, the DC8 and the Comet.

8. Most of the amphibians have a tri-cycle landing gear configuration. The Beriev M12 of Fig.3.31d is an interesting exception.

9. Landing gear wells in water based airplanes have to be sealed to prevent water from entering the hull. The hulls themselves must have a number of sealed, watertight compartments. This is to prevent damage to a small area from causing the entire machine to sink.

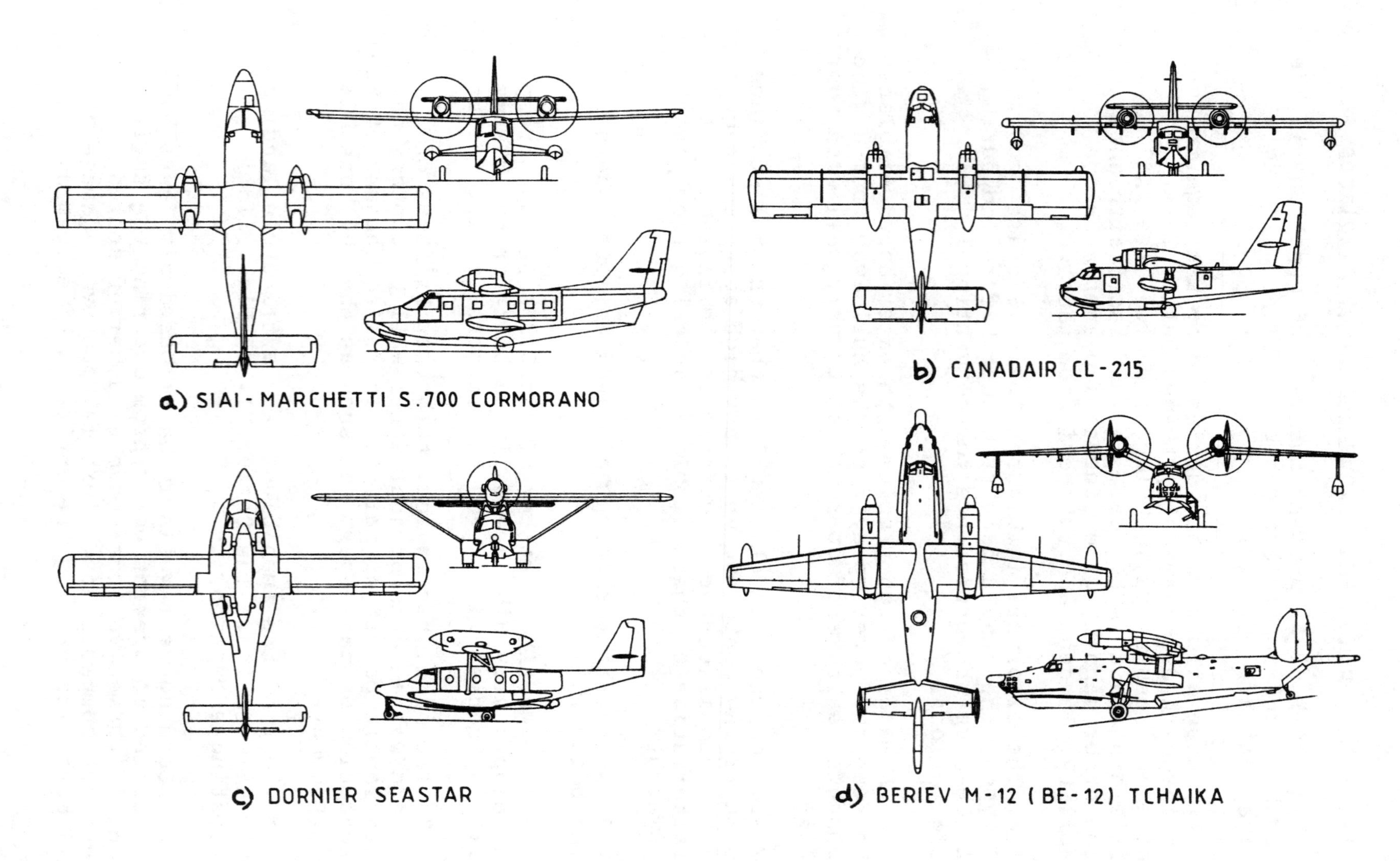

Figure 3.31 Flying Boats, Amphibious and Float Airplanes

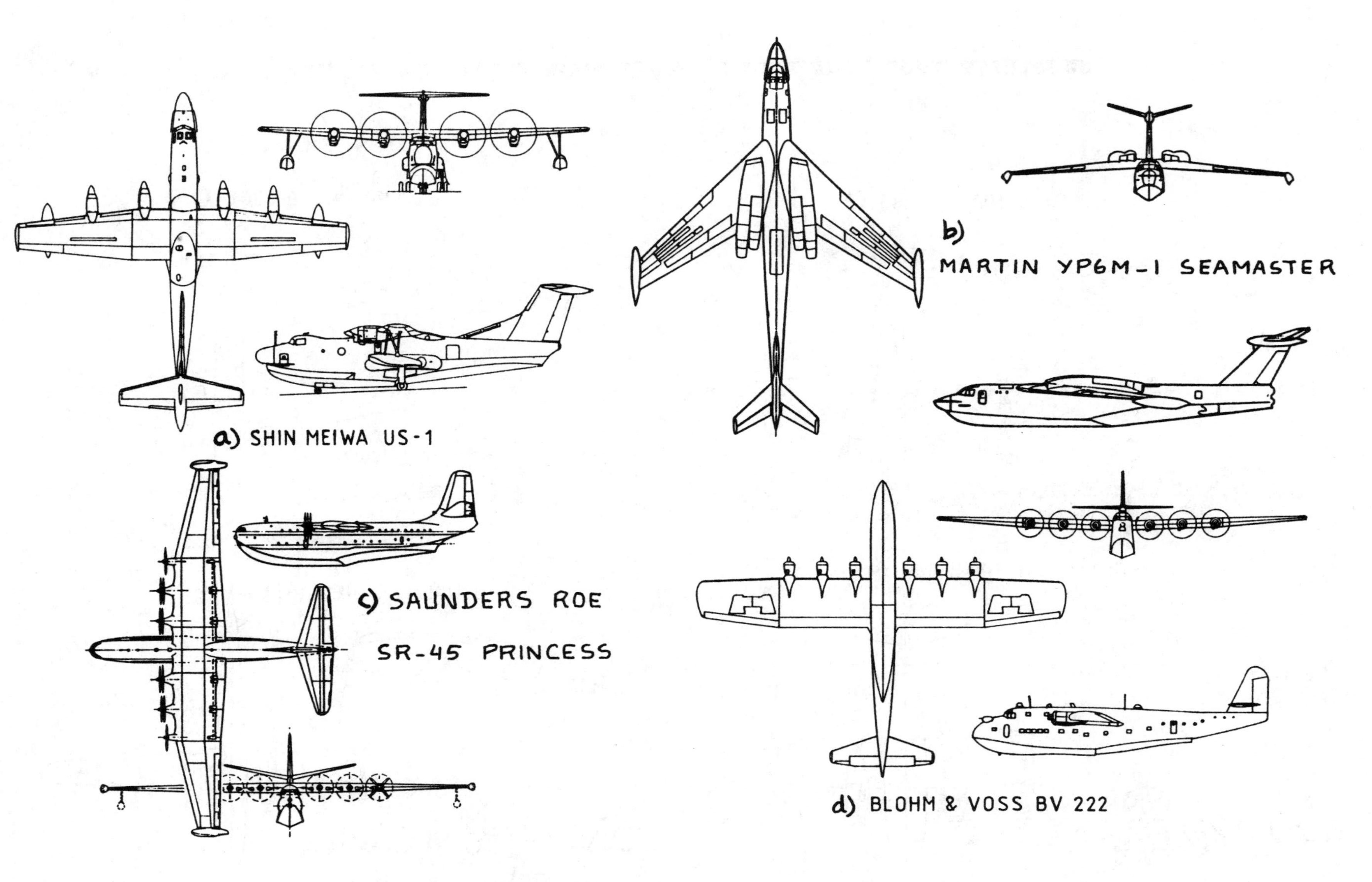

Figure 3.32 Flying Boats, Amphibious and Float Airplanes

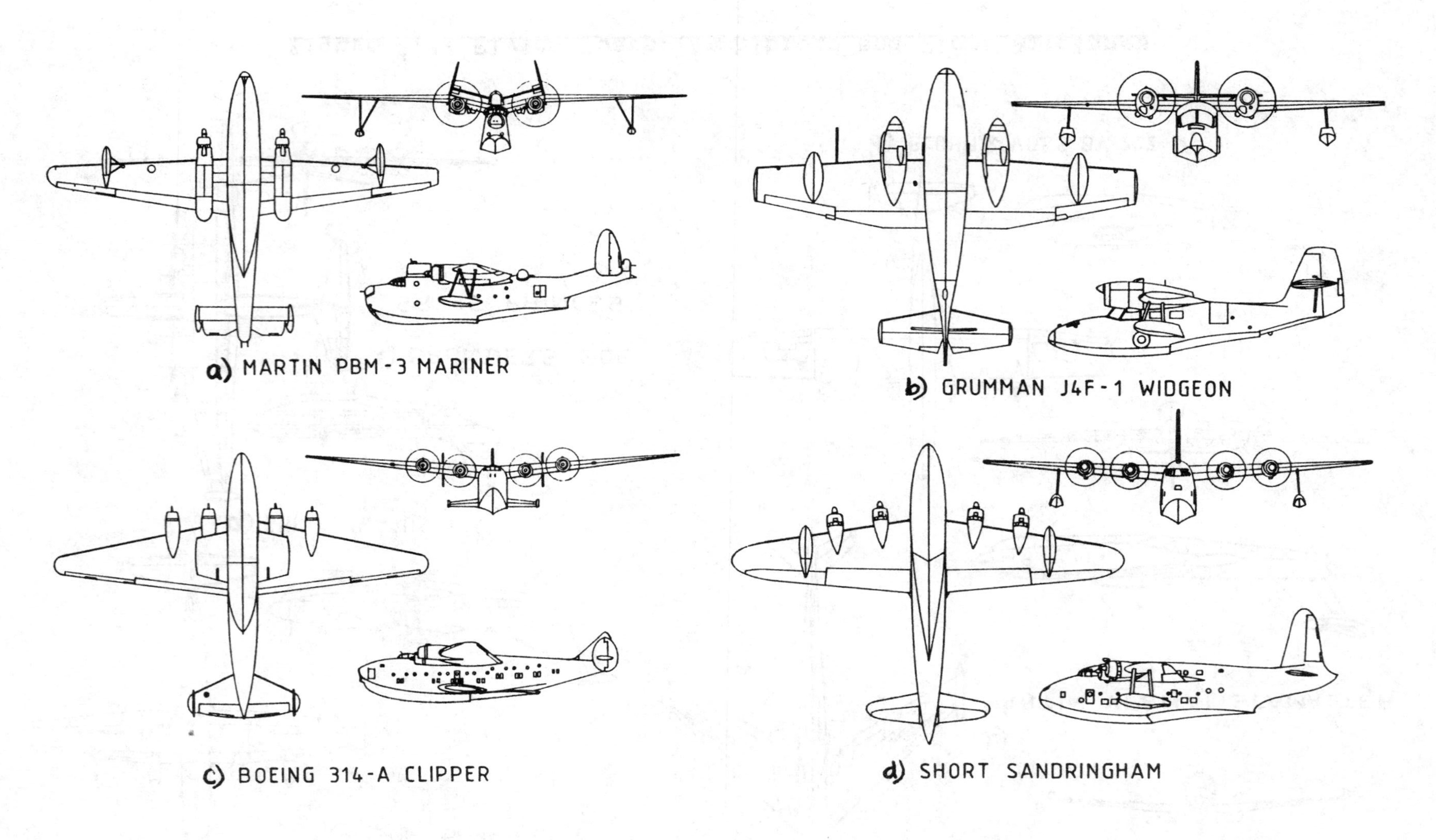

Figure 3.33 Flying Boats, Amphibious and Float Airplanes

3.1.12 Supersonic Cruise Airplanes

Figures 3.34-36 present twelve configurations of supersonic cruise airplanes. The following observations are offered:

1. The airplanes of Figures 3.34 and 3.35 have flown and except for the XB-70 have been or still are operational. The airplanes of Figure 3.36 are design studies only in the sense that they have not been built.

2. Note the large sweep angles on all supersonic airplanes. The airplanes shown all have 'subsonic' leading edges in supersonic cruise. That means the leading edge of the wing is behind the Mach cone. Supersonic cruise vehicles are dominated by the requirement to minimize wave drag. The cross sectional area distribution of these airplanes is therefore very critical.

3. Because of the large l.e. sweep, the lift-curve slope of these airplanes is low. At approach speeds this results in a high angle of attack which makes visibility over the nose a major problem. In the airplanes of Figs. 3.35c, d and 3.36a, b this problem was solved by a 'drooped nose'. In the B1-B of Fig.3.35b a variable sweep wing is used to allow the airplane to cruise with reasonable efficiency at subsonic speeds. This VSW feature can make it unnecessary to use a drooped nose. Note that in the Boeing SST proposal of Fig.3.36a both features are employed.

4. A major design problem with commercial supersonic transports is the sonic boom. It is very difficult to design an SST with acceptable sonic boom characteristics during overland flight. That is the reason why sofar most countries (including the USA) prohibit supersonic flight overland. Military airplanes are exempted from this requirement as long as they stay within certain corridors.

5. Inlet placement in supersonic airplanes is another critical design consideration. Note that most have the inlet far aft under the wing. Such an arrangement results in favorable pressure interference.

6. Trimmed cruise lift-to-drag ratios at supersonic speeds are typically 7 to 9. For the subsonic transports these values are 14 to 18. Here lies an aerodynamic design problem with serious implications for economic feasibility.

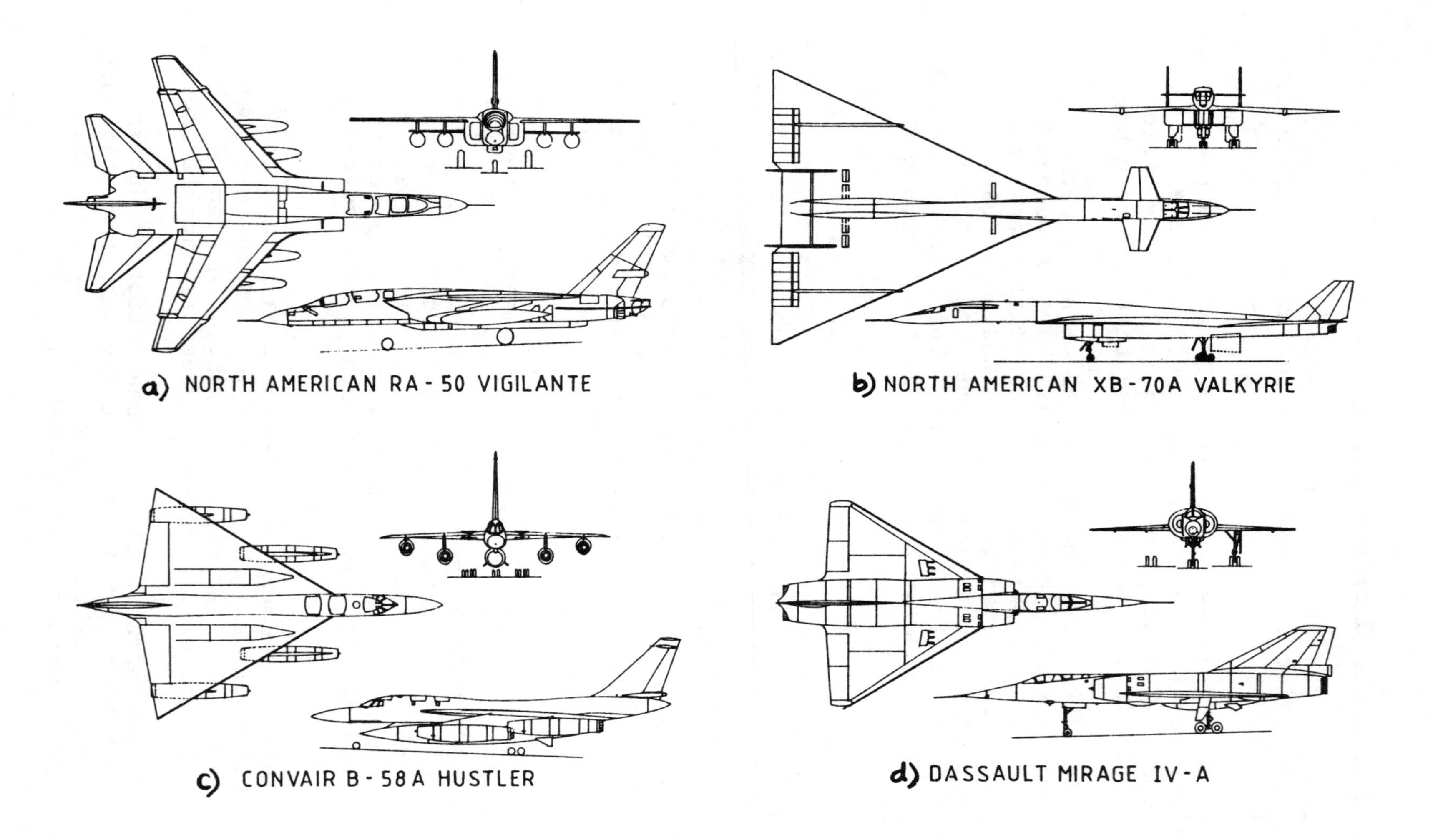

Figure 3.34 Supersonic Cruise Airplanes

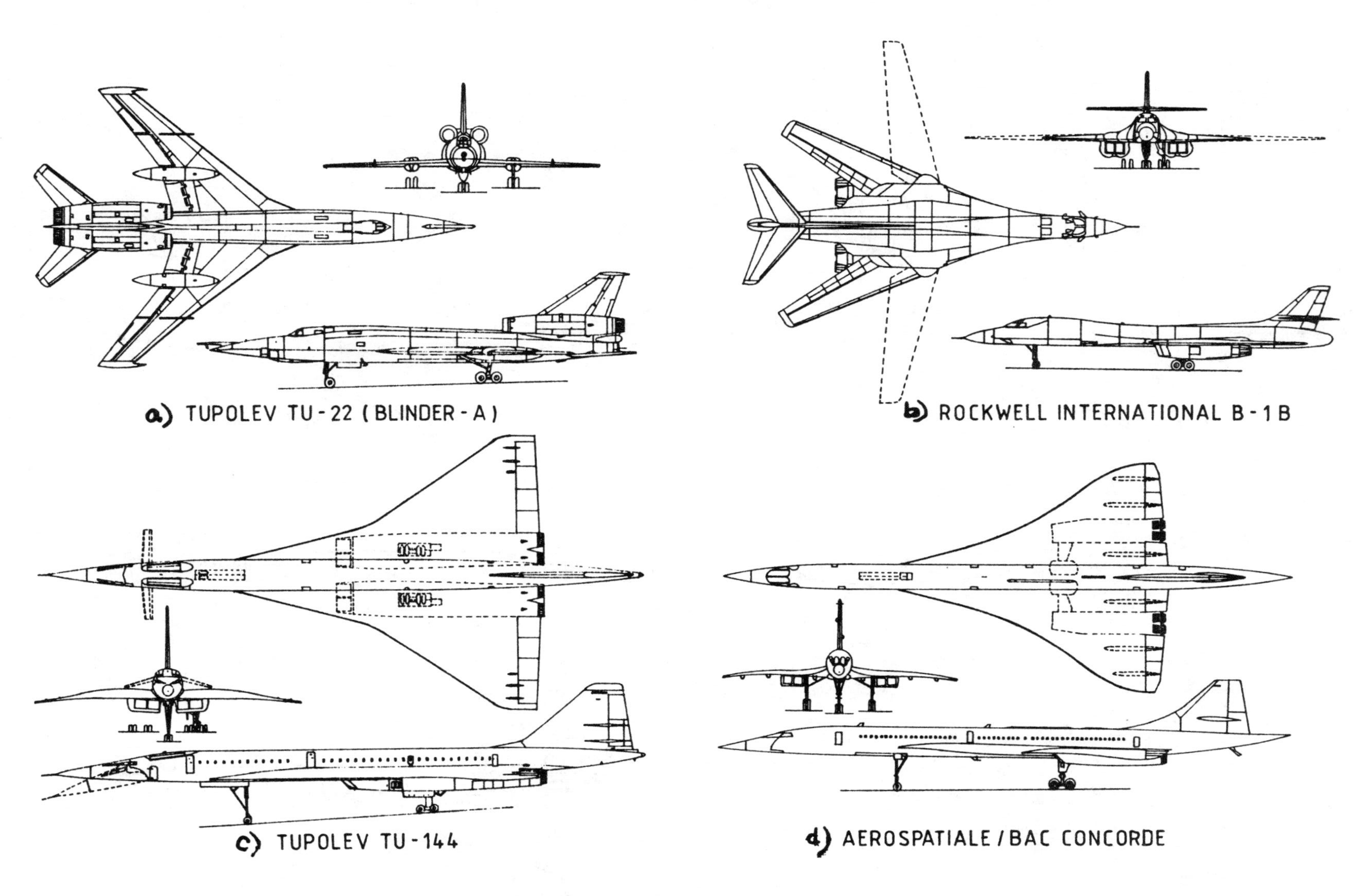

Figure 3.35 Supersonic Cruise Airplanes

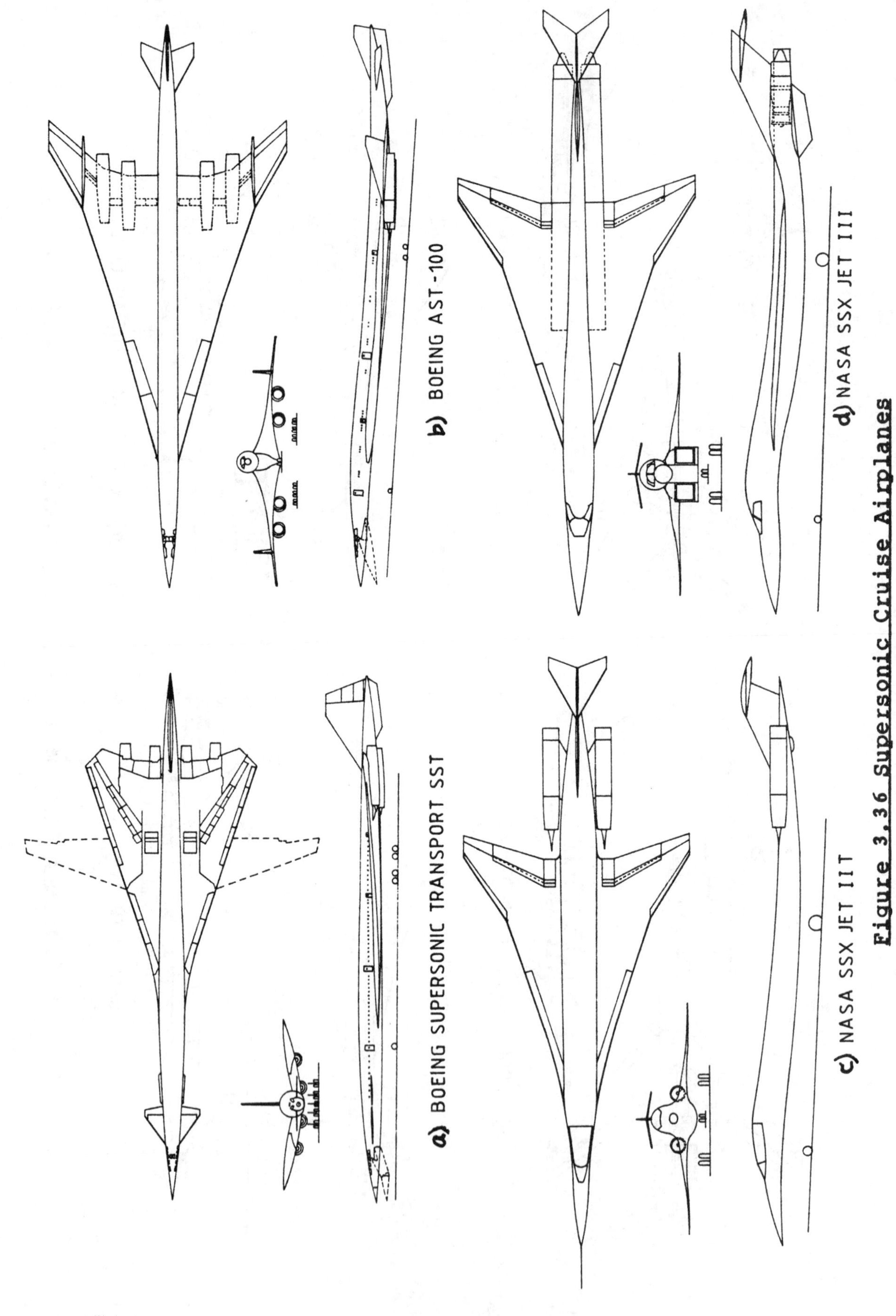

Figure 3.36 Supersonic Cruise Airplanes

3.2 UNUSUAL CONFIGURATIONS

The reader will find that while studying the historical references listed in Section 14.2 a large number of 'unusual' configurations have actually been built and flown. Some of these were successful, others were not. Therefore, when trying to innovate in the area of configuration design the reader will also find that it is very difficult indeed to come up with something which has not (in one form or other) been tried before.

The purpose of this section is to discuss a number of such unusual configurations. The discussion is organized as follows:

3.2.1 Canard and tandem wing configurations.
3.2.2 Joined wing configurations
3.2.3 Three-surface configurations
3.2.4 Double fuselage configurations
3.2.5 Flying wings
3.2.6 Burnelli configurations
3.2.7 Oblique wing configurations
3.2.8 Roadable airplanes

3.2.1 Canard and Tandem Wing Configurations

The world's first powered, controllable airplane was the Wright Flyer. Its configuration was that of a twin-propeller (single engine), pusher, pure canard design. Figure 3.37 shows a threeview of the Wright Flyer.

It is difficult to pinpoint the reason why canard designs were dropped shortly after the Wright Flyer. The main reason probably was a lack of aerodynamic understanding of the subtleties of canard design as known today.

Just before and during WWII a number of canard designs were evolved, the most notable probably were the Miles M39B Libellula, the Curtiss XP-55 Ascender and the Kyushu J7W1 Shinden. Figures 3.38 through 3.40 show three views of these airplanes.

Observe that the Libellula was in fact a tractor: the propeller disks are forward of the center of gravity. The Ascender and the Shinden were pushers.

Note that the Ascender is very similar in layout to the Rutan Varieze of Figure 3.41. The inboard strake and the winglets are the primary features which make the

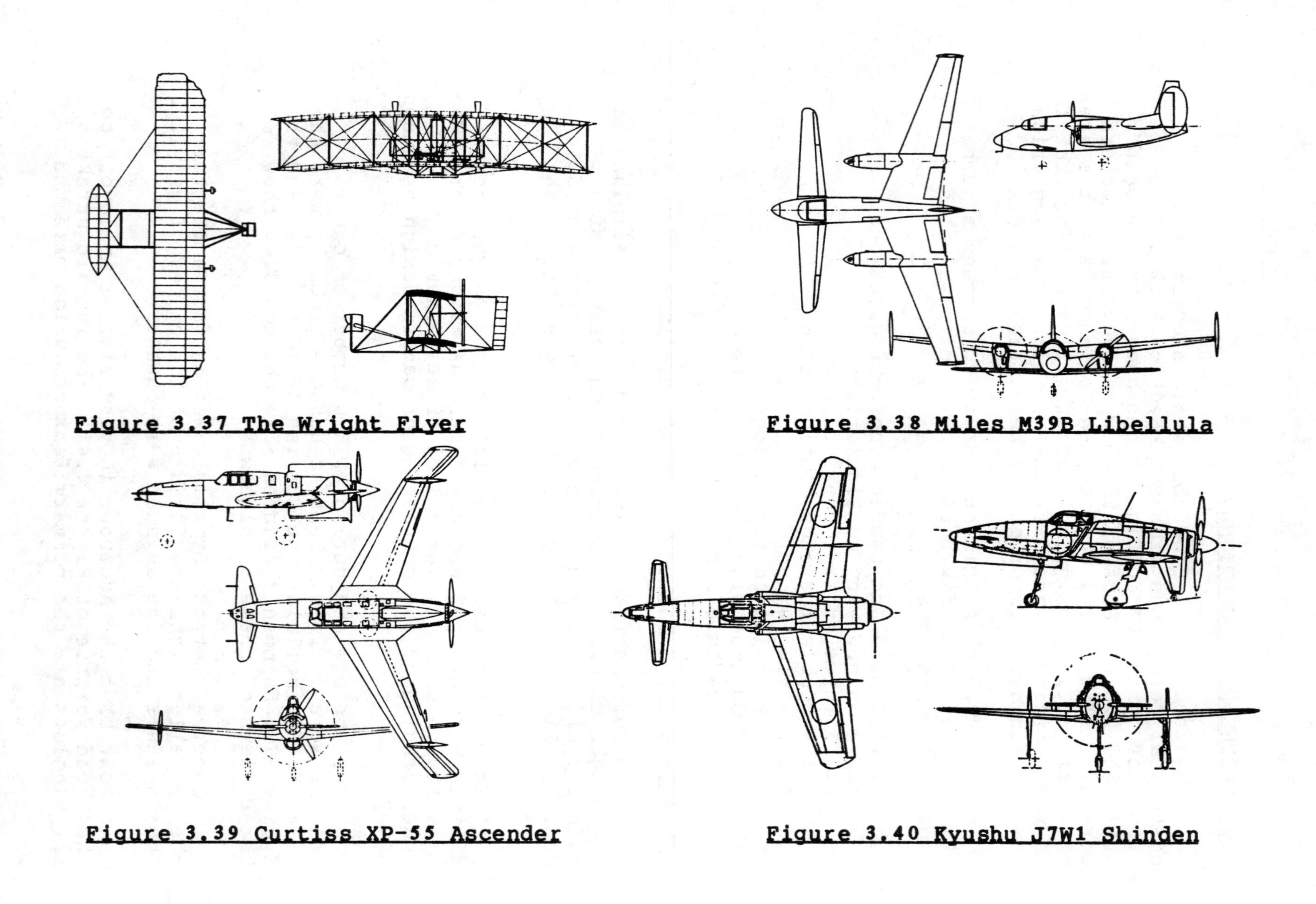

Figure 3.37 The Wright Flyer

Figure 3.38 Miles M39B Libellula

Figure 3.39 Curtiss XP-55 Ascender

Figure 3.40 Kyushu J7W1 Shinden

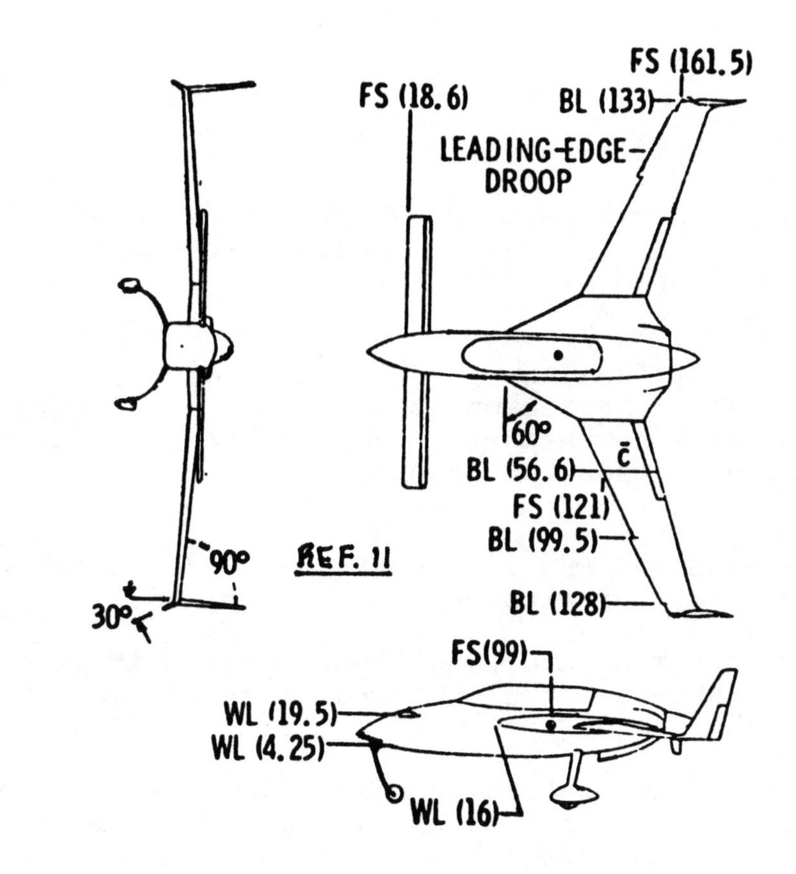

Figure 3.41 Rutan Varieze

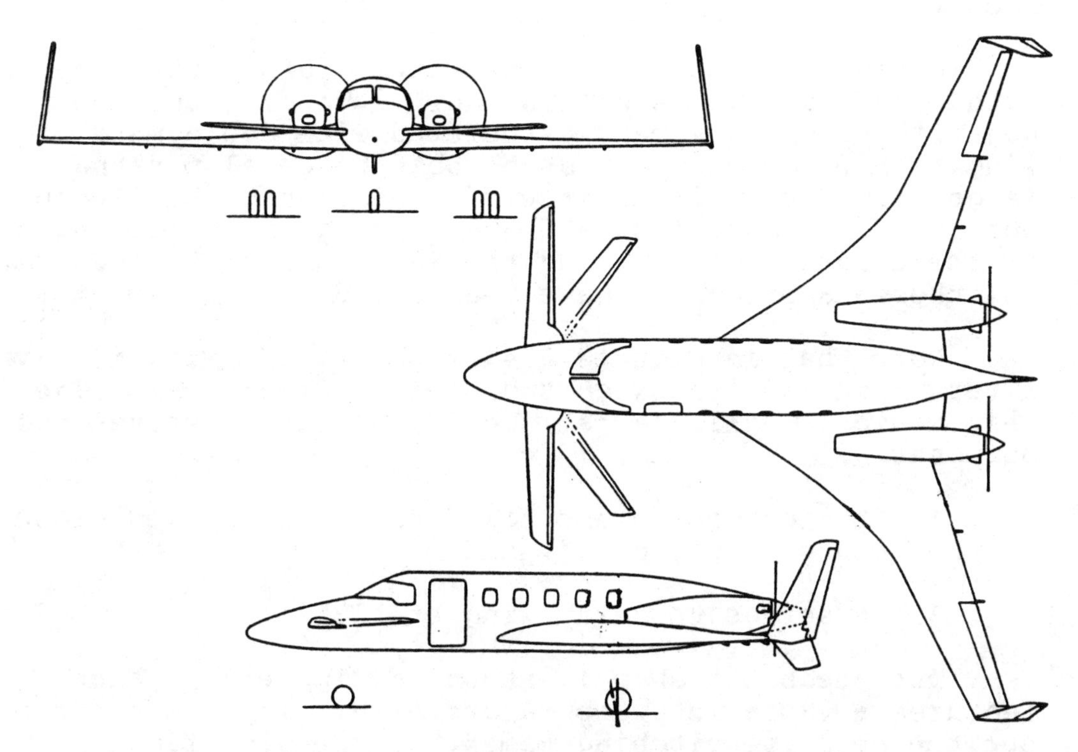

Figure 3.42 Beech Starship I (Tentative Threeview)

Varieze layout different from the Ascender.

A logical development from the Varieze configuration into an executive airplane is the twin turboprop pusher now being developed by Beech Aircraft Corp., Starship I, shown in Figure 3.42.

Why this rekindling of interest in canard configurations? The reason is that canards do have certain inherent advantages. Some of these advantages are presented here on the assumption that 'everything else is the same':

1. Trimmed maximum lift coefficient for a canard is higher than that for a conventional airplane.

2. By proper canard/wing layout design it is possible to achieve better trimmed lift-to-drag ratios with a canard design.

A problem with canard airplanes is that the canard must be designed so that it stalls before the wing. This way a stable 'pitch-break' is obtained. If this is not done, and the wing is allowed to stall before the canard, an uncontrollable and sometimes violent pitch-up can occur.

Obviously, the canard must stall before the wing with wing flaps up as well as down. To trim out the negative pitching moment associated with deployment of wing flaps, the canard must be able to develop rather large lift coefficients itself. This can be handled by putting flaps on the canard, by varying the sweep angle of the canard or by varying the incidence of the canard. All these 'approaches' have been tried.

Note that in Figures 3.41 and 3.42 the wing is given a very high inboard sweep angle: in a fighter airplane this would be called a 'strake'. The strake serves two purposes:

1. It provides volume for fuel to be carried close to the 'empty weight c.g.', and:

2. It serves to delay wing stall.

The Beech Starship I, shown in Figure 3.42 also features a variable sweep canard. This is used to trim out the negative pitching moment of the wing flaps.

Arranging the propulsion system so that it is

'pushing' instead of 'pulling' the airplane through the air is a feature which seems to be increasing in popularity. It is shown in Ref.9 that pusher configurations exhibit a stabilizing tendency in both pitch and yaw when compared to a tractor configuration. This feature can be capitalized upon by a slight reduction in tail surface requirements.

Another potential advantage of a pusher propeller configuration is that it can serve to lower cabin interior noise. This is a major problem in conventional propeller driven airplanes. Many of these have cabin noise levels well into the decibel regime where permanent hearing damage occurs.

An example of a tandem wing configuration is shown in Figure 3.43. The reader will recognize that it can be a matter of semantics whether a configuration is called a pure canard or a tandem wing layout. This is one reason why some designers prefer to refer to the canard as a front wing.

Reference 10 shows that the particular configuration of Fig.3.43 has some serious handling quality problems. In a high angle of attack flight condition with power off, the result of rapidly adding power is to:

1. Increase the lift on the front wing.

2. Decrease the lift on the rear wing due to the downwash from the front wing.

Both effects cause a large positive (nose-up) pitching moment which may be impossible to control.

Reference 11 contains more discussions of the handling characteristics of 'unusual' configurations.

A major design problem with any canard or tandem wing layout is the aerodynamic induction effect of the front wing on the rear wing. The vortex system generated by the front wing will influence the rear wing in a manner strongly dependent on:

1. Relative wing area and wing span sizes

2. Longitudinal and vertical separation between the wings

3. Angle of attack

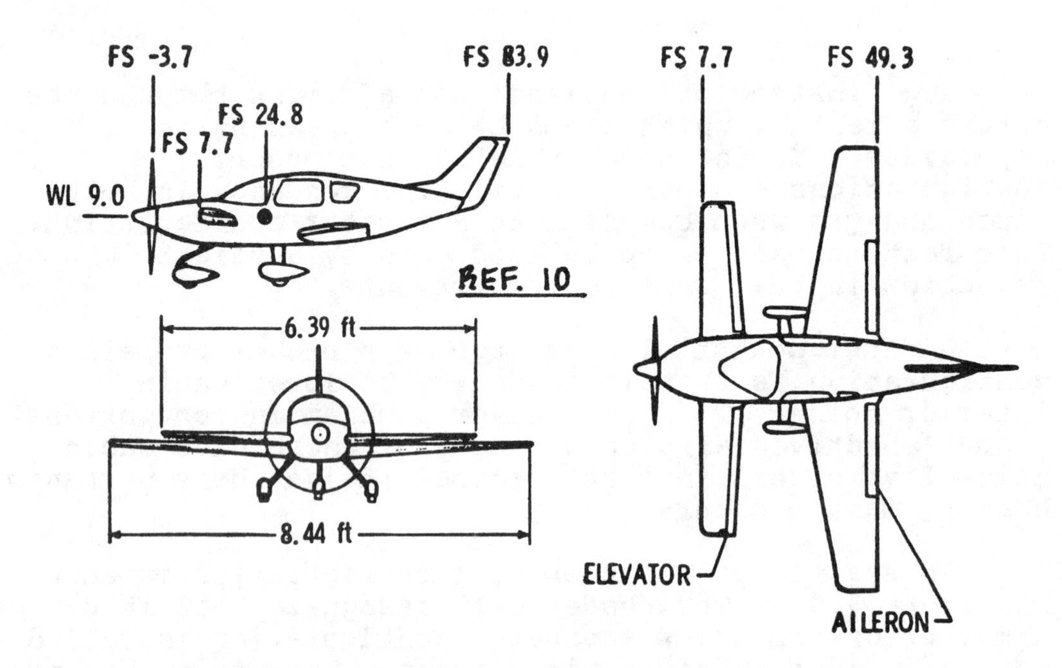

Figure 3.43 Tandem Wing Configuration

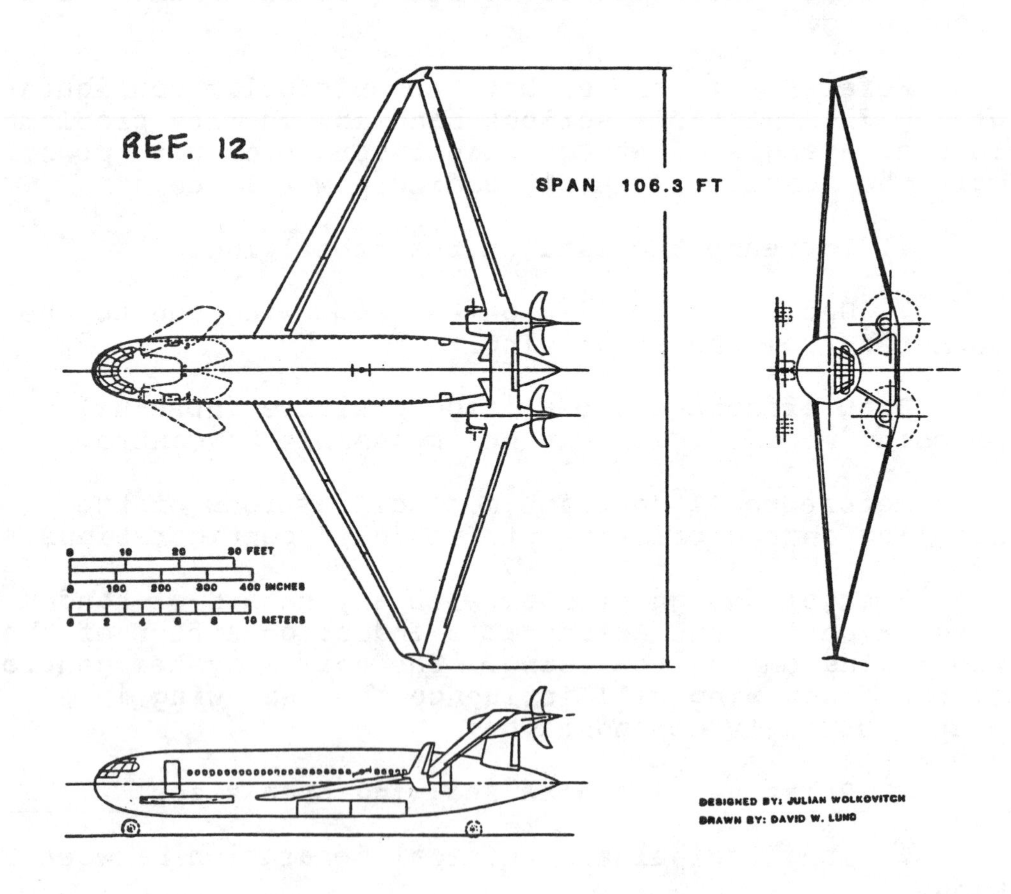

Figure 3.44 Joined Wing Transport Configuration

The canard (or front wing) tip vortex will induce an upwash on the wing outboard of the canard span. At the same time this canard tip vortex will induce a downwash on the wing inboard of the canard span. This results in poor induced drag behavior of the wing and also increases the root bending moment of the wing.

These effects can be deminished by:

1. Locating the canard far forward and below the wing.

2. Applying opposite camber and twist to the wing at the wing station corresponding to the canard span.

By closely coupling the canard to the wing (as has been done in the fighter configurations of Figures 3.27d and 3.46) it is possible to use the canard wash to enhance wing lift and reduce induced drag.

3.2.2 Joined Wing Configurations

Figures 3.44 and 3.45 show examples of projected joined wing configurations. Based on work done by J.Wolkovitch (Refs.12 and 13) the following advantages are claimed for the joined wing when compared to a conventional configuration:

1. Lower structural weight because of improved stiffness in torsion as well as in bending.

2. Built-in direct lift and direct side-force capability

3. Reduced induced drag.

4. Reduced transonic and supersonic wave drag as well as improved area ruling.

3.2.3 Three Surface Configurations

Figures 3.46 and 3.47 show examples of recent three surface layouts: the Grumman X-29 and the Gates-Piaggio GP180.

The three surface layout for these widely differing airplanes came about for the following reasons:

For the X-29:

1. In a transonic fighter configuration with a

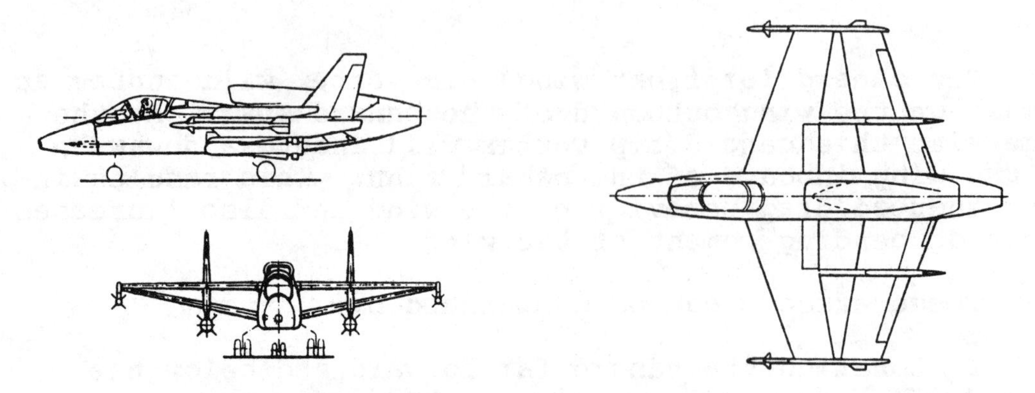

Figure 3.45 Joined Wing Fighter Configuration

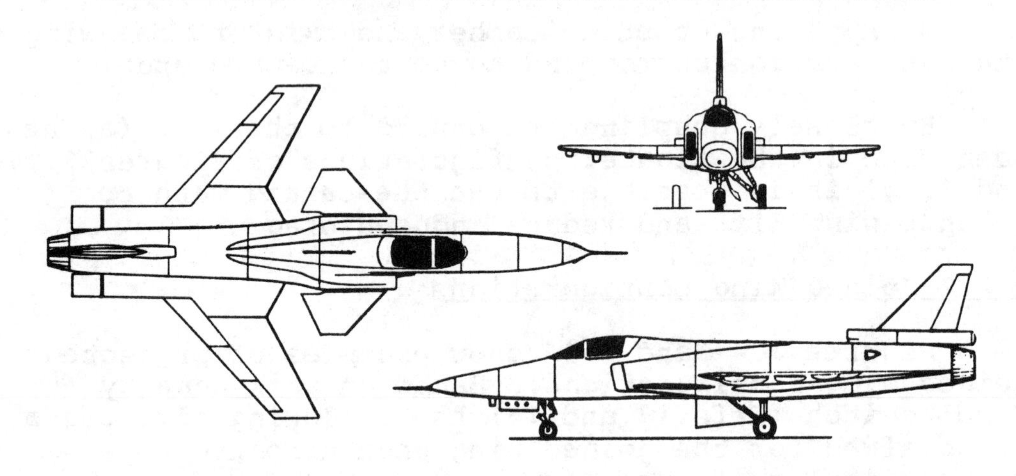

Figure 3.46 Grumman X-29A FSW Demonstrator

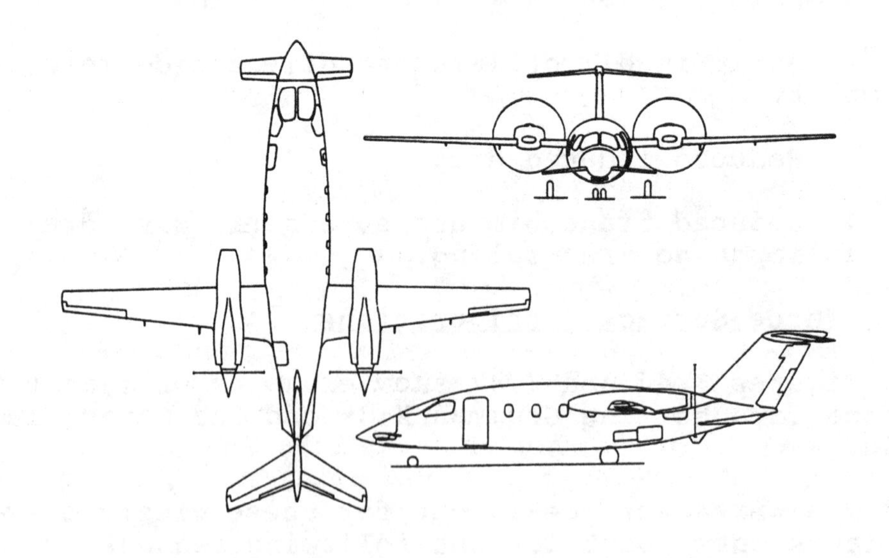

Figure 3.47 Gates Piaggio GP-180

requirement for very high sustained maneuvering at high subsonic speeds, a closely coupled canard with a forward swept wing results in reduced trim drag and in reduced wave drag.

2. An additional aft surface for trim in off-c.g. conditions results in less trim drag than by employing the canard for this purpose.

It is noteworthy to point out that the X-29 is designed to a level of inherent static longitudinal instability of 35 percent. The all-digital flight control system assures the de-facto stability of this airplane.

For the GP-180:

1. The three surface layout allows for minimization of induced trimmed drag over a wider range of center of gravity than do two surface layouts.

2. The longitudinal primary and trim controls are incorporated in the horizontal tail as in a conventional configuration.

3. Trim of flap induced pitching moments is done by a geared flap on the canard (front wing). This canard flap is mechanically geared to the wing flaps.

4. The wing torque box, the aft pressure bulkhead and the main landing gear share the same primary structure in the fuselage. This results in structural weight savings.

3.2.4 Double Fuselage Configurations

Figures 3.48 and 3.49 show examples of double fuselage airplanes.

There appear to be wetted area advantages to the double fuselage layout in subsonic as well as in supersonic applications. In addition, there may be significant development cost savings involved in 'growing' an airplane from one existing fuselage to two such fuselages.

3.2.5 Flying Wings

Flying wing configurations were pioneered by designers like Northrop, DeHavilland, Handley Page and Lippisch.

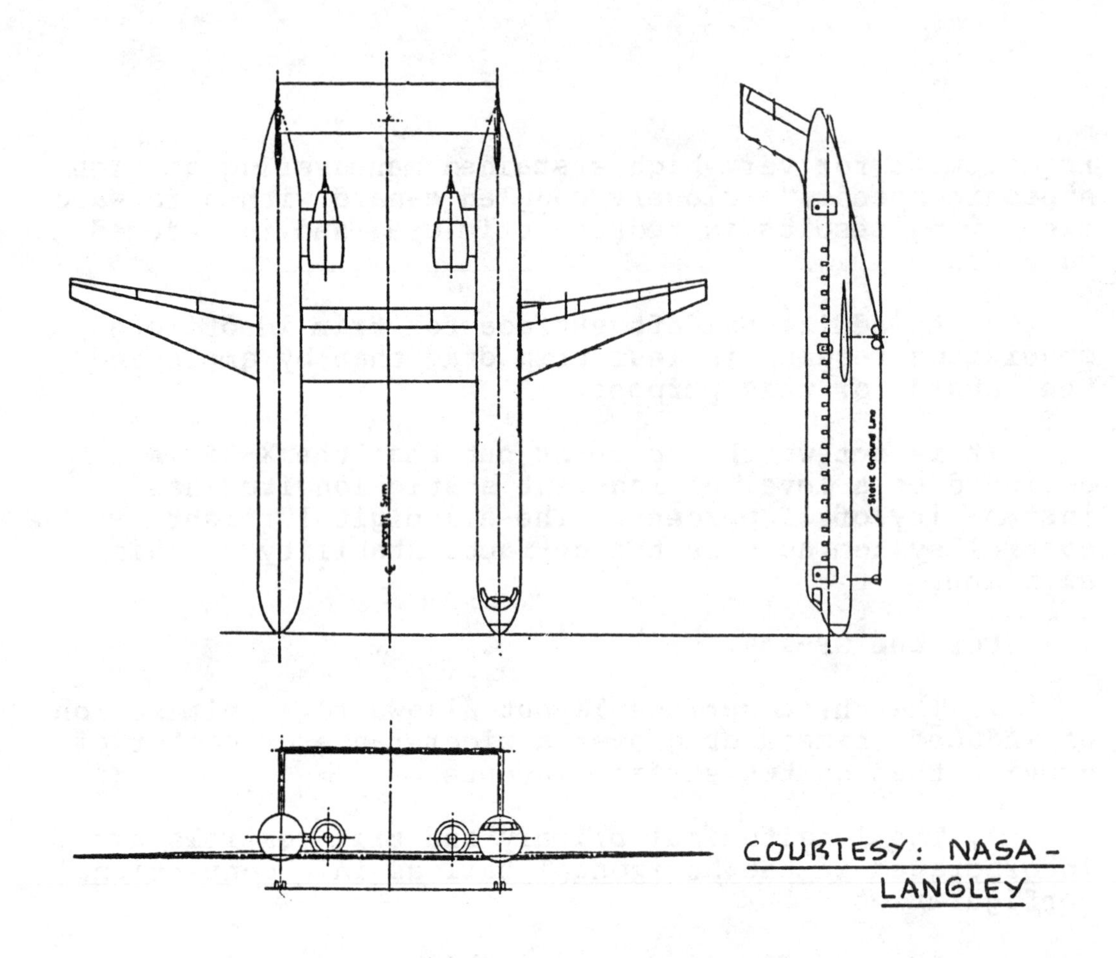

Figure 3.48 Double Fuselage Configuration: Example 1

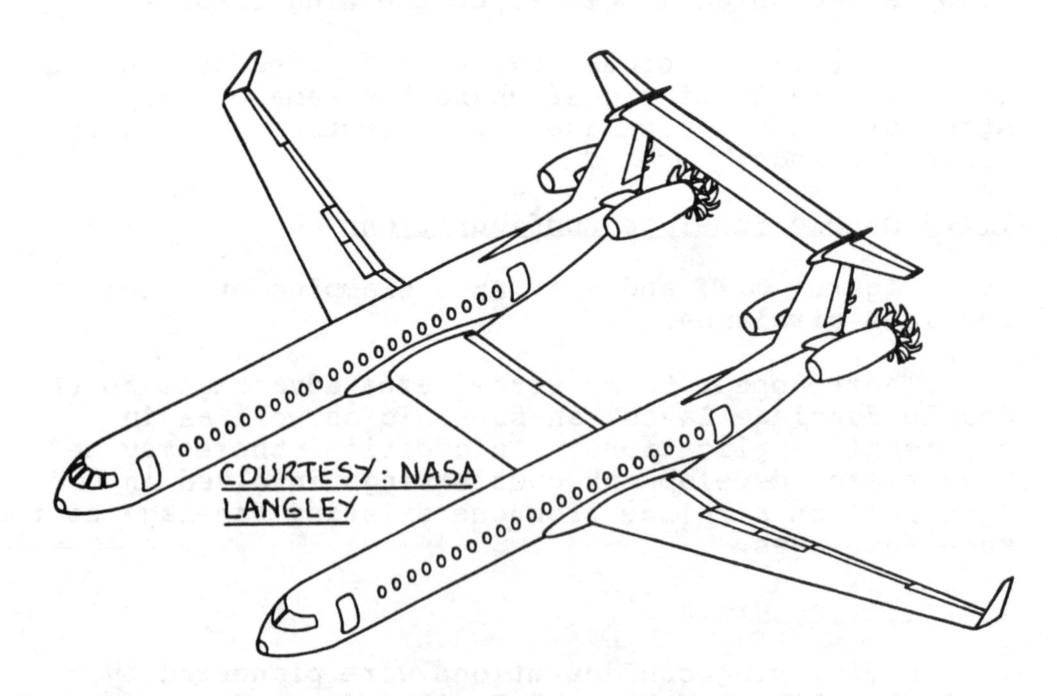

Figure 3.49 Double Fuselage Configuration: Example 2

References 12,17, 21 and 27 in sub-section 14.2 provide detailed information on some of the flying wing designs built and flown by these designers.

Reference 14 defines a flying wing as an airplane without an empennage. In this text a vertical tail is allowed.

Figures 3.50 through 3.54 are examples of several flying wing projects. Except for the configuration of Figure 3.52 all of these have flown and some even became operational.

An interesting variation on the flying wing theme is the so-called double-delta shape exhibited by the SAAB Draken of Figure 3.55. More extensively tailored versions of this wing shape are those of the Concorde (Fig.3.35d) and the F-16XL (Fig.3.25d).

Another variation on the flying wing concept is the so-called span-loader design by Lockheed as shown in Figure 3.56.

Pure flying wings tend to have higher trimmed L/D values compared with other configurations. They also have favorable payload weight fractions. With a conventional flight control system a flying wing can have serious dynamic handling deficiencies due to low inherent pitch damping. With today's highly reliable digital flight control and feedback systems these deficiencies are no longer a detriment.

For military applications a major advantage of the flying wing is its very small radar cross section (stealth).

3.2.6 Burnelli Configurations

Figure 3.57 shows an example of a so-called Burnelli airplane. Here the idea is to make the fuselage participate in the production of lift. A problem is that such a fuselage shape becomes heavy when used in a pressurized airplane. For certain large freighter applications the Burnelli configuration may warrant further consideration.

3.2.7 Oblique Wing Configurations

Figure 3.58 shows two oblique wing configurations. Note that one is also a double fuselage arrangement.

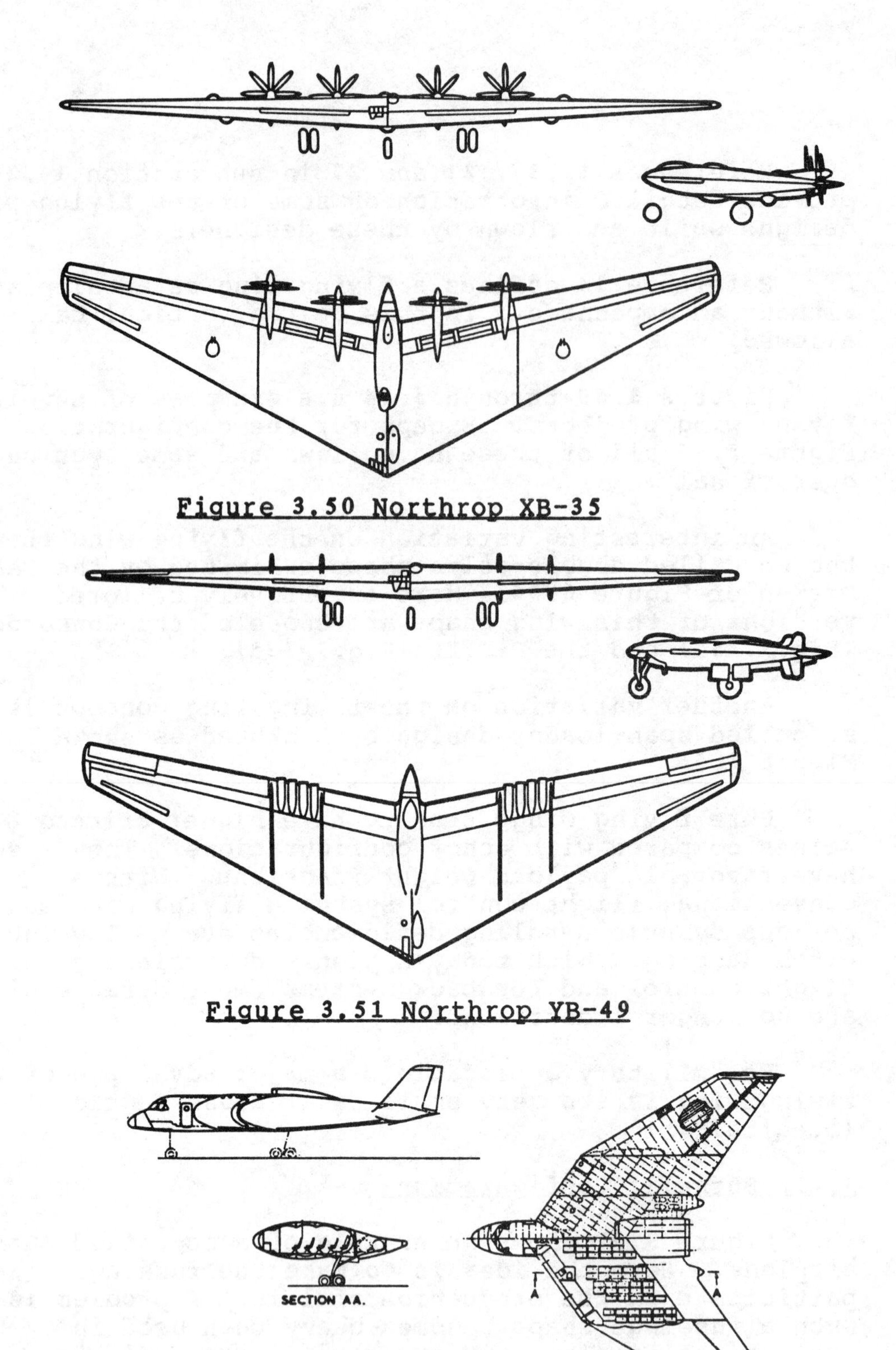

Figure 3.50 Northrop XB-35

Figure 3.51 Northrop YB-49

Figure 3.52 Handley Page 126 Aerobus Design

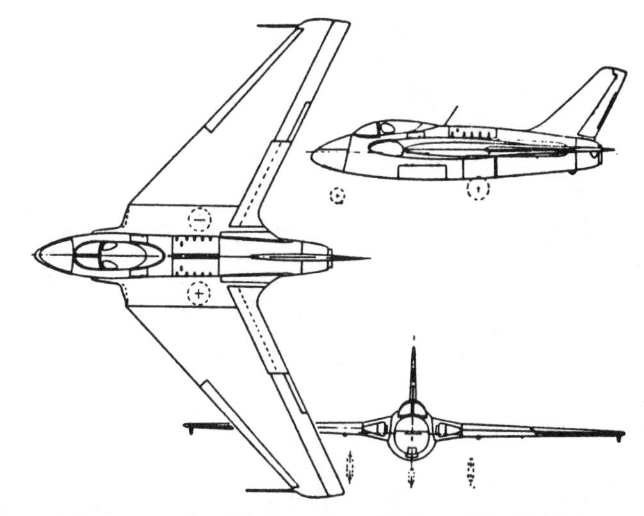

Figure 3.53 DeHavilland DH 108

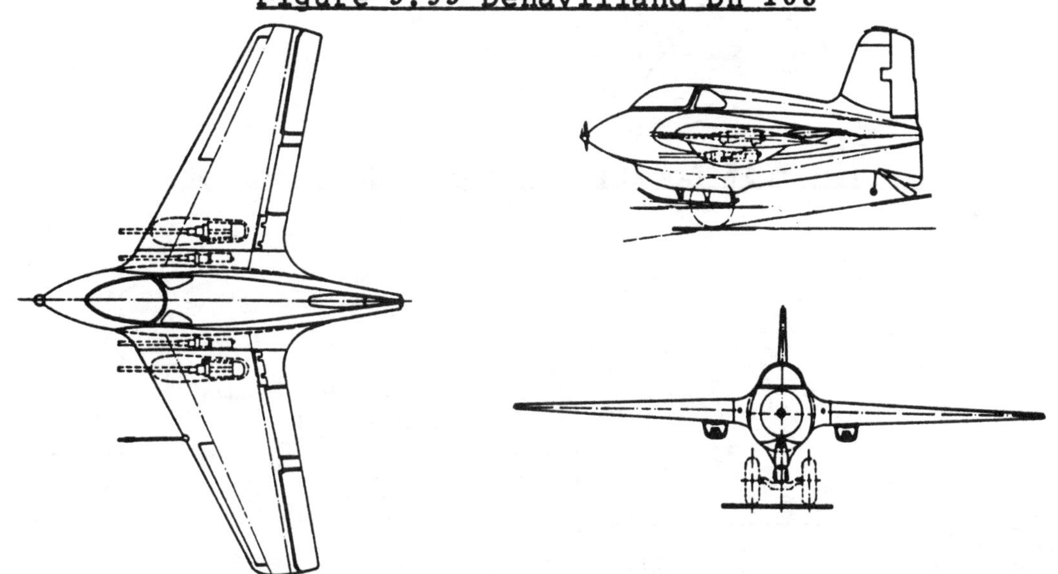

Figure 3.54 Messerschmitt (Lippisch) 163B Rocket Fighter

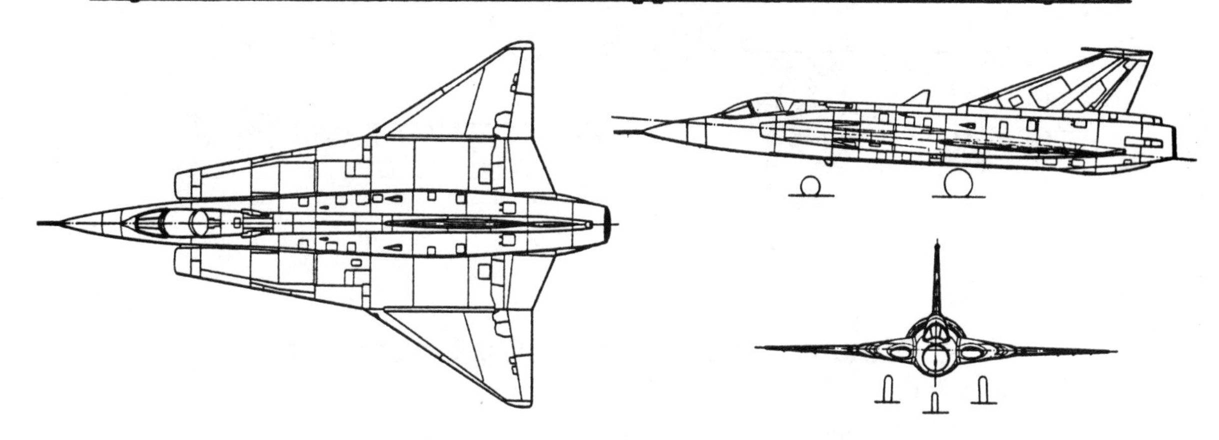

Figure 3.55 SAAB 35 Draken

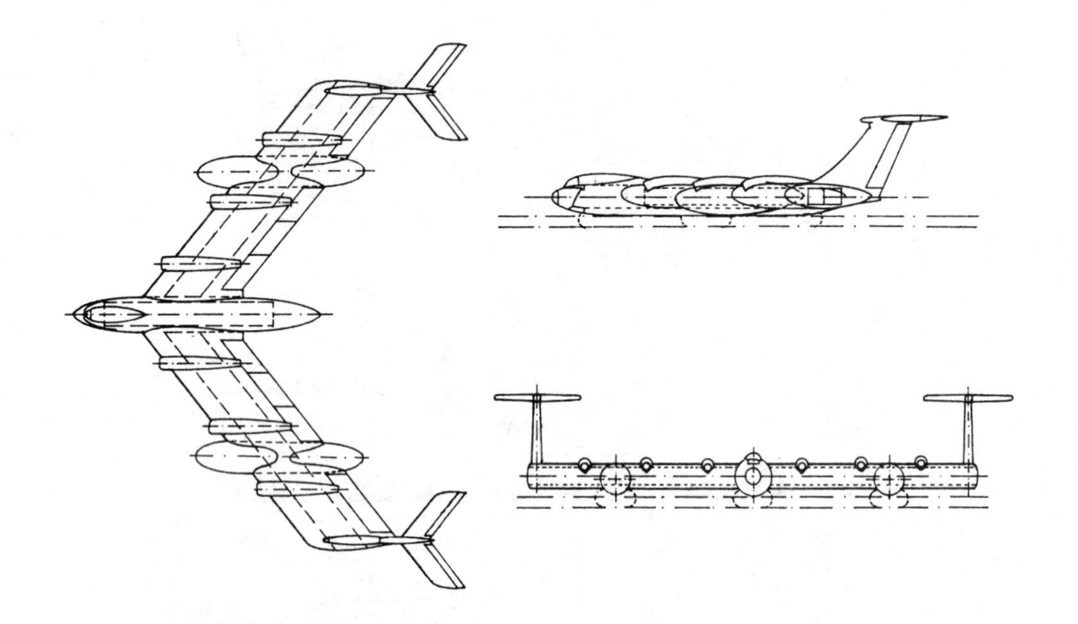

Figure 3.56 Lockheed Span-Loader Concept

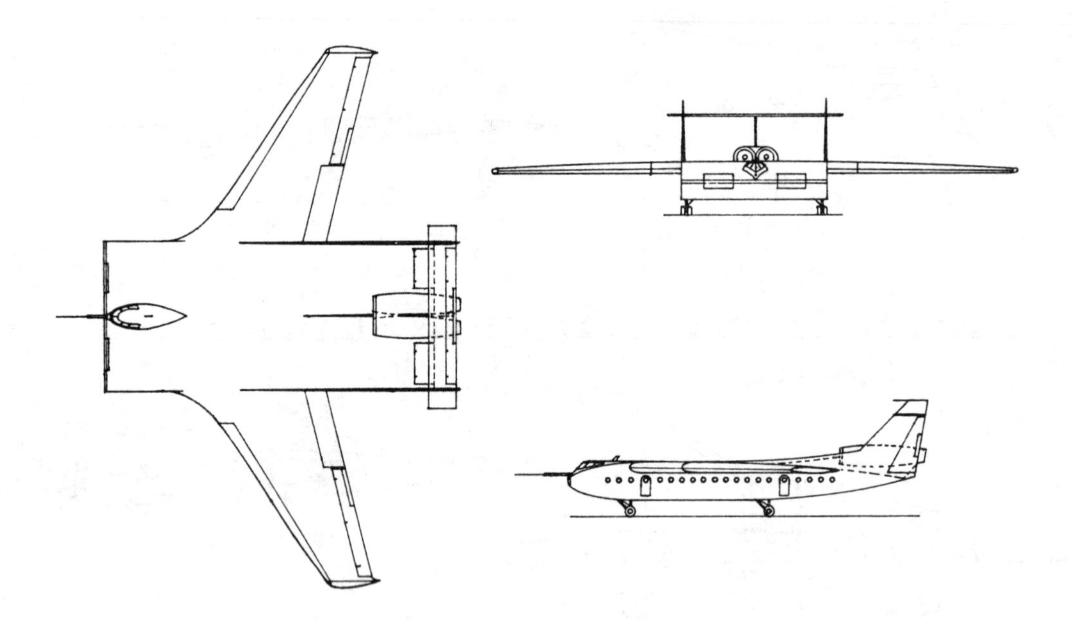

Figure 3.57 Burnelli Configuration

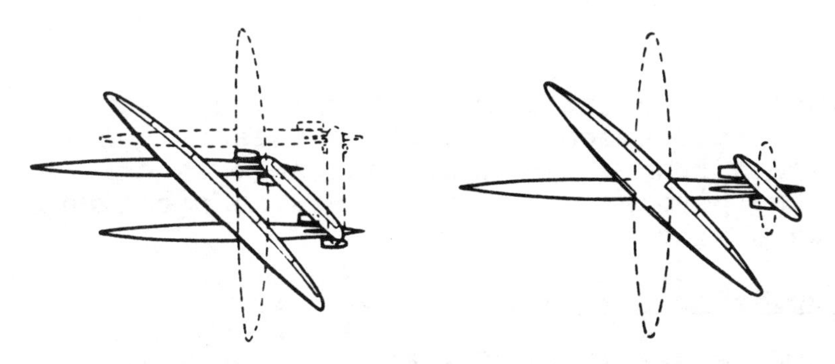

Figure 3.58 Oblique Wing Configurations

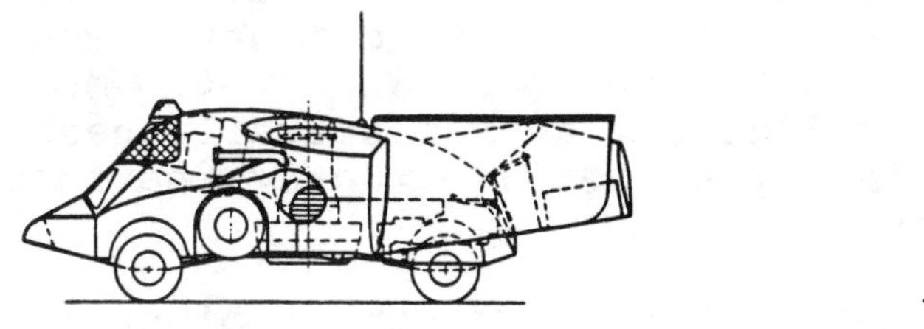

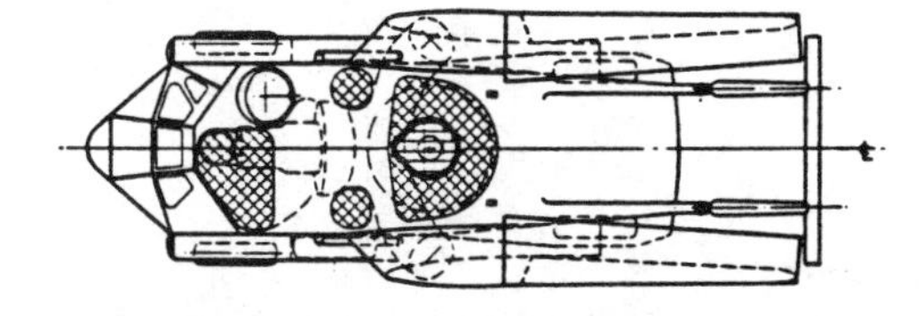

Figure 3.59 Handley Page 120 Roadable V/STOL Design

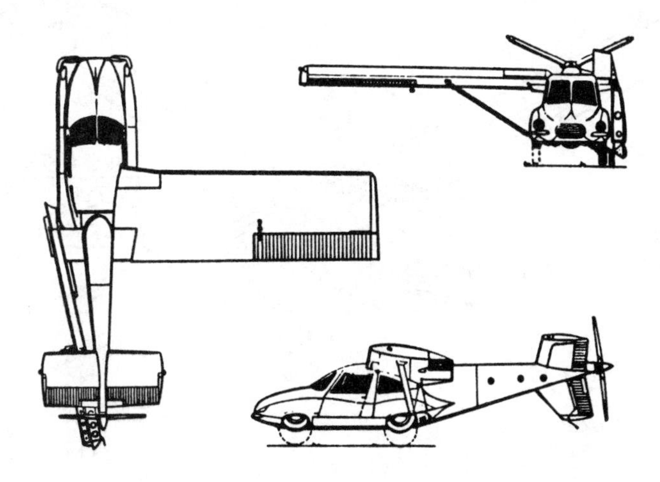

Figure 3.60 Taylor Aerocar III

Oblique wings have significantly lower drag than conventional fixed sweep or variable sweep wings in the transonic speed range. In addition there is only one instead of two pivots as is the case with a conventional variable sweep wing.

3.2.8 The Roadable Airplane

The idea of combining a roadworthy vehicle and an airworthy vehicle into one is an old idea which sofar has not been translated into commercial or military reality. Several attempts at realizing this idea have been made. Examples are shown in Figures 3.59 and 3.60. Molt Taylor's Aerocar of Figure 3.60 has actually been flown and certified to FAR 23 standards. Sofar the reaction of the market has been cool.

A major problem is the large number of design compromises which must be made to create a vehicle which can fulfill both roles. These design compromises result in performance penalties which apparently have been too large to offset the flexibility which such vehicles would offer.

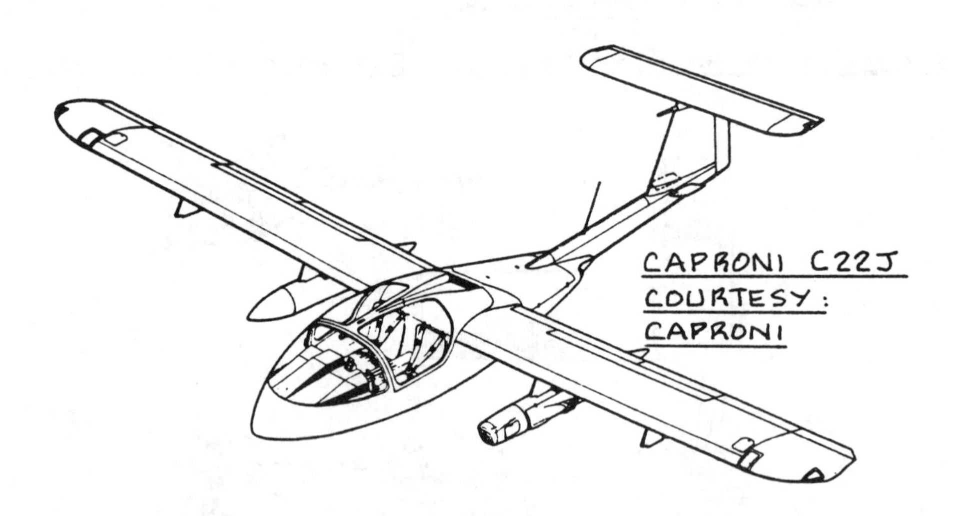

3.3 OUTLINE OF CONFIGURATION POSSIBILITIES

The purpose of this section is to present an outline of configuration possibilities. This outline is addressed to aerospace engineering students and not to experienced configuration designers.

The outline covers the following aspects of configuration design choices:

3.3.1. Overall configuration
3.3.2 Fuselage configuration
3.3.3 Engine type, number of engines and engine disposition
3.3.4 Wing configuration
3.3.5 Empennage configuration
3.3.6 Landing gear type and disposition

3.3.1 Overall Configuration

From a basing point of view airplanes can be classified as follows:

1. Land based
2. Water based
3. Amphibious

Within these basing modes the following overall configurations are possible:

1. Conventional (that means tail aft)
2. Flying wing (that means no horizontal tail or canard
3. Canard or Tandem wing
4. Three surface
5. Joined wing

Most airplanes which have been built or are being built today are of a conventional configuration. With certain exceptions, designers have not felt compelling reasons to deviate from the conventional configuration. One reason is that the data base and the experience base dealing with conventional configurations is very large. This data base is narrow and even non-existent in some of the other configurations.

Section 3.4 presents a step-by-step guide which should be useful to aeronautical engineering students in selecting the overall configuration of an airplane.

Within each overall configuration (1-5), it is

possible to utilize a wide variety of choices for the arrangement of the major airplane components. These choices are discussed in the following sub-sections:

3.3.2 Fuselage configuration
3.3.3 Engine type, number of engines and engine disposition
3.3.4 Wing type and placement
3.3.5 Empennage type and placement
3.3.6 Landing gear type and placement

Most airplanes have the XZ plane as a plane of symmetry. In some instances there may be a good reason to deviate from a symmetrical configuration. The oblique wings of Figure 3.58 are examples of this.

3.3.2 Fuselage Configuration

Fuselage configurations can be broadly classified as follows:

1. Conventional (Example: virtually all airplanes in Figures 3.1 - 3.36 have a conventional fuselage.)
2. Twin fuselage (Example: Figures 3.48 and 3.49)
3. Twin boom with center fuselage (Example: Figures 3.9c and 3.11c)
4. Burnelli (Example: Figure 3.57)

Chapter 4 presents a step-by-step guide to cockpit and fuselage layout design. Part III (Ref.2) contains detailed discussions and data useful in the design of cockpit and fuselage layouts.

3.3.3 Engine Type, Number of Engines and Engine Disposition

3.3.3.1 Engine type

The selection of engine type depends mostly on the matching of desired airplane performance to the inherent performance of an engine type. From a pragmatic (cost and certification) viewpoint, the choice of engine type for the next 10 years is probably limited to:

1. Piston/propeller combinations
2. Turbo/propeller combinations
3. Propfans
4. Unducted fans
5. Turbojets
6. Turbofans

7. Rockets
8. Ramjets

Any combination 1 through 8 which makes sense in a given application also presents a viable choice of engine type.

Several engine types are under research and development. Examples of such types are:

9. Diesel and turbo/diesel engines
10. Rotary engines for a variety of fuels
11. Variable cycle jet engines (primarily for supersonic cruise applications)
12. Electrical propulsion using Lithium fuel cells (these latter have as an interesting but important feature the fact that airplane weight will increase in flight due to the formation of certain chemical compounds: see Ref.15.)
13. Electrical propoulsion with photo-voltaic cells
14. Electrical propulsion with microwave beams

Items 13 and 14 are probably of interest primarily in very high altitude long endurance platforms.

Whether or not any of these propulsion types will materialize will depend on a combination of need, fuel prices and fuel availability. It will take a minimum of five to ten years to bring anyone of these types to maturity.

Section 5.1 contains a step-by-step procedure for selecting the engine type(s) to be used.

3.3.3.2 Number of engines

Selection of the number of engines depends on a combination of the following factors:

1. Total power or thrust required and availability of engines in a given power or thrust class.

2. Relationship between critical field and climb performance and the probability of engine failure

3. Other safety considerations

4. Cost of acquisition and of maintenance

Historically the number of engines used on any given airplane type has ranged from 1 to 10. The B36D (Ref.28,

Section 14.2) was an example of the latter. The range of 1 to 4 engines has proven to be the most practical for many airplanes.

Section 5.2 presents a step-by-step procedure for determining the number of engines to be used.

3.3.3.3 Engine disposition

Broadly speaking, engines can be arranged as:

1. Tractors (point of thrust application ahead of the center of gravity)
2. Pushers (point of thrust application behind the center of gravity)
3. Combination tractor and pusher

Within these three basic arrangements, engines can be installed in the following manner:

1. In pods or nacelles
2. Buried

Whether podded or buried, engines can be dispositioned on or in:

1. The wing: below, above or in-line
2. The fuselage
3. The empennage

The disposition of engines has major consequences for:

* airplane weight
* airplane vibration and noise
* engine efficiency
* handling characteristics from a pilot viewpoint
* maintenance

Section 5.3 presents a step-by-step procedure for determining the disposition of the engines. Part III (Ref.2) contains many examples of propulsion system integration.

3.3.4 Wing Configuration

From a structural viewpoint wing configurations can be classified as follows:

1. Cantilever wing
2. Braced (or strutted) wing

Note that joined and tandem wing arrangements were already accounted for under the overall airplane configuration possibilities discussed in sub-section 3.3.1.

In terms of wing/fuselage arrangement, wings can be classified as follows:

1. High wing
2. Mid wing
3. Low wing

From a sweep angle viewpoint, wings can be classified in the following manner:

1. Zero or negligible sweep
2. Aft sweep (also called positive sweep)
3. Forward sweep (also called negative sweep)
4. Variable sweep (meaning symmetrically variable sweep)
5. Oblique sweep (meaning asymmetrically variable sweep)

Most wings are given a fixed wing incidence angle on the fuselage. In certain cases however, the wing is given a variable incidence angle. An example of the latter is the Vought F8U naval fighter (See Ref. 8, 1969-1970 issue).

In addition to these overall wing configuration possibilities, the following wing design characteristics are important to the weight, the performance and the stability and control characteristics of an airplane:

1. Aspect ratio
2. Thickness ratio
3. Airfoil(s)
4. Taper ratio
5. Twist
6. Incidence angle
7. Dihedral angle
8. High lift and control surface requirements
9. Winglets

Chapter 6 presents a step-by-step procedure for the selection of all major wing configuration design characteristics.

Chapter 7 contains a step-by-step method for selecting the high lift devices which may be required.

Part III (Ref.2) contains more detailed information on the subject of wing and high lift layout design.

3.3.5 Empennage Configuration

The word empennage as used here can mean:

1. Horizontal tail(s)
2. Vertical tail(s)
3. Canard(s): horizontal and/or vertical

The empennage configuration is intimately tied up with the selection of the overall configuration.

In principle, all that has been said about the wing configuration, applies to the empennage.

In addition, the following configurational choices must be made:

For the horizontal tail:

1. Fuselage mounted, usually far aft on the fuselage
2. Boom mounted, such as in twin boom designs
3. Vertical tail mounted as either a cruciform or a T-tail installation
4. Butterfly or V-tail (Examples are the Beech V35 Bonanza and the Potez CM570 Magister of Ref.8, 1963-1964 edition)

For the vertical tail:

1. Fuselage mounted
2. Boom mounted, such as in twin boom designs
3. Single or multiple vertical tail(s)
4. Butterfly or V-tail

For the canard:

For horizontal and for vertical canards the configurational choices are essentially those of the horizontal and/or the vertical tail.

In many airplanes it is found necessary to add strakes, ventral fins and/or dorsal fins to the empennage. Examples of these may be seen in many of the airplane configurations presented in Section 3.1.

Chapter 8 provides a step-by-step method for determining the size and location of the empennage. Parts III and VII (Refs 2 and 6) contain more detailed information on the layout design and sizing of the empennage.

3.3.6 Landing Gear Type And Disposition

From a systems viewpoint landing gears can be classified as:

1. Fixed or non-retractable (Many single engine, propeller driven types of Section 3.1)
2. Retractable (Most airplanes in Section 3.1)

According to their layout, landing gears can be classified as:

1. Taildraggers (See Figs 3.10a,c,d)
2. Conventional or tricycle (Most airplanes in Section 3.1)
3. Tandem (See Fig.3.28a)
4. Outrigger (See Fig.3.28a)

Landing gears can be mounted in or on:

1. Wing and/or nacelle
2. Fuselage

Many flying boats employ outrigger floats for lateral stability on the water. Sometimes these outrigger floats are retractable. Figs 3.33a,b,d are examples of fixed outrigger floats while Figs 3.32 c,d are examples of retracting outrigger floats.

Retracting water skis have also been tried. The water based Convair Seadart (See Ref.22 in Section 14.2) was an example.

The following landing gear design aspects have a major impact on the ultimate configuration of the landing gear:

* Number of main gear struts
* Number of tires per strut
* Retraction kinematics and available volume to receive the gear

Selection of the number of struts and tires is intimately tied to the type of surface the airplane needs to operate from.

Chapter 9 presents a step-by-step procedure for deciding on the type of gear, the disposition of the gear and the size of struts and tires. Part IV contains more detailed information on the problem of designing landing gears, assuring their satisfactory disposition and designing the retraction system.

3.4 A PROCEDURE FOR SELECTING THE OVERALL CONFIGURATION

The following step-by-step procedure is offered to assist in arriving at the decision which overall configuration to use:

Step 3.1: Determine whether or not the airplane to be designed falls into one of the eight categories described in Section 3.2.

If it does, read the appropriate sub-section. This will help in familiarizing yourself with what the competition has been doing.

If it does not, proceed to Step 3.2.

Step 3.2: Review the study results of Step 1, Section 2.1.

Step 3.3: Obtain a historical perspective by reviewing the appropriate references listed under 'historical bibliography' in Section 14.2. Consult older versions of Ref.8.

Step 3.4: Review Section 3.3 and write down which overall configuration candidates are considered suitable. List the reasons why.

Step 3.5: If time and/or available manpower don't allow for the red, white and blue team approach, select one configuration and go with it.

Step 3.6: Document the decisions made in selecting the configuration.

3.5 EXAMPLE APPLICATIONS

Three example applications will now be presented:

3.5.1 Twin Engine Propeller Driven Airplane
3.5.2 Jet Transport
3.5.3 Fighter

The applications are all presented in the Step 3.1 through 3.5 sequence of Section 3.4.

3.5.1 Twin Engine Propeller Driven Airplane

For easy future reference the twin engine propeller driven airplane will be given the name 'Selene'. Selene is the goddess of the moon in Greek mythology.

Step 3.1: As a propeller driven twin the Selene belongs to category 3 of the categories listed on p.28. Figures 3.7-3.9 contain twelve 3-views of airplanes in this category.

Steps 3.2 and 3.3: To save space these steps are not presented in detail.

The following tabulation compares the Selene with several potential competitors. All data are from Part I, sub-section 2.6.1.

Airplane Type	W_{PL} (lbs)	W_{TO} (lbs)	$V_{cr_{max}}$ (kts)	Range (nm)
Beech Duke B60	1,300	6,775	239	1,080
Beech Baron M58	1,500	5,400	200	1,200
Cessna T303	1,650	5,150	196	1,000
Piper PA-44-180	1,250	3,800	168	725
Selene	1,250	7,900	250	1,000

Step 3.4: The following configurations are suitable candidates for the Selene:

*conventional *canard or tandem *three surface

The flying wing is not considered a suitable candidate: it would cause problems in packaging passengers and payload. It would also suffer from poor pitch damping which can be solved only with a SAS. This is thought to be unacceptable from a cost viewpoint in this type of airplane.

The joined wing is not considered a suitable candidate primarily because of lack of a data base. Fear of adverse market reactions to such a 'radical' configuration also plays a role in rejecting this configuration.

The Beech Starship I and the Gates-Piaggio GP180 employ the canard and the three surface layout respectively. Figures 3.42 and 3.47 give threeviews of these airplanes.

Step 3.5: For the Selene a conventional configuration will be selected, but with a twist: a high wing layout combined with a pusher layout will be used. This proposed layout is similar to that of the Piaggio P166 of Figure 3.7b. Two advantages of a pusher configuration are:

1. Less cabin noise because the propellers are behind the cabin.
2. Pusher propellers are stabilizing in longitudinal and directional stability: this can lead to savings in tail area and thus in drag and weight.

3.5.2 Jet Transport

For easy future reference this jet transport will be named the 'Ourania', after the Greek muse of astronomy.

Step 3.1: By definition, the Ourania falls in category 7 of those listed on p.28. Figures 3.19 - 3.21 present twelve 3-views of airplanes in this category.

Steps 3.2 and 3.3: To save space, these steps are not presented in detail.

The following tabulation compares the Ourania with several competitors. These data are taken from sub-section 2.6.2 in Part I.

Airplane Type	W_{TO} (lbs)	W_{TO} (lbs)	$V_{cr_{max}}$ (kts)	Range (nm)
Boeing 737-200	35,000	135,000	460	1,620
McDD DC9-80	38,000	140,000	M=.8	2,000
Airbus A320	42,000	145,000	450	2,700
Ourania	30,750	127,000	473	1,500

Step 3.4: The following configurations are suitable candidates for the Ourania:

*conventional *canard or tandem *three surface
*joined wing

The flying wing is not considered suitable because of packaging problems with passengers and baggage. Access would have to be from the leading edge or via stairways from below. Sealing access door on the leading edge might be a problem. Servicing access from below is not compatible with existing servicing equipment.

The other configuration candidates should be evaluated against each other. The red, white and blue team approach would have to be employed.

Step 3.5: For reasons of conservatism a conventional configuration will be selected for the Ourania. However, the airplane will be designed for relaxed static stability and will employ a digital fly-by-wire primary flight control system. This, to save weight and wetted area.

3.5.3 Fighter

For easy future reference the fighter will be given the name of Eris, goddess of war in greek mythology.

Step 3.1: The Eris belongs to category 9 of the airplane categories listed on p.28. Figures 3.25 - 3.27 present twelve 3-views of airplanes in this category.

Steps 3.2 and 3.3: To save space these steps are not presented in detail.

The following tabulation compares the Eris with several competitors. All data are those from Part I, sub-section 2.6.3.

Airplane Type	W_{PL} (lbs)	W_{TO} (lbs)	V_{max} (kts)	Range (nm)
F.R. A10A	15,000	50,000	450	540
Grumman A6	17,000	60,400	689	1,700
Tornado F.Mk2	16,000	58,400	600*	750
Eris	12,000	64,500	400*	800*

*with external stores

Step 3.4: The following configurations are suitable for the Eris:

*conventional *flying wing *canard or tandem
*three surface *joined wing

None of these configurations can be ruled out.

The flying wing is attractive because of its obvious stealth qualities. Experience with the B35 and YB49 flying wing bombers (See Figures 3.50 and 3.51) indicated that these airplanes were very difficult to detect on the radars of their era.

The joined wing may present a problem in this regard. However, by making the joined wing out of composites a very small radar cross section should be obtainable. The proposed joined wing configuration of Figure 3.45 does represent an attractive possibility for an attack fighter.

Since there is no requirement for transonic/supersonic performance, a three surface layout like that of the X29 (See Fig.3.46) may not be appropriate.

That leaves the canard and the conventional layout. Because an attack fighter must have excellent forward visibility a canard configuration could present some problems. This would have to be verified before accepting or rejecting the canard in this case.

Step 3.5: The conventional layout with engines buried in the fuselage, a triangular fuselage cross section (for stealth) and a twin boom tail arrangement will be selected for the Eris. Figure 3.61 shows an example of a british fighter which employed this type of layout.

The airplane will be designed for negative inherent stability. It will employ a digital FBW flight control system. This should save on wetted area as well as on trim drag.

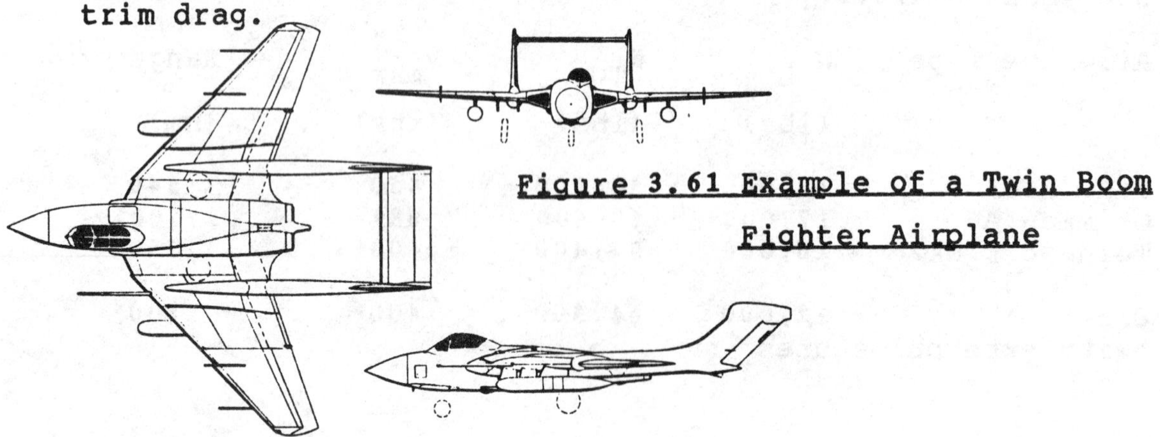

Figure 3.61 Example of a Twin Boom Fighter Airplane

4. DESIGN OF COCKPIT AND FUSELAGE LAYOUTS

The purpose of this chapter is to provide a step-by-step guide to the preparation of cockpit and fuselage layouts so that the mission requirements in terms of crew, passengers and payload are met.

For military airplanes this includes the necessary weapons and stores layouts on the fuselage.

The method is presented as part of Step 4 in p.d. sequence I as outlined in Chapter 2.

Section 4.1 presents the step-by-step guide. Example applications are contained in Section 4.2.

4.1 A PROCEDURE FOR THE DESIGN OF COCKPIT AND FUSELAGE LAYOUTS

Step 4.1: Referring to the mission specification, make a list of crew, payload and operational items which need to be located in the fuselage.

Note that this step assumes that the overall configuration is not a flying wing.

Typical items to be included on this list are:

1. number and weight of cockpit crew members
2. number and weight of cabin crew members
3. number and weight of 'special duty' crew members (such as radar and systems operators)
4. number and weight of passengers
5. weight and volume of 'carry-on' baggage
6. weight and volume of 'check-in' baggage
7. weight and volume of cargo
8. number, weight and size of cargo containers
9. weight and volume of 'special operational equipment' (such as sensor and computer equipment required by patrol airplanes)
10. weight and volume of military payload (such as: guns, stores, bombs, torpedoes, missiles etc.)
11. weight and volume of fuel carried in fuselage
12. radar equipment
13. auxiliary power unit (APU)
14. beaching requirements such as in the case of flying boats

Step 4.2: Translate the list obtained in Step 4.1 into a dimensioned drawing of a proposed cabin interior layout.

This step includes making a decision on the size and shape of the fuselage cross section to be used, the location of the cabin floor in that cross section and a check of volumetric requirements imposed by any of the items 1-14 in Step 4.1. Part III (Ref.2) contains detailed information on cabin and fuselage layouts used by a number of existing airplanes.

This step involves the definition of access doors, hatches and emergency exits. Depending on the certification base of the airplane, there are very definite minimum requirements for size, placement and number of exits which need to be provided. Part III contains detailed information on these important items.

In passenger/troop transport airplanes and in business airplanes it is important to consider carefully the following choices:

1. Number of persons abreast
2. Number and size of aisles
3. Type of seating to be employed: first class, business class, tourist class or economy class
4. Cabin provisions required in terms of: closets, toilets, overhead storage compartments, galleys
5. Seating provisions for the cabin crew

Part III contains data on all these items.

In certain cargo airplanes there may be a requirement for loading and off-loading from both ends of the fuselage. This usually requires large doors and ramps. These items can dominate the fuselage design of such airplanes and need detailed attention in terms of the structural layout. How to prepare an initial structural layout is discussed in Part III.

In many military applications it is necessary to account for the installation of guns, ammo containers, missiles and other weapons. Data on sizes and volumes for such military items are also included in Part III.

Step 4.3: Add the appropriate distances to the cabin interior layout of Step 4.2, to allow for the required structural depth for fuselage frames, fuselage bulkheads and fuselage skins.

Typical distances which allow for sufficient structural depth are:

for small commercial airplanes: 1.5 inches
for fighters and trainers: 2 inches
for large transports: $0.02d_f$ + 1 inch

Step 4.4: Finish the exterior lines which define the cabin part of the fuselage.

Step 4.5: Translate the cockpit crew requirement into a dimensioned drawing of the cockpit.

Part III (Ref.2) contains detailed data with which civil and military cockpits can be laid out while observing typical requirements for pilot visibility and for pilot ability to reach the essential cockpit controls.

Make certain that the aerodynamic 'fairing' of the cockpit exterior into the fuselage exterior causes as little extra drag as possible.

Step 4.6: Prepare a dimensioned drawing of the entire fuselage, including the rear fuselage cone.

Figure 4.1 defines several important geometric parameters for the fuselage. Table 4.1 shows ranges of these parameters which are currently employed. Unless there is a good reason, these ranges should not be exceeded.

The fuselage cone is normally a smooth transition from the maximum fuselage cross section to the 'end' of the fuselage. When the 'fineness ratio' of this cone is too low, there will be a large base drag penalty although the fuselage weight may be reduced. When the 'fineness ratio' of this cone is too large, there will be a large friction drag penalty as well as a large weight penalty.

It will be obvious to the reader, that a long fuselage cone tends to increase the tail moment arm thereby reducing required tail area and vice versa.

The decision on the fuselage cone fineness ratio is therefore one that involves a number of trade-offs.

Caution 1. The geometry of the fuselage cone can also have an impact on the ability of the airplane to

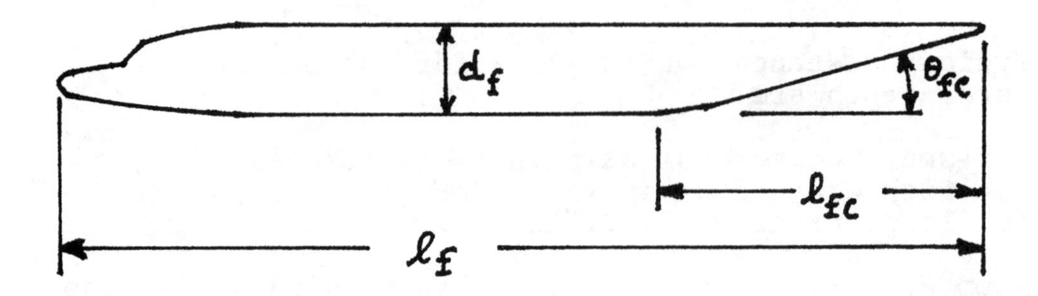

Figure 4.1 Definition of Geometric Fuselage Parameters

Table 4.1 Currently Used Geometric Fuselage Parameters

Airplane Type	l_f/d_f	l_{fc}/d_f	θ_{fc} (deg)
Homebuilts	4 - 8	3*	2 - 9
Single Engine	5 - 8	3 - 4	3 - 9
Twins	3.6** - 8	2.6 - 4	6 - 13
Agricultural	5 - 8	3 - 4	1 - 7
Business Jets	7 - 9.5	2.5 - 5	6 - 11
Regionals	5.6 - 10	2 - 4	15 - 19***
Jet Transports	6.8 - 11.5	2.6 - 4	11 - 16
Mil. Trainers	5.4 - 7.5	3*	up to 14
Fighters	7 - 11	3 - 5*	0 - 8
Mil. Transports, Bombers and Patrol Airplanes	6 - 13	2.5 - 6	7 - 25****
Flying Boats	6 - 11	3 - 6	8 - 14
Supersonics	12 - 25	6 - 8	2 - 9

*Tailcone as defined by Figure 4.1 not easily defined
**Cessna 336 (Fig.3.9c) ***Embraer Brasilia (Fig.3.16d)
****Lockheed Hercules (Fig.3.29d)

rotate about its rear gear during take-off. Make sure that the selected cone geometry does not interfere with take-off rotation.

Table 4.1 shows ranges of rear fuselage angles used on existing airplanes.

Caution 2. In the case of twin boom configurations, the fuselage tends to have a rather small fineness ratio. Examples are the AW Argosy (Ref.14, Section 14.2) and the Fairchild C-119 (Ref.29, Section 14.2). These airplanes all experienced high drag due to the fuselage configuration. The obvious trade-off between a larger fineness ratio for the fuselage to reduce drag and the greater weight caused by such a larger fineness ratio will have to be established and a decision made.

Caution 3. In the case of flying boats it is essential that the lower part of the fuselage (called hull) has the 'correct' hydrodynamic lines. The reader should refer to Part III for data on these shapes.

Step 4.7: Document the decisions made under steps 4.1 - 4.6 in a brief descriptive report including clear, dimensioned drawings.

One of these drawings should be a so-called 'inboard profile'. Examples of inboard profiles may be found in Part III.

4.2 EXAMPLE APPLICATIONS

Three example applications will be presented:

4.2.1 Twin Engine Propeller Driven Airplane: Selene
4.2.2 Jet Transport: Ourania
4.2.3 Fighter: Eris

The applications are all presented in accordance with the Step 4.1 through Step 4.7 sequence presented in Section 4.1.

4.2.1 Twin Engine Propeller Driven Airplane

Step 4.1: Table 2.17 of Part I defines the mission of the Selene. The following items from Table 2.17 need to be carried in the fuselage:

1. Six passengers (this includes the pilot)
2. 200 lbs of luggage

The mission specification does not stipulate the required baggage volume. Comparison with competitive airplanes (Ref.8) shows that a baggage volume of 40 cubic would be acceptable.

Step 4.2: A two abreast layout is selected for the Selene. This type of layout is common to most airplanes in this category. Two cockpit seats and four cabin seats are therefore required, for a total of three rows.

The selection of cabin cross section is critical to passenger comfort and to weight and wetted area. Looking at the fuselage cross sections for this type of airplane in Part III shows most of them to be rather flat sided. For an unpressurized fuselage that is acceptable. It also is easy to manufacture. For a pressurized fuselage the perfect cross section would be circular. The reader should try and prepare a layout of a circular cross section for the Selene. Because of the human anatomy it will be discovered that the fuselage will become rather bulky. This is another reason why the fuselage cross section of most smaller general aviation airplanes is more or less rectangular.

Since it is forseen that future versions of the Selene will have to be pressurized, the double circle cross section of Figure 4.2a was selected. Note the slab sides which connect the two circles. The internal cabin dimensions of the Selene were selected after comparison with four competitors:

Airplane Type	Internal cabin dimensions in ft		
	Length	Max. Width	Max. Height
Beech Duke	11.8	4.2	4.3
Beech Baron M58	12.6	3.5	4.2
Cessna T303	13.6	4.0	4.0
Piper PA-44-180	8.0	3.5	4.0
Selene	18.5	4.25	4.4

Most cabin type twins have an access door in the rear. Because Selene will be configured as a high wing pusher with the propellers behind the wing trailing edge, a rear access door would be awkward: the propellers are to close to the door. Therefore, the cabin access door will be located directly behind the pilot on the left side. This arrangement is also used in several business jets. Figure 4.2b shows the proposed interior arrangement of the cabin.

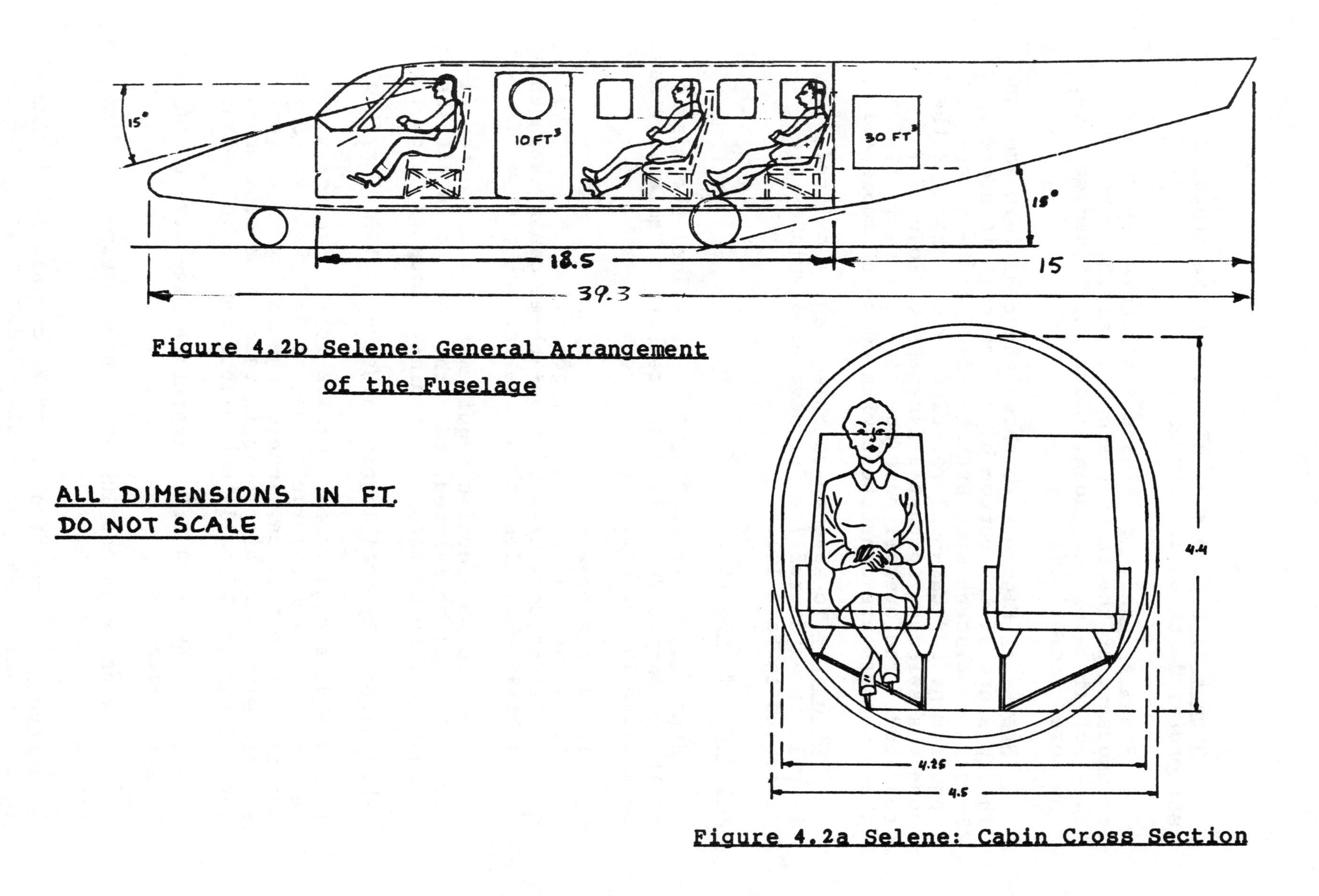

Figure 4.2b Selene: General Arrangement of the Fuselage

ALL DIMENSIONS IN FT.
DO NOT SCALE

Figure 4.2a Selene: Cabin Cross Section

Step 4.3: Figure 4.2a also shows the proposed structural depth of 1.5 inches.

Steps 4.4 and 4.5: Figure 4.2b shows the general arrangement of the cockpit and the fairing into the exterior lines of the cabin. Note the 15 degree 'over the nose' visibility.

Step 4.6: Figure 4.2b shows the rear fuselage cone. The up-slope of the bottom of the cone is 15 degrees. This is consistent with attached flow and with the requirement for take-off rotation. The length of the cone was selected so that a fineness ratio of 2.7 resulted. The overall fuselage fineness ratio is 7.2. These numbers are consistent with those of Table 4.1.

Step 4.7: To save space this step is omitted. Example inboard profiles for several airplanes are presented in Part III.

4.2.2 Jet Transport

Step 4.1: Table 2.18 of Part I defines the mission of the Ourania. The following items from Table 2.18 must be carried in the fuselage:

1. 150 passengers
2. 150x30 = 4,500 lbs of luggage
3. flight deck crew of two + three cabin attendants
4. 5x30 = 150 lbs of luggage for the crew

There is no specific requirement for cargo containers. It will be assumed, that the total of 4,650 lbs of luggage will be carried in containers located below the cabin floor. Typical luggage density is 12.5 lbs/ft^3. This yields a requirement for 372 ft^3 of baggage volume. Because of the large number of 727's and 737's which are in airline service, interchangeability of cargo containers with these airplanes is felt to be desirable. Typical Boeing 727 belly containers have a volumetric capacity of about 80 ft^3. Therefore five such containers will be necessary.

Data on cargo and luggage containers may be found in Part III.

Step 4.2: According to Ref.8, comparable airplanes to the Ourania have five or six abreast seating. A circular fuselage cross section is required to keep the weight of the pressurized shell down.

Five abreast seating results in 30 seat rows.
Six abreast seating results in 25 seat rows.

A future problem with a 5-abreast arrangement may be that any growth version will end up with a very long fuselage. This is one reason to opt for 6-abreast seating for the Ourania.

The next question to be decided is the seat and aisle width to be used. Part III contains detailed data on this subject. It is decided here to opt for the seats shown in Figure 4.3 with an aisle of 22 inches. Figure 4.4 shows the proposed seating/aisle arrangement. At this point a circle needs to be drawn such that the aisle height is reasonable and such that the shoulders of passengers seated in window seats do not touch the interior side wall. Figure 4.3 also shows the proposed interior circle.

Airline experience shows that an item high on the list of passenger preferences is easy to reach and liberally sized overhead storage. Figure 4.3 also shows the overhead storage.

The seat pitch needs to be selected next. Part III shows that a 34 inch seat pitch is reasonable for this type airplane. The cabin floor arrangement can now be drawn. Figure 4.5 shows the proposed floor arrangement. Note that provisions are made for door and emergency exits. Part III also contains data on the required number and size of doors and emergency exits in passenger airplanes.

Figure 4.5 also shows the proposed arrangement of galleys, toilets and wardrobes. Part III contains data on the dimensions of these items also.

The following data compare the cabin interior dimensions of the Ourania with those of three competitors:

Airplane Type	Seats Abreast	Internal cabin dimensions in ft Length	Max.Width	Max.Height
Boeing 737-300	6	68.5	11.5	7.2
McDD DC9-80	5	101	10.1	6.8
Airbus 320	6	NA	12.2	7.3
Ourania	6	76.6	12.4	7.5

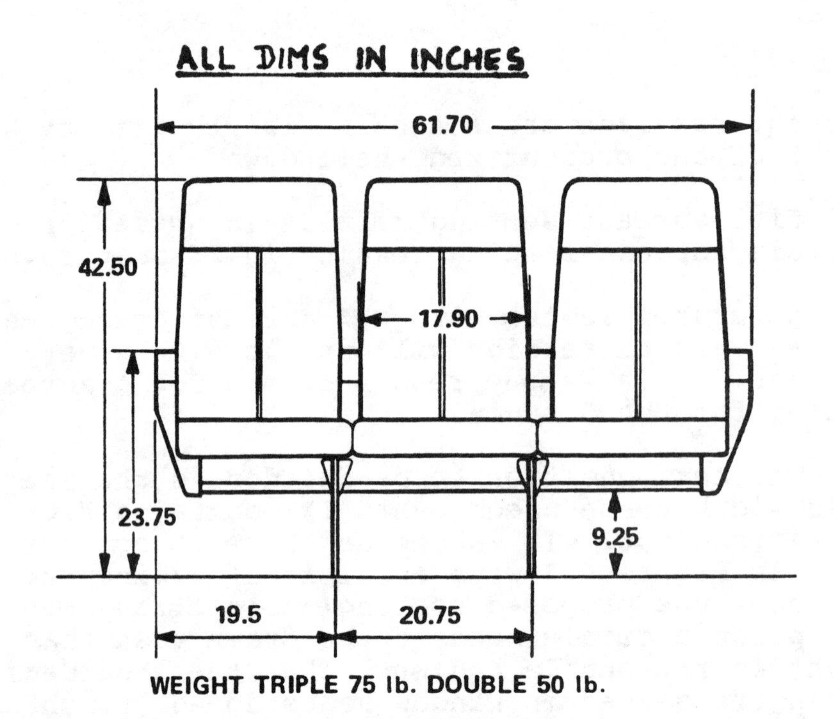

Figure 4.3 Ourania: Proposed Triple Seats

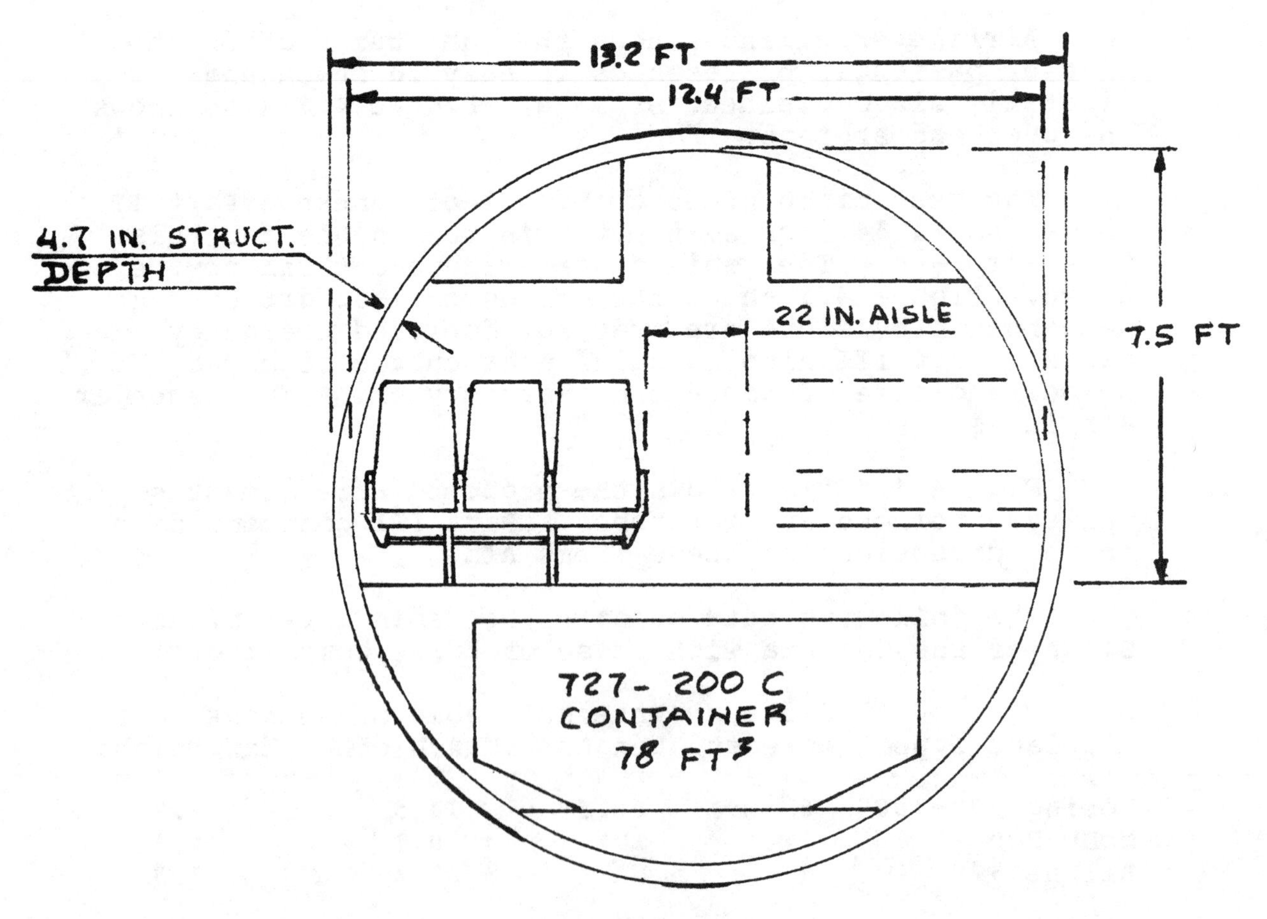

Figure 4.4 Ourania: Cabin Cross Section

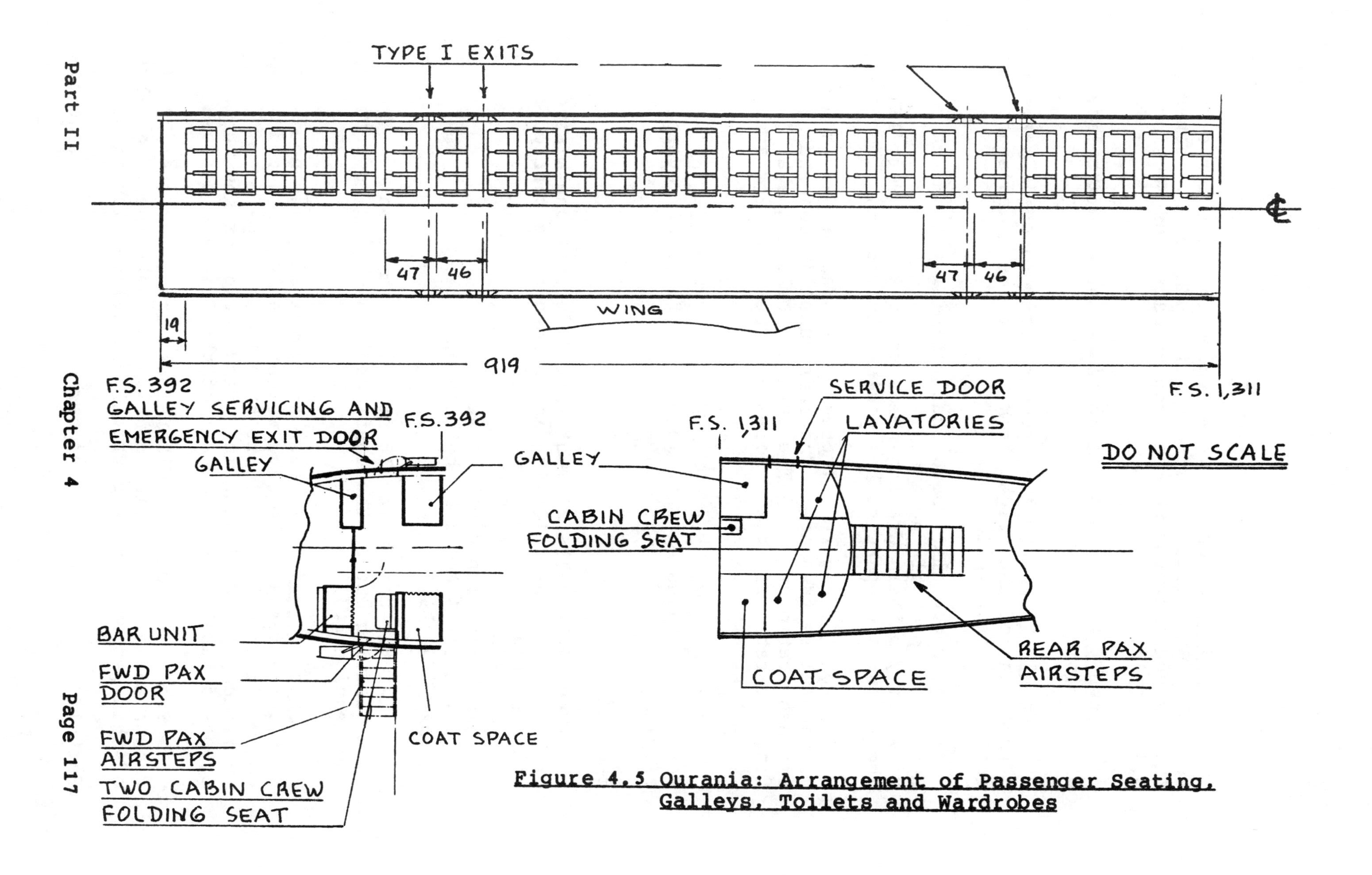

Figure 4.5 Ourania: Arrangement of Passenger Seating, Galleys, Toilets and Wardrobes

Step 4.3: Figure 4.4 also shows the exterior cross section. Note that the structural depth is 4.7 inches. This is consistent with the recommendation of Section 4.1, Step 4.3.

Step 4.4: Figure 4.5 also shows the exterior lines of the cabin.

Step 4.5: Figure 4.6 presents the proposed interior arrangement of the flight deck. Note the added seats for carrying 'check' pilots.

Figure 4.6 also shows that visibility from the cockpit is probably acceptable. To make sure a visibility pattern drawing needs to be made. Part III shows how to prepare such a visibility pattern.

Step 4.6: Figure 4.7 presents a dimensioned drawing of the entire fuselage. The rear fuselage cone has a fineness ratio of 3.5. The entire fuselage has a fineness ratio of 10.1. Note that these numbers are consistent with Table 4.1.

Step 4.7: To save space this step has been omitted. Part III contains example inboard profiles of several airplanes.

4.2.3 Fighter

Step 4.1: Table 2.19 of Part I defines the mission of the Eris. The following items need to be carried in the fuselage:

1. Pilot with ejection seat
2. GAU 8/A multi barrel cannon
3. Two engines

Item three is a result not of the mission specification but of the configuration choice made in sub-section 3.5.3.

Step 4.2 - 4.7: Because a fighter airplane needs to be tightly 'packed' to save weight, wetted area and volume it is not feasible to take these steps individually. Following is a description of how the proposed fuselage arrangement of the Eris was arrived at.

Figure 4.8 shows a dimensioned sketch of the GAU 8/A cannon and its ammunition container. Note the large size of this weapon. It is currently installed also in the

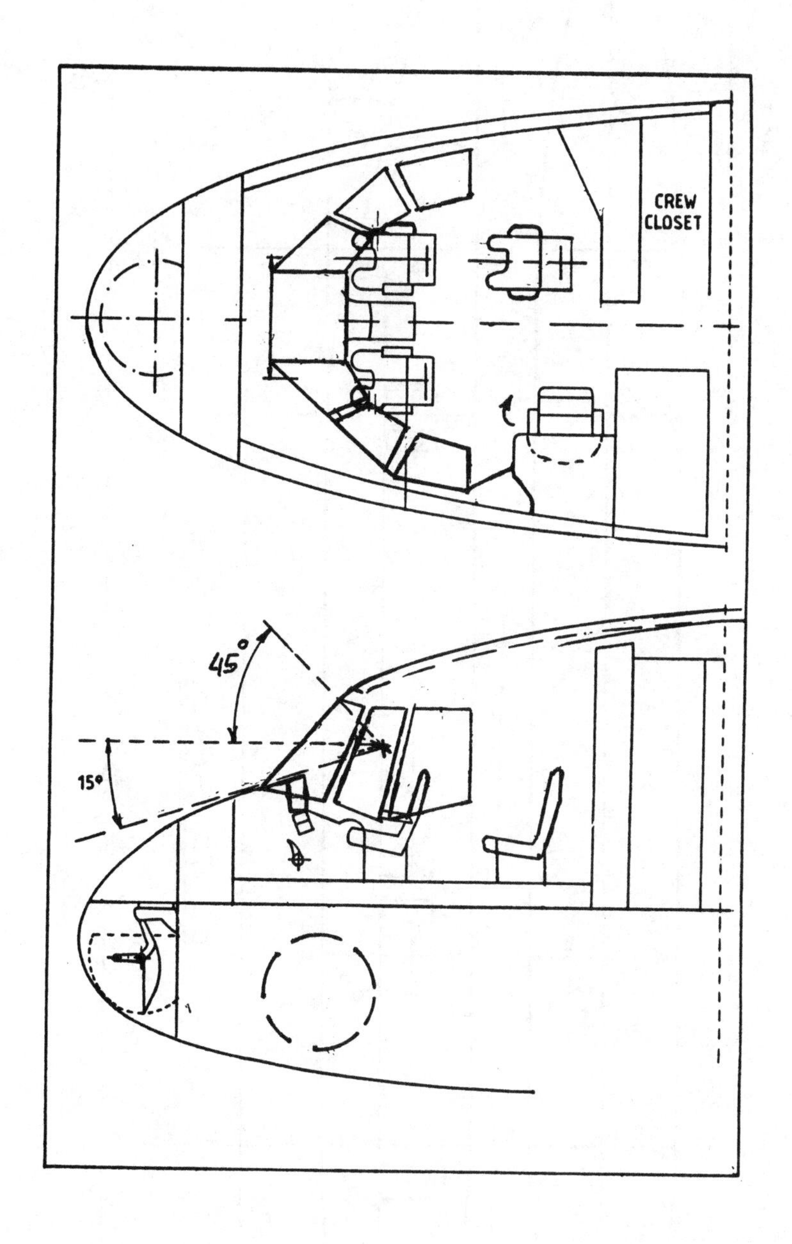

Figure 4.6 Ourania: Flight Deck Arrangement

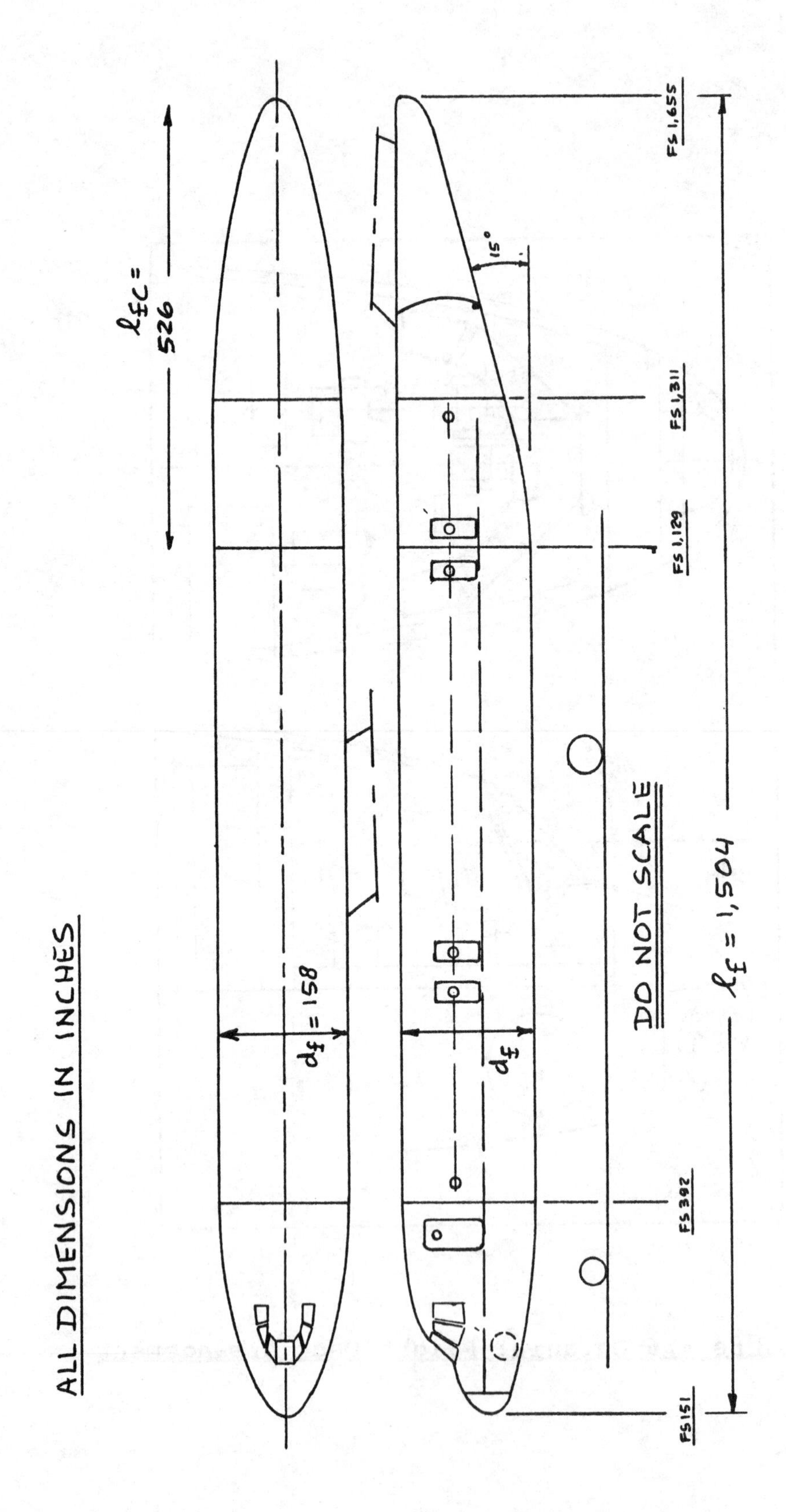

Figure 4.7 Ourania: General Arrangement of the Fuselage

Fairchild Republic A10 attack airplane.

Figure 3.61 shows the threeview of the DeHavilland DH110 SeaVixen. The overall configuration of this airplane is the one selected for the Eris. It can therefore be used as a guide.

To keep the length of the fuselage within reasonable bounds, the large ammo container will be placed behind the pilot. The cannon itself will be placed forward of and below the pilot. The nose gear will be retracted forward into the nose. Because nosegear and cannon compete for the same space, they will be separated laterally. This results in the cannon being on the right side and the nose gear on the left side.

The engines will be mounted as closely behind the ammo container as possible.

The wing torque box must pass through the fuselage above or below the ammo container. To reduce fuselage depth as much as possible it was decided to mount the wing on the fuselage above the ammo container. This results in a high wing configuration. In turn this forces the inlet ducts to be of the so-called 'armpit' type. A potential problem is that the exhaust gasses from the cannon can enter the inlets. To prevent this a special exhaust gas deflector is installed on the nose of the fuselage.

Figure 4.9 shows the proposed fuselage arrangement. Note the 15 degree downward visibility over the nose.

The mission specification of the Eris also calls for twenty 500 lbs bombs to be carried externally. It is decided to try the following arrangement:

- 8 bombs mounted conformally under the fuselage
- 12 bombs mounted in racks under the wings at the same spanwise station which carries the tail-booms.

Example inboard profiles for fighters and trainers are contained in Part III.

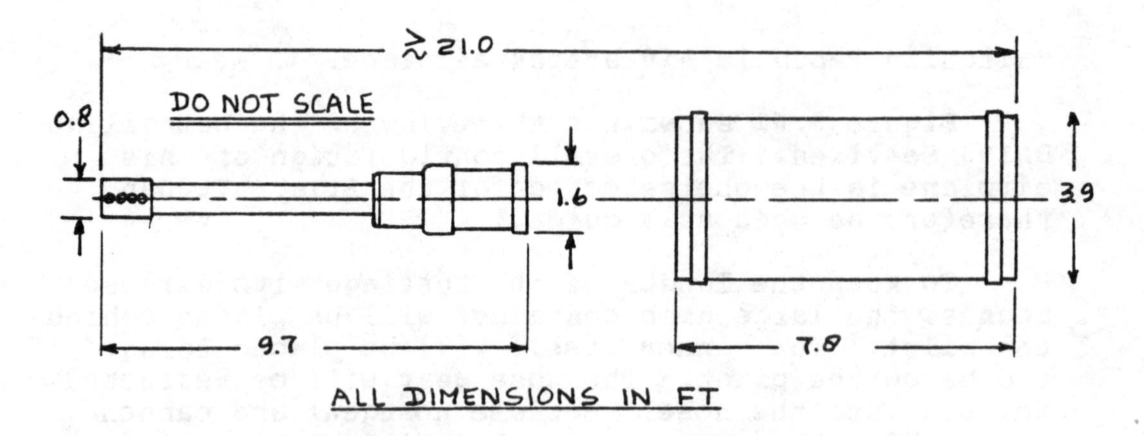

Figure 4.8 Eris: GAU 8/A Cannon Dimensions

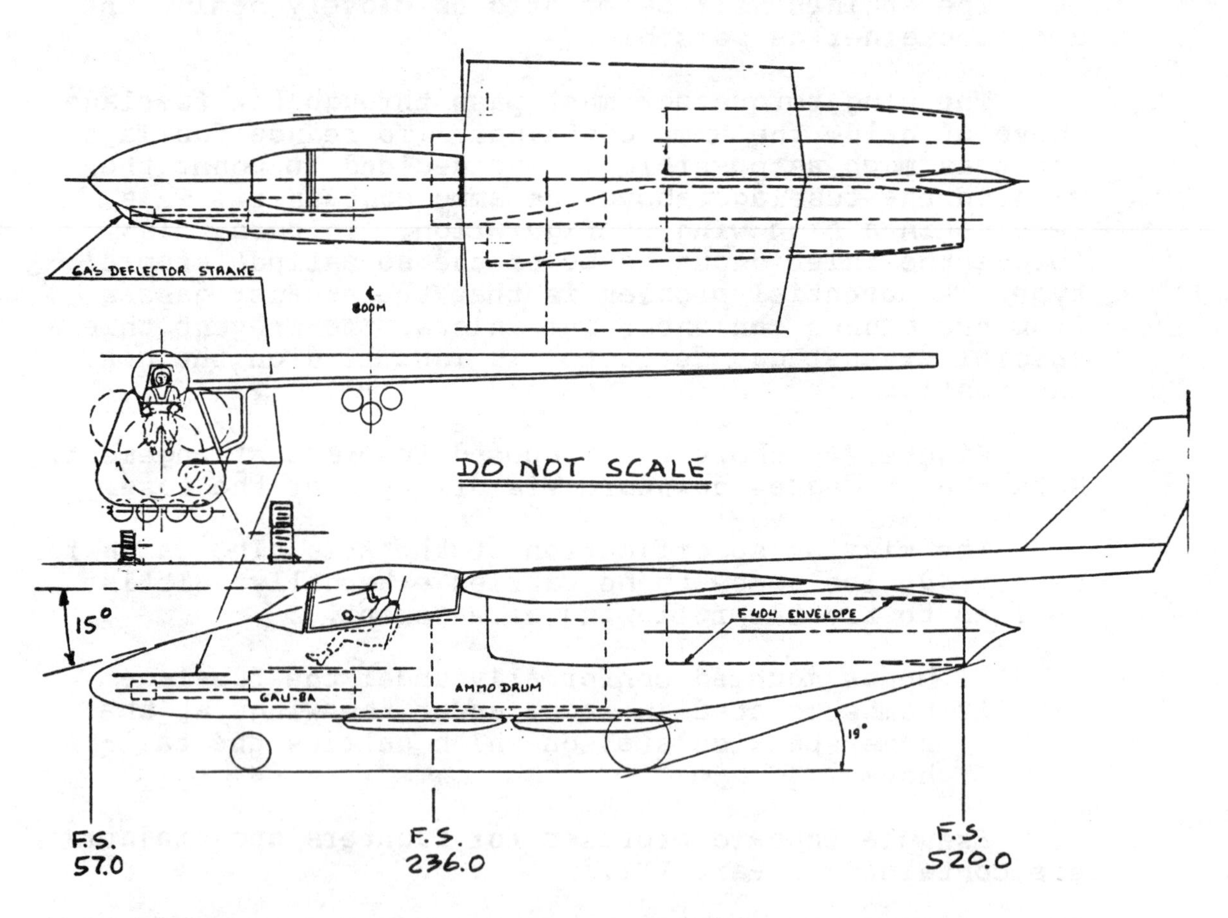

Figure 4.9 Eris: General Arrangement of the Fuselage

5. SELECTION AND INTEGRATION OF THE PROPULSION SYSTEM

The purpose of this chapter is to provide a guide to the selection and to the integration of the propulsion system. The method is presented as part of Step 5 in p.d. sequence I as outlined in Chapter 2.

Selection and integration of the propulsion system involves the following three decisons:

1. Selection of the propulsion system type or types.

2. Determination of the number of engines to be used and the power (or thrust) level of each.

3. Disposition of these engines, i.e. integration of these engines into the configuration.

Sections 5.1 through 5.3 address these decisions in a step-by-step manner. Example applications are discussed in Section 5.4

5.1 SELECTION OF PROPULSION SYSTEM TYPE

The following factors play a role in selecting the type of propulsion system to be used:

1. Required cruise speed and/or maximum speed
2. Required maximum operating altitude
3. Required range and range economy
4. FAR 36 noise regulations (applies to civil airplanes only)
5. Installed weight
6. Reliability and maintainability
7. Fuel amount needed
8. Fuel cost
9. Fuel availability
10. Specific customer or market demands
11. Timely certification

Overall fuel efficiency and installed weight often dominate the arguments pro and con a certain type of propulsion system. Figure 5.1 provides an overview of trends in propulsion system application as it relates to the flight envelope of airplanes. The data are based on 1985+ technology.

It is clear from Figure 5.1 that the flight envelope (speed-altitude envelope) of an airplane has an important bearing on the choice of the type of propulsion system.

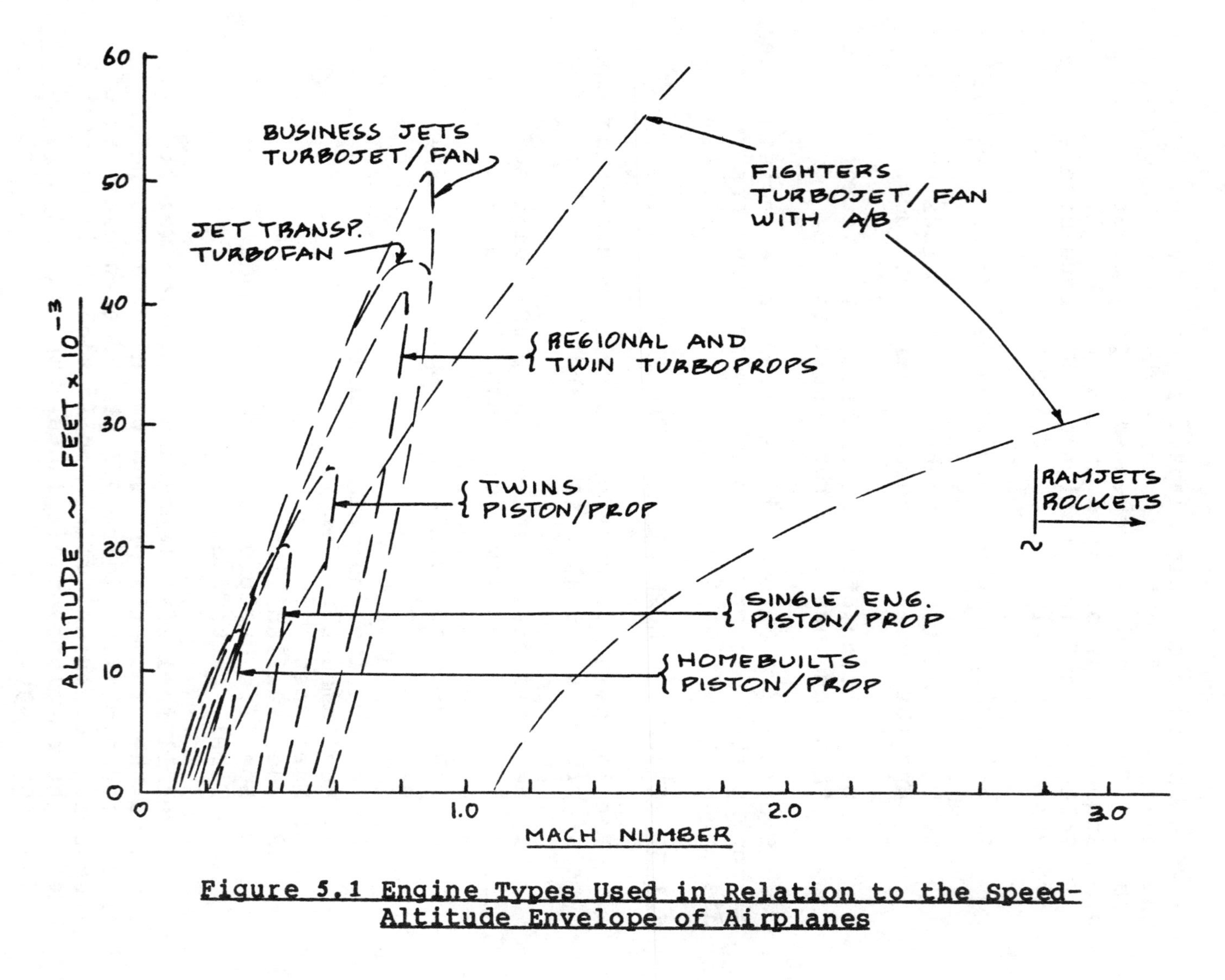

Figure 5.1 Engine Types Used in Relation to the Speed-Altitude Envelope of Airplanes

From a certification point of view (civil and military), only the following propulsion system types will be viable for application during the next 5-10 years:

1. Piston/propeller with or without supercharging
2. Turbo/propeller
3. Propfan
4. Unducted fan
5. Turbojet
6. Turbofan
7. Rocket
8. Ramjet

Propulsion types 1-4 can be expected to be offered with single as well as with contra rotating propellers and/or fans.

References 16 - 18 contain excellent discussions on the characteristics of these propulsion systems.

The following step-by-step procedure is suggested to arrive at a decision on the type(s) of propulsion system to be used:

Step 5.1: Check the mission specification for any definition of the type of powerplant required. Frequently the type of powerplant is specified in the mission specification. If so, proceed to Step 5.4. If not, proceed to Step 5.2.

Step 5.2: Draw a preliminary Speed (or Mach) versus Altitude envelope for the airplane.

This can usually be done from the preliminary sizing work described in Part I (Ref.1).

Step 5.3: Compare the airplane speed-altitude envelope with those of Figure 5.1 and decide which type of powerplant provides the best overall match.

Conventional wisdom says that it is undesirable to 'mix' different types of powerplant in one airplane. An important argument in favor of this standpoint is that different types of propulsion system call for different operating procedures. This certainly increases the crew workload which is not desirable.

Another argument if favor of this standpoint is that

maintenance will become more costly when different types of propulsion system are used in the same airplane.

While these arguments are certainly correct, there have been several successful deviations from this rule. Examples of such deviations are:

1. The Convair B36 bomber, which used six piston/propeller engines and four turbojet engines.

2. The DeHavilland Comet, which used rockets in addition to its four turbojet engines to improve the field performance at 'hot-and-high' airports.

3. The Lockheed P2V Neptune, which used two piston/propeller engines and two turbojet engines.

5.2 SELECTION OF THE NUMBER OF ENGINES AND THE POWER OR THRUST LEVEL PER ENGINE

The reader is reminded of the fact, that the total required power or thrust level required for take-off is already known from the preliminary sizing work done in Section 3.7 of Part I (Ref.1). The type of propulsion system was decided upon in Section 5.1, Step 5.3. What is needed now is a decision on the number of engines.

There are two possibilities at this point:

1. A new engine will be developed for the proposed design.

In this case, the engine(s) can be tailored to the existing design. The reader must be aware of the fact that the development and certification of a new powerplant is expensive and takes a long lead time. For new jet engines a typical lead time is 7-10 years.

2. An existing engine must be used.

Reference 8 provides data on existing aircraft engines. Because the power or thrust level of existing engines is basically 'frozen', the number of engines is determined by dividing the required take-off power or thrust level by an integer: usually 1,2,3 or 4. In the past more than four engines have been employed on a number of airplanes. The concensus today is that beyond four engines the problems of maintenance, rigging and failure probabilities become unacceptable. If in the future there is a requirement for very large airplanes, it may be that the cost of developing new, large engines becomes prohibitive. Design studies performed by Lockheed and Boeing for such airplanes indicate thet in such cases more than four engines is again a reasonable solution.

Table 5.1 relates the numerical engine failure probability to the number of engines used.

Table 5.1 Relation Between Engine Failure Probability and the Number of Engines Used

Failure of:	1 Engine	2 Engines	3 Engines
Airplane with:			
two engines	$2P_{ef}$	P_{ef}^2	not appl.
three engines	$3P_{ef}$	$3P_{ef}^2$	P_{ef}^3
four engines	$4P_{ef}$	$6P_{ef}^2$	$4P_{ef}^3$

Conventional wisdom says that it is not desirable to use engines of differing power (or thrust) levels in one airplane. The main arguments for this position are the same arguments advanced in Section 5.1 for not using more than one type of powerplant.

While these arguments are generally correct, there have been several instances of successful deviations from this rule as well. Examples of such deviations are:

1. The DeHavilland 121 Trident IIIE which uses four jet engines, three large, one small. The fourth smaller engine was added to allow for higher take-off weights and to do so with minimum development and production cost.

2. Rutan's Voyager, which uses two piston/propeller engines of different power output. Because of the extreme range requirement placed on this airplane it was important to match best fuel consumption to power required. In this application, the solution of two different power levels was a sensible one.

In many instances the mission specification will define how many power plants are to be used. If this is not the case, the following step-by-step procedure may be followed:

Step 5.4: Determine the maximum power (or thrust) requirement for the airplane.

The reader is reminded of the fact that the maximum

power, P_{TO} (or thrust, T_{TO}) requirement was already established from the preliminary sizing work outlined in Section 3.7, Part I (Ref.1).

<u>Step 5.5:</u> Decide on the number of engines and on the specific engine model to be used.

The number of engines to be used in an airplane is often specified in the mission specification. If this is not the case, make a list of candidate engines which are available on the market. This information can be found in Reference 8 or in brochures from engine manufacturers.

The power (or thrust) levels of the candidate engine should be as close as possible to the take-off power (or thrust) levels divided by an integer. Don't worry about being off the mark by +/- 10 percent: the sizing calculations of Part I have the same accuracy.

<u>Step 5.6:</u> If the airplane being designed is a propeller driven airplane, determine the required propeller diameter and the number of propeller blades with the following Class I method:

Tables 5.2, 5.3 and 5.4 list typical take-off power and propeller data for six types of airplanes. Note that the so-called 'blade-power-loading' number, P_{bl} is within a certain range for these four types of airplanes.

By assuming a suitable value for P_{bl} and for the number of blades, n_p, it is possible to determine the propeller diameter from:

$$D_p = \{4P_{max}/(\pi n_p P_{bl})\}^{1/2} \qquad (5.1)$$

<u>5.3 INTEGRATION OF THE PROPULSION SYSTEM</u>

Having decided on the type and the number of engines to be employed, the next decision is: where should these engines be located?

As may be seen from the configurations presented in Chapter 3, the number of possible arrangements is very large indeed. The following factors play a role in deciding on the engine disposition:

Table 5.2 Relation Between Max. Engine Power, Propeller Diameter and Number of Propeller Blades for Homebuilts and for Single Engine FAR23 Certified Airplanes

Airplane Type	Prop. Pitch	Max. Power per Engine, P_{max}, hp	Prop. Diam., D_p, ft	Number of Prop. Blades, n_p,	Power Loading per Blade, P_{bl}, hp/ft^2
<u>Homebuilts</u>					
Jurca MJ5	Fixed	115	6.1	2	2.0
Piel CP1320	Fixed	160	5.9	2	2.9
Piel CP80	Fixed	90	5.0	2	2.3
Pottier P70S	Fixed	60	4.3	2	2.1
Pazmany PL4A	Fixed	50	5.7	2	1.0
Variviggen	Fixed	150	5.8	2	2.8
Rand/R KR-1	2-pos.	90	4.4	2	3.0
Van's RV-3	Fixed	125	5.7	2	2.5
Sequoia F8L	Fixed	135	6.2	2	2.2
Per. Osprey II	Fixed	150	5.5	2	3.2
			P_{bl} range: 1.0-3.2		
<u>Single Engine FAR23 Certified</u>					
CESSNA					
152	Fixed	108	5.8	2	2.0
Skyhawk	Fixed	160	6.3	2	2.6
Skylane	C.Spd	230	6.8	2	3.2
Skywagon (185)	C.Spd	300	6.7	3	2.8
Caravan I	C.Spd	600	8.3	3	3.7
BEECH					
V35B Bonanza	C.Spd	285	7.0	2	3.7
38P Lightning	C.Spd	550	7.7	3	3.9
PIPER					
PA28 Warrior II	Fixed	160	6.2	2	2.6
Mooney 201	C.Spd	200	6.2	2	3.3
Mooney 301	C.Spd	360	6.5	3	3.6
			P_{bl} range: 2.0-3.9		

Note: $P_{bl} = 4P_{max}/\pi n_p D_p^2$

Table 5.3 Relation Between Max. Engine Power, Propeller Diameter and Number of Propeller Blades for Agricultural Airplanes and for Military Propeller Driven Trainers

Airplane Type	Prop. Pitch	Max. Power per Engine, P_{max}, hp	Prop. Diam., D_p, ft	Number of Prop. Blades, n_p,	Power Loading per Blade, P_{bl}, hp/ft^2
Agricultural Airplanes					
Schweiz. AgCat	C.Spd	750	9.0	2	5.9
Airtruk PL12	C.Spd	300	7.3	2	3.6
EMB 201A	C.Spd	300	7.0	2	3.9
PZL-104	C.Spd	260	8.7	2	2.2
PZL-106A	C.Spd	592	8.6	4	2.5
PZL-M18A	C.Spd	1,000	10.8	4	2.7
NDN Fieldmaster	C.Spd	750	8.8	3	4.1
Cessna AgTruck	C.Spd	300	7.2	2	3.7
Air Tr. AT-301A	C.Spd	600	9.1	2	4.6
Ayr. Thrush S2R	C.Spd	600	9.0	2	4.7
			P_{bl} range: 2.2-5.9		
Military Propeller Driven Trainers					
EMB 312 Tucano	C.Spd	750	7.8	3	5.2
Indaer Pillan	C.Spd	300	6.3	3	3.2
Aerosp. Epsilon	C.Spd	300	6.5	2	4.5
RFB 600 Fantr.	C.Spd	420	4.0	5*	6.7
SM SF-260	C.Spd	260	6.3	2	4.2
FFA AS32T	C.Spd	420	7.2	3	3.4
Pilatus PC-7	C.Spd	650	7.8	3	4.5
NDN-1 Firecr.	C.Spd	260	6.3	3	2.8
NDN-1T Firecr.	C.Spd	715	7.0	3	6.2
Beech T34C	C.Spd	715	7.5	3	5.4
			P_{bl} range: 2.8-6.7		

Note: $P_{bl} = 4P_{max}/\pi n_p D_p^2$

*This airplane has a ducted fan instead of a propeller

Table 5.4 Relation Between Max. Engine Power, Propeller Diameter and Number of Propeller Blades for Twin Engine FAR23 and for Regional Turbopropeller Driven Airplanes

Airplane Type	Prop. Pitch	Max. Power per Engine, P_{max}, hp	Prop. Diam., D_p, ft	Number of Prop. Blades, n_p,	Power Loading per Blade, P_{bl}, hp/ft^2
Twin Engine FAR23 Certified Airplanes					
PIPER					
PA-31 Navajo	C.Spd	325	6.7	3	3.1
PA-31T Chey. II	C.Spd	620	7.8	3	4.3
CESSNA					
T303	C.Spd	250	6.2	3	2.8
340A	C.Spd	310	6.4	3	3.2
Conquest I	C.Spd	450	7.8	3	3.1
Conquest II	C.Spd	636	7.5	3	4.8
BEECH					
Baron 95-B55	C.Spd	260	6.5	2	3.9
Duke B60	C.Spd	380	6.2	3	4.2
King Air C90-1	C.Spd	550	7.8	3	3.8
BN2B Islander	C.Spd	260	6.5	2	3.9
			P_{bl} range: 2.8-4.8		
Regional Turbopropeller Driven Airplanes					
EMB-110 Bandar.	C.Spd	750	7.8	3	5.2
EMB-120 Brasil.	C.Spd	1,500	10.5	4	4.3
SF-340	C.Spd	1,630	10.5	4	4.7
Fokker F27-200	C.Spd	2,140	11.5	4	5.2
Brit.Aer. 748	C.Spd	2,280	12.0	4	5.0
Casa Nurt. 235	C.Spd	1,700	10.8	4	4.6
Beech C99	C.Spd	715	7.8	3	5.0
Beech 1900	C.Spd	1,100	9.1	4	4.2
ATR-42	C.Spd	1,800	13.0	4	3.4
IAI Arava 201	C.Spd	750	8.5	3	4.4
			P_{bl} range: 3.4-5.2		

Note: $P_{bl} = 4P_{max}/\pi n_p D_p^2$

1. Effect of power changes or power failures on stability and control: longitudinal, lateral and directional. The vertical and/or lateral location of the thrustline(s) are critically important in this respect.

2. Drag of the proposed installation.

3. Weight and balance consequences of the proposed installation.

4. Inlet requirements and resulting effect on 'installed' power and efficiciency.

5. Accessibility and maintainability.

The following step-by-step procedure is offered as a guide in deciding on the integration of the propulsion system:

<u>Step 5.7:</u> Decide on a pusher, a tractor or a mixed installation.

As a general rule, when the propeller or inlet plane is forward of the c.g., the installation is referred to as a tractor installation. When the propeller or the inlet plane is located behind the c.g. the installation is referred to as a pusher installation.

Tractor installations tend to be destabilizing while pusher installations tend to be stabilizing in both static longitudinal and static directional stability. This feature can be used to save some empennage area in pusher installations.

Methods for computing these effects are discussed in Parts VI and VII (Refs 5 and 6).

If it is decided to go with a pusher propeller installation with the propeller behind the trailing edge of the wing (such as the airplanes of Figures 3.42 and 3.47), make certain that the distance between the wing trailing edge and the propeller plane is at least one half the local wing chord. This is to alleviate dynamic excitation of the propeller blades by the wing vortex system.

<u>Step 5.8:</u> Decide on mounting the engines on:

a. the wing
b. the fuselage
c. the empennage
d. any combination of a through c.

The reader should again refer to the configuration discussions in Sections 3.1 and 3.2.

Before deciding where to mount the engines, refer to the factors 1-5 listed at the beginning of this section and carefully consider the various trade-offs involved. Document all decisions and list the reasons for and/or against.

In the case of propeller installations it is highly desirable to maintain a clearance between the propeller tips and the fuselage of 20 - 40 inches, depending on the blade power loading and on the propeller tipspeed. This clearance is necessary to avoid acoustic fatigue of the adjacent structure and to avoid excessive noise entering the cabin.

In the case of jet engines, make sure that no primary structure is placed too close to exhaust gases.

Step 5.9: Obtain the necessary information on:

1. engine geometry and clearance envelope
2. engine mounting (attachment) points
3. engine air-ducting requirements
4. engine thrust reversing requirements
5. engine exhaust system requirements
6. engine accessory requirements
7. engine c.g. location
8. engine firewall requirements
9. in the case of a propeller/pusher installation, verify that the propeller thrust bearings are suitable for a pusher installation.
10. engine inlet requirements can play a major role in the layout of those jet engine installations where long inlets are needed. This is the case in many 'buried' installations.
11. for supersonic airplanes a variable geometry inlet duct is often required.

The reader should refer to Part III for more details on engine installations.

Items 1 - 9 are normally obtained directly from the engine manufacturer.

Step 5.10: Make dimensioned drawings of all engine installations required by your airplane.

These drawings should identify the engine envelope, nacelle envelope and any required inlet ducts. Example engine installations are shown in Part III.

Step 5.11: Make certain that the proposed engine installations are compatible with such requirements as:

1. acceptable FOD characteristics
2. geometric clearance when static on the ramp: no nacelle or propeller tip may touch the ground with deflated landing gear struts and tires
3. geometric clearance during take-off rotation: no scraping of nacelles or of propeller tips is allowed, with deflated landing gear struts and tires
4. geometric clearance during a low speed approach with a five degree bank angle
5. no gun exhaust gasses may enter the inlet a jet engine. Such gun exhaust gasses are highly corrosive to fan, compressor and turbine blades.

Step 5.12: Draw the engine installation in the threeview. The amount of detail here depends on the type of threeview being drawn.

The reader should refer to Part III for more details on engine installations.

Step 5.13: Document the decisions made in Steps 5.1 through 5.11 in a brief, descriptive report. Include clear, dimensioned drawings where applicable.

5.4 EXAMPLE APPLICATIONS

Three example applications will be presented:

5.4.1 Twin Engine Propeller Driven Airplane: Selene
5.4.2 Jet Transport: Ourania
5.4.3 Fighter: Eris

The applications are all presented in accordance with the Step 5.1 through Step 5.13 sequence as presented in Sections 5.1 through 5.3.

5.4.1 Twin Engine Propeller Driven Airplane

Step 5.1: The mission specification of Table 2.17 in Part I specifies that two piston engine/propeller combinations are to be used.

Note: Steps 5.2 and 5.3 can be omitted. They are presented here as a help to the reader.

Step 5.2: Figure 5.2 shows the preliminary speed-altitude envelope of the Selene. All necessary data were taken from Part I.

Step 5.3: Comparison of Figure 5.2 with Figure 5.1 shows that the piston/propeller combination is an acceptable choice for the Selene.

Step 5.4: The maximum take-off power required for the Selene was determined to be P_{TO} = 898 hp, according to the matching results of page 178, Part I.

Step 5.5: The number of engines was specified as: two, in Table 2.17, Part I. Per engine, a maximum power level of 898/2 = 449 hp is therefore required.

Consulting with Ref. 8 (1983-84), the following engines are available with roughly this power level:

1. AVCO-Lycoming TIGO-541-E1A, with 425 maximum hp output from sealevel to 15,000 ft (supercharged) and a dry weight of 700 lbs.
2. Teledyne-Continental GTSIO-520-F,K with 435 maximum hp output from sealevel to 11,000 ft (supercharged) and a dry weight of 502 lbs.

An arbitrary decision was made to use the AVCO-Lycoming engine. This engine is 24 hp short of the required power. However, the accuracy of the sizing calculations in Part I is such that this difference can

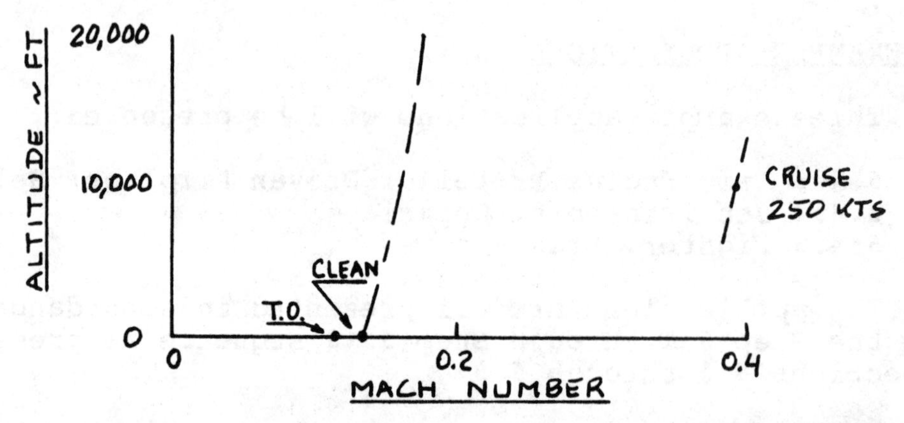

Figure 5.2 Selene: Preliminary Speed-Altitude Envelope

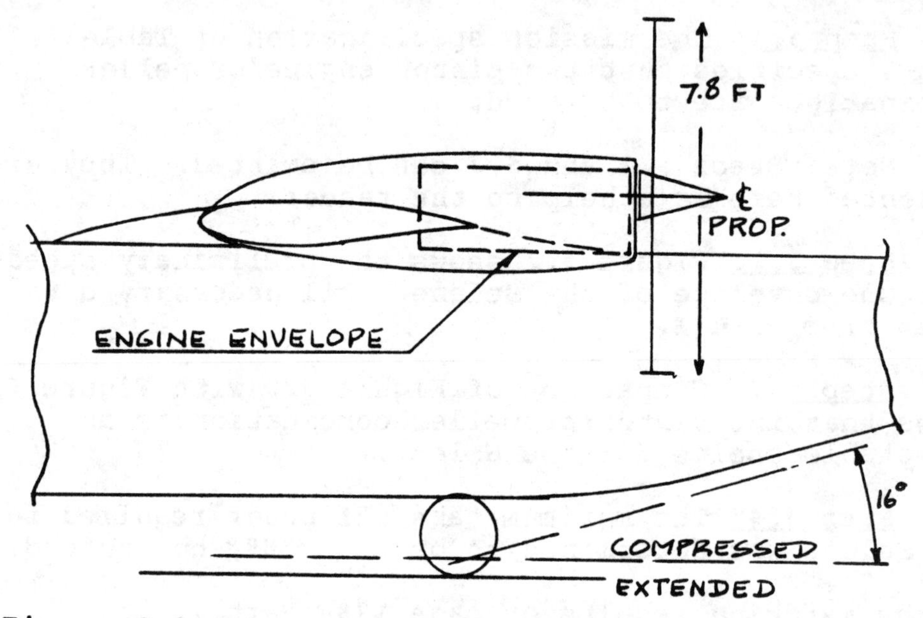

Figure 5.3 Selene: Preliminary Engine Installation

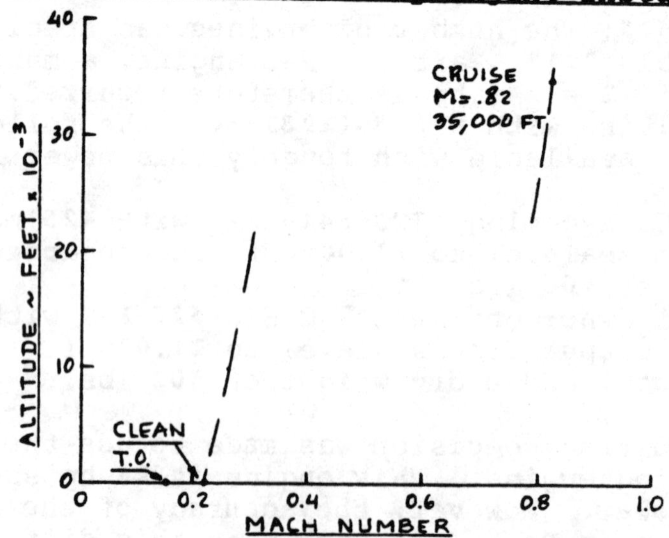

Figure 5.4 Ourania: Preliminary Speed-Altitude Envelope

be safely disregarded at this stage of the design process.

Step 5.6: Table 5.3 shows that for twins three blades per propeller are normal: therefore $n_p = 3$. For the power loading per blade a value of $P_{bl} = 3.0$ will be selected. With Eqn.(5.1) it is found that $D_p = 7.8$ ft.

Step 5.7: It was already decided in Step 3.5, that a pusher configuration was to be selected.

Step 5.8: In Step 3.5 it was decided to mount the engines in the wing. The propellers are located behind the wing trailing edge.

Step 5.9: The necessary engine information was obtained from AVCO-Lycoming as Specification No.2397-C.

Step 5.10: Figure 5.3 shows the preliminary engine installation.

Step 5.11: Figure 5.3 also shows that the installation satisfies requirements 2, 3 and 4 of this step. Requirements 1 and 5 do not apply.

Step 5.12: The threeview of Figure 13.1 shows the proposed installation.

Step 5.13: To save space this step is omitted.

5.4.2 Jet Transport

Step 5.1: The mission specification of Table 2.18 of Part I specifies that two turbofan engines are to be used.

Note: Steps 5.2 and 5.3 can be omitted. They are presented here as a help to the reader.

Step 5.2: Figure 5.4 shows the preliminary speed-altitude envelope of the Ourania. The necessary data were obtained from Part I.

Step 5.3: Comparison of Figure 5.4 with Figure 5.1 shows that the turbofan is an appropriate choice.

Step 5.4: The preliminary matching results for the Ourania as presented on pages 183-184 of Part I show that: $T_{TO} = 47,625$ lbs.

Step 5.5: Two engines are required, according to Table 2.18, Part I. The maximum required thrust per engine is therefore: 23,813 lbs.

Consultation with Ref. 8 (1983-84) shows that the CFM56-2 turbofan is the only engine which satisfies this thrust requirement: T_{max} = 24,000 lbs with a dry weight of 4,612 lbs.

Step 5.6: Not applicable.

Step 5.7: It is decided to mount the engines under the wing, forward of the center of gravity. This makes the airplane a tractor.

Step 5.8: See Step 5.7.

Step 5.9: The engine envelope information was obtained from Ref. 8 (1983-84).

Step 5.10: Figure 5.5 shows the proposed engine installation.

Step 5.11: In terms of FOD characteristics, the engine installation of the Ourania is very similar to that of the Boeing 737-300. The latter satisfies FOD requirements. It will be assumed that these requirements are also satisfied for the Ourania.

Figure 5.5 shows that requirements 2-4 are also satisfied.

Requirement 5 is not applicable.

Step 5.12: Figure 13.2 shows the proposed engine installation in the threeview.

Step 5.13: To save space this step is omitted.

5.4.3 Fighter

Step 5.1: Table 2.19 of Part I specifies the use of two turbofans.

Step 5.2: Figure 5.6 shows a preliminary speed-altitude envelope for the Eris. All necessary data were obtained from Part I.

Step 5.3: Comparison of Figure 5.6 with Figure 5.1 shows that the choice of turbofans is an appropriate one.

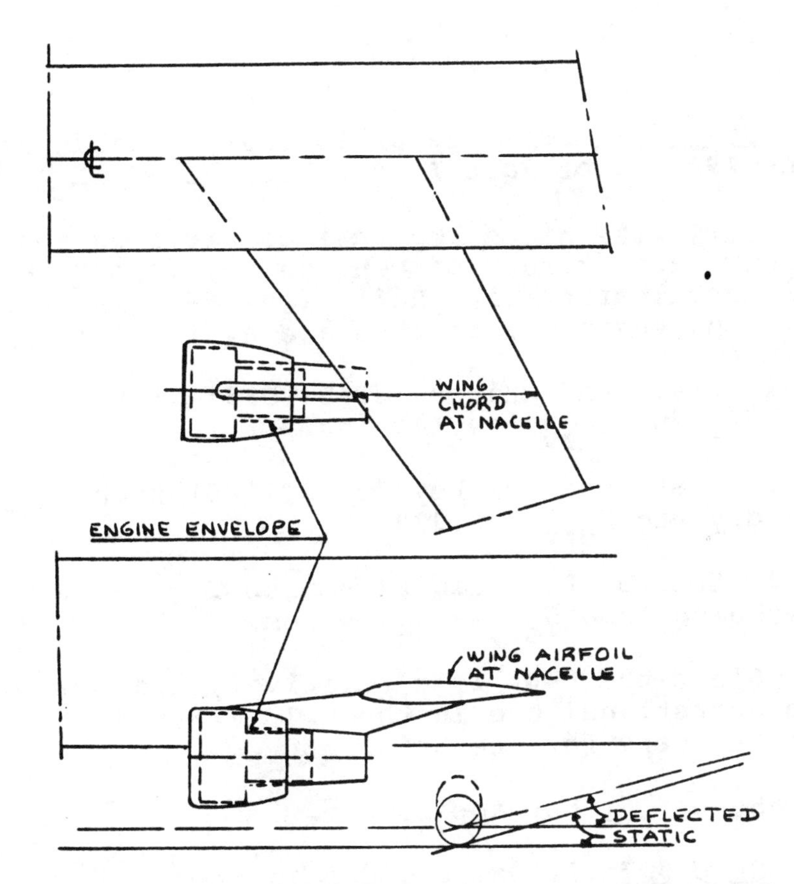

Figure 5.5 Ourania: Preliminary Engine Installation

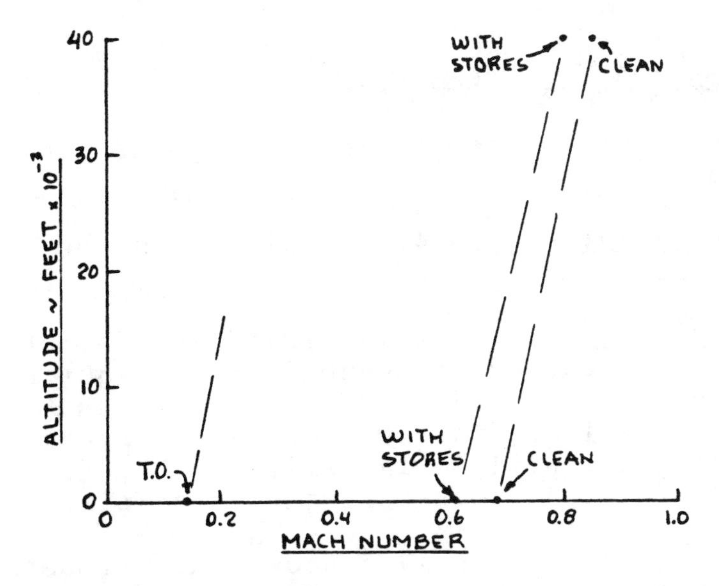

Figure 5.6 Eris: Preliminary Speed-Altitude Envelope

Step 5.4: From the preliminary matching results of pages 190-191 of Part I it follows that T_{TO} = 29,670 lbs.

Step 5.5: Since two engines are required, the maximum rated thrust per engine is: 14,835 lbs.

Consultation with Ref.8 (1983-84) shows that the following engine candidates are available:

1. Pratt and Whitney JT3D(TF33) with T_{max} = 18,000 lbs, dry and W_{dry} = 4,340 lbs.

2. Pratt and Whitney JTF22(F100) with T_{max} = 14,670 lbs, dry and W_{dry} = 3,033 lbs.

3. General Electric F404 with T_{max} = 16,000 lbs in afterburner and W_{dry} = 2,000 lbs.

Since the F404 is a relatively light weight engine with operational use in the F17, F18 and X29 it is selected here for the Eris.

Step 5.6: Not applicable.

Step 5.7: It was decided in Step 3.5, page 106 that the engines are to be mounted in the fuselage as in the DH110 of page 106. From an installation viewpoit that makes the Eris a tractor since the inlets are ahead of the c.g.

Step 5.8: See Step 5.7.

Step 5.9: The geometric envelope of the F404 was obtained from Ref.8(1983-84).

Step 5.10: Figure 4.9(p.122) shows the proposed engine installation.

Step 5.11: The Eris is similar to the DH110 of p.106. It is therefore assumed, that requirement1 is satisfied. Figure 4.9(p.122) indicates that requirements 2-4 are satisfied. To accomodate requirement 5 a gun-gas deflector plate will be installed on the fuselage nose. Figure 4.9(p.122) shows this deflector plate.

Step 5.12: Figure 13.3 shows the proposed installation in a threeview.

Step 5.13: To save space this step is omitted.

6. CLASS I METHOD FOR WING PLANFORM DESIGN AND FOR SIZING AND LOCATING LATERAL CONTROL SURFACES

The purpose of this chapter is to present a step-by-step methodology for determining the following planform design characteristics of the wing:

1. Size (i.e. area), S
2. Aspect ratio, A
3. Sweep angle, Λ
4. Thickness ratio, t/c
5. Airfoils
6. Taper ratio, λ
7. Incidence angle, i_w and twist angle, ε_t
8. Dihedral angle, Γ_w
9. Lateral control surface size and layout

The method is presented as part of Step 6 in p.d. sequence I as outlined in Chapter 2.

The reader will recall that items 1 and 2 for the wing are already known: these were determined by the preliminary sizing process of Part I. Items 3 through 9 for the wing remain to be determined.

As a result of Step 3 in p.d. sequence I (Chapter 2, p.11) it has already been decided whether the overall configuration of the airplane is one of the following:

1. Conventional (that means tail aft)
2. Flying wing (that means no horizontal tail or canard)
3. Tandem Wing
4. Canard
5. Three surface
6. Joined wing

Section 6.1 presents a step-by-step procedure for determining the wing design characteristics listed as 3-9 at the beginning of this chapter. Example applications are discussed in Section 6.2.

6.1 A PROCEDURE FOR WING PLANFORM DESIGN AND FOR SIZING AND LOCATING LATERAL CONTROL SURFACES

Step 6.1: If the airplane is a flying wing, all items discussed in Chapter 4 must somehow be integrated into the wing. This will have a major impact on the wing layout and therefore needs to be looked into first.

If the airplane is not a flying wing, proceed to Step 6.2.

Step 6.2: Decide on the overall structural wing configuration.

The choices here are between:

1. Cantilever wing
2. Braced (or strutted wing)

Tables 6.1 through 6.12 provide an initial guide to this choice. The reader will note that braced wings are used primarily on relatively low speed airplanes. The reason is: the trade between profile and interference drag increments (due to the struts) and wing weight is generally unfavorable to strutted arrangements above a speed of around 200 kts.

Step 6.3: Decide on the overall wing/fuselage arrangement.

The choices here are:

1. High wing 2. Mid wing 3. Low wing

Tables 6.1 through 6.12 provide an initial guide to this choice. The reader should also review the pertinent configurations presented in Chapter 3.

The following ratings of overall wing/fuselage configurations are correct only if 'everything else' is the same. The number 1 means 'preferred' and the number 3 means 'least preferred'.

	High wing	Mid Wing	Low Wing
Interference Drag	2	1	3
Lateral Stability	1	2	3
Visibility from Cabin*	1	2	3
Landing Gear Weight	3**	2	1

* strongly dependent on where the wing passes through the fuselage

** if the gear is retracted into the fuselage, gear weight is not necessarily a factor. In that case the landing gear often requires a 'bump fairing' which causes additional drag.

Table 6.1 Homebuilt Airplanes: Wing Geometric Data

Type	Dihedral Angle, Γ_w, deg.	Incidence Angle, i_w, root/tip deg.	Aspect Ratio, A	Sweep Angle, $\Lambda_{c/4}$, deg.	Taper Ratio, λ_w	Max. Speed, V_{max}, kts	Wing Type
PIK-21	0	0	3.8	0	1.0	NA	ctl/low
Duruble							
RD-03C	6.5	3/0	7.0	0	0.51	182	ctl/mid
PIEL							
CP-750	5.7	4.2	5.9	0	0.55	183	ctl/low
CP-90	5.7	3	5.4	0	0.44	171	ctl/low
POTTIER							
P-50R	4.4	NA	5.1	2	0.54	167	ctl/low
P-70S	0	2	4.8	0	1.0	129	ctl/mid
O-O							
Aerosport	2.5	NA	5.7	0	1.0	76	ctl/low
Aerocar							
Micro-Imp	0	4	4.7	0	1.0	260	ctl/high
Coats							
SA-III	4	1.5	5.6	0	1.0	165	ctl/low
Sequoia							
300	3	3.5/1.5	6.9	0	0.55	243	ctl/low
Ord-Hume							
OH-4B	3	3	5	5.0	1.0	95	brcd/parasol
Procter							
Petrel	5	0	6.6	0	1.0	113	ctl/low
Bede BD-8	0	3	3.9	0	1.0	238	ctl/low

ctl = cantilever brcd = braced (strutted)

Table 6.2 Single Engine Propeller Driven Airplanes: Wing Geometric Data

Type	Dihedral Angle, Γ_w, deg.	Incidence Angle, i_w, root/tip deg.	Aspect Ratio, A	Sweep Angle, $\Lambda_{c/4}$, deg.	Taper Ratio, λ_w	Max. Speed, V_{max}, kts	Wing Type
CESSNA							
Skywagon 207	1.7	1.5/-1.5	7.4	0	0.69	182	brcd/high
Cardinal RG	1.5	4.1/0.7	7.3	0	0.73	156	ctl/high
Skylane RG	1.7	0.8/-2.8	7.4	0	0.67	187	brcd/high
PIPER							
Cherokee Lance	7.0	2/-1	6.2	0	1.0	188	ctl/low
Cher. Warrior	7.0	2/-1	7.2	5	0.67	152	ctl/low
Turbo Sarat.SP	6.8	NA	7.3	0	0.68	195	ctl/low
Bellanca							
Skyrocket	2	2	6.7	0	0.57	287	ctl/low
Grumman Am.							
Tiger	5	1.4	7.1	0	1.0	148	ctl/low
Rockwell Commander							
112A	7	2	7.0	-2.5	0.50	180	ctl/low
Trago Mills							
SAH-1	5	3/1	7.5	0	0.54	202	ctl/low
Scottish Aviation							
Bullfinch	6.5	1.2	8.4	0	0.57	150	ctl/low
Robin HR100/4	6.3	4.7	5.4	0	1.0	180	ctl/low
Socata Rallye							
235E	7	4	7.6	0	1.0	148	ctl/low
Fuji FA-200	7	2.5	6.3	0	1.0	123	ctl/low
Gen Avia F15F	6	4	7.7	0	0.49	167	ctl/low

ctl = cantilever brcd = braced (strutted)

Table 6.3 Twin Engine Propeller Driven Airplanes: Wing Geometric Data

Type	Dihedral Angle, Γ_w, deg.	Incidence Angle, i_w, root/tip deg.	Aspect Ratio, A	Sweep Angle, $\Lambda_{c/4}$, deg.	Taper Ratio, λ_w	Max. Speed, V_{max}, kts	Wing Type
CESSNA							
310R	5	2.5/-.5	7.3	0	0.67	236	ctl/low
402B	5 (outer)	2/-.5	7.5	0 L.E.	0.67	227	ctl/low
414A	5	2.5/-.5	8.6	0 L.E.	0.60	232	ctl/low
T303	7	3/0	8.1	0 L.E.	0.71	216	ctl/low
PIPER							
PA-31P	6	1/-1.5	7.2	0	0.39	243	ctl/low
PA-44-180T	7.2	NA	8.1	0	0.63	196	ctl/low
Chieftain	5	1/-1.5	7.2	1.9	0.40	231	ctl/low
Cheyenne I	5	1.5/-1	7.4	0	0.37	249	ctl/low
Cheyenne III	5	1.5	7.8	0	0.31	296	ctl/low
BEECH							
Duchess 76	6.5	3/.6	8.0	0	0.80	194	ctl/low
Duke B60	6	4/0	7.2	0	0.32	246	ctl/low
Learfan 2100	4	1.5	9.5	0	0.45	369	ctl/low
Rockwell Commander 700	7	NA	9.0	0	0.43	231	ctl/low
Piaggio P166-DL3	21.5/2.5*	2.7	7.3	7.5	0.35	215	ctl/gull
EMB-121	7	3	7.2	0.33	0.61	316	ctl/low

ctl = cantilever brcd = braced (strutted)
*21.5 inboard, 2.5 outboard on this gull wing configuration

Table 6.4 Agricultural Airplanes: Wing Geometric Data

Type	Dihedral Angle, Γ_w, deg.	Incidence Angle, i_w, root/tip deg.	Aspect Ratio, A	Sweep Angle, $\Lambda_{c/4}$, deg.	Taper Ratio, λ_w	Max. Speed, V_{max}, kts	Wing Type
IAR-822	5 (outer)	5	6.3	0	1.0	92	ctl/low
UTVA-65	2	2.5	7.2	0	0.7	95	brcd/low
IA-53	7.5 (out)	4.3	6.3	0	0.7	116	ctl/low
EMB-200	7	3	7.0	0	1.0	116	ctl/low
Ag-cat	3	6	8.7	0	1.0	113	brcd/bipl
WSK M-15	NA	NA	NA	0	NA	146	brcd/bipl
PZL M-18A	1.3	3	7.8	0	1.0	128 138*	ctl/low
PZL 106A	4	6.5	7.8	4	1.0	114*	brcd/low
NDN-6	4.3	4.5	7.5	0	0.7	135	brcd/low
Cessna AgHusky	9	1.5/-1.5	8.5	0	0.7	106	brcd/low
Antonov AN-2M	2.5 both wings	NA	NA	0	1.0	136	brcd/bipl
HAL-31	6	0	6.0	0	1.0	108	ctl/low

*speed without spray equipment installed
ctl = cantilever brcd = braced (strutted) bipl = biplane

Table 6.5 Business Jets: Wing Geometric Data

Type	Dihedral Angle, Γ_w, deg.	Incidence Angle, i_w, root/tip deg.	Aspect Ratio, A	Sweep Angle, $\Lambda_{c/4}$, deg.	Taper Ratio, λ_w	Max. Speed, V_{max}, kts	Wing Type
DASSAULT/BREGUET							
Falcon 10	1.5	NA	7.1	27	0.36	492(25K)	ctl/low
Falcon 20F	2	1.5	6.4	30	0.31	465(25K)	ctl/low
Falcon 50	0	NA	7.6	24	0.32	475	ctl/low
CESSNA							
Citation I 500	4	2.5/-0.5	7.8	0	0.39	277(28K)	ctl/low
Citation II	4.7	NA	8.3	2	0.32	277(28K)	ctl/low
Citation III	2.8	NA	8.9	25	0.35	472(33K)	ctl/low
GATES LEARJET							
24	2.5	1	5.0	13	0.50	473(31K)	ctl/low
35A	2.5	1	5.7	13	0.50	464	ctl/low
55	2.9	NA	7.3	13	0.42	470(30K)	ctl/low
IAI							
1124 Westw. I	2	1/-1	6.5	5	0.33	471	ctl/mid
1125 Astra	2.6 (out)	NA	8.8	34/25 at LE	0.30	472(35K)	ctl/low
Canadair CL601	2.3	3	8.5	25	0.26	450	ctl/low
BAe 125-700	2	2.1/-0.3	6.3	20	0.28	436(28K)	ctl/low
GA Gulfst. III	3	3.5/-0.5	6.5	28	0.31	487	ctl/low
Mu Diamond I	2.7	3/-3.5	7.5	20	0.35	431(30K)	ctl/low
L. Jetstar II	2	1/-1	5.3	30	0.37	475(30K)	ctl/low

ctl = cantilever (30K) = 30,000 ft altitude

Table 6.6 Regional Turbopropeller Driven Airplanes: Wing Geometric Data

Type	Dihedral Angle, Γ_w, deg.	Incidence Angle, i_w, root/tip deg.	Aspect Ratio, A	Sweep Angle, $\Lambda_{c/4}$, deg.	Taper Ratio, λ_w	Max. Speed, V_{max}, kts	Wing Type
CASA C-212-200							
SHORTS							
330	3 (outer)	NA	12.3	0	1.0	190(10K)	brcd/high
360							
BEECH							
1900	6	3.5/-1.1	9.8	0	0.42	263(8K)	ctl/low
B99	7	4.8	7.5	0	0.5	247(12K)	ctl/low
CESSNA CONQUEST							
I							
II							
GA Gulfstr. Ic							
GAF N22B							
Fokker F27-200	2.5	3.5	12.0	0	0.41	259(20K)	ctl/high
DeHAVILLAND CANADA							
DHC-6-300							
DHC-7	4.5	3	10.0	0	0.44	231(8K)	ctl/high
DHC-8	2.5 (out)	NA	12.3	0	0.45	270(15K)	ctl/high
EMB 110	7	3	9.9	0	0.50	248(8K))	ctl/low
EMB 120	6.5	2	9.9	0	0.50	NA	ctl/low
BRITISH AEROSPACE							
Jetstream 31	7	2	10.0	0.5	0.37	263(20K)	ctl/low
748	7	3	12.7	2.9	0.36	244(15K)	ctl/low

ctl = cantilever (30K) = 30,000 ft altitude

Table 6.7 Jet Transports: Wing Geometric Data

Type	Dihedral Angle, Γ_w, deg.	Incidence Angle, i_w, root/tip deg.	Aspect Ratio, A	Sweep Angle, $\Lambda_{c/4}$, deg.	Taper Ratio, λ_w	Max. Speed, V_{max}, kts	Wing Type
BOEING							
727-200	3	2	7.1	32	0.30	549(22K)	ctl/low
737-200	6	1	8.8	25	0.34	462(33K)	ctl/low
737-300	6	1	8.0	25	0.28	462(33K)	ctl/low
747-200B	7	2	7.0	37.5	0.25	523(30K)	ctl/low
747SP	7	2	7.0	37.5	0.25	529(30K)	ctl/low
757-200	5	3.2	7.9	25	0.26		ctl/low
767-200	6	4.3	7.9	31.5	0.27		ctl/low
McDONNELL DOUGLAS							
DC-9 Super 80	3	1.3	9.6	24.5	0.16	500	ctl/low
DC-9-50	1.5	NA	8.7	24	0.18	537	ctl/low
DC-10-30	5.3/3	+/-	7.5	35	0.25	530(25K)	ctl/low
AIRBUS							
A300-B4	5	NA	7.7	28	0.35	492(25K)	ctl/low
A310	11.1/4.1	5.3	8.8	28	0.26	483(30K)	ctl/low
Lockh.1011-500	7.5/5.5	NA	7.0	35	0.30	525(30K)	ctl/low
Fkr F28-4000	2.5	NA	8.0	16	0.31	390	ctl/low
Rombac 111-495	2	2.5	8.5	20	0.32	470(21K)	ctl/low
BAe 146-200	-3	3.1/0	9.0	15	0.36	420(26K)	ctl/high
Tupolev Tu154	0	NA	7.0	35	0.27	526(31K)	ctl/low

ctl = cantilever (30K) = 30,000 ft altitude

Table 6.8 Military Trainers: Wing Geometric Data

Type	Dihedral Angle, Γ_w, deg.	Incidence Angle, i_w, root/tip deg.	Aspect Ratio, A	Sweep Angle, $\Lambda_{c/4}$, deg.	Taper Ratio, λ_w	Max. Speed, V_{max}, kts	Wing Type
<u>Propeller Driven</u>							
EMB-312 Tucano	5.5	1.4/-0.8	6.4	0.7	0.47	292	ctl/low
Pilatus PC-7	7 (outer)	NA	6.5	1	0.55	270	ctl/low
NDN-1	5 (outer)	3	5.4	0	0.79	247	ctl/low
Beech T-34C	7	4/1	6.2	0	0.41	280	ctl/low
Aerosp.Epsilon	5	2	7.0	0	0.63	281	ctl/low
SM SF-260M	6.3	2.8/0	6.3	0	0.49	235	ctl/low
Yak-52	2	2	5.8	0	0.54	194	ctl/low
Neiva T-25	6	2	7.1	0	0.54	269	ctl/low
<u>Jet Driven</u>							
Aero L-39C	2.5	2	4.4	2	0.52	491	ctl/low
Microjet 200B	5	3	8	0	0.39	300	ctl/low
DB/D Alphajet	-6	NA	4.8	28	0.36	495(33K)	ctl/shldr
Aermac. MB339A	2.6	NA	5.3	9	0.58	500	ctl/low
SM S-211	-2	2.2/-1.3	5.1	16	0.46	400	ctl/shldr
PZL TS-11	2.7	NA	5.7	7	0.51	404	ctl/mid
CASA C-1-1	5	1	5.6	2	0.60	428(25K)	ctl/low
Bae Hawk Mk1	2	NA	5.3	22	0.34	572	ctl/low
Tupolev Tu154	0	NA	7.0	35	0.27	526(31K)	ctl/low

ctl = cantilever shldr = shoulder (30K) = 30,000 ft altitude

Table 6.9 Fighters: Wing Geometric Data

Type	Dihedral Angle, Γ_w, deg.	Incidence Angle, i_w, root/tip deg.	Aspect Ratio, A	Sweep Angle, $\Lambda_{c/4}$, deg.	Taper Ratio, λ_w	Max. Speed, V_{max}, kts	Wing Type
DASSAULT BREGUET							
Mirage III-E	-1	0	1.9	61(LE)	0	1,268(39K)	ctl/low
Mirage F1-C	-4.5	NA	2.8	48(LE)	0.29	1,260	ctl/shldr
Mirage 2000	-1	NA	2.0	58(LE)	0	1,260	ctl/low
Super Etendard	-3.5	NA	3.2	45	0.50	573	ctl/mid
Fairch.R.A-10A	7 (outer)	-1	6.5	0	0.66	450	ctl/low
Grumman A-6E	0	NA	5.3	25	0.30	700	ctl/mid
Grumman F14A	-1.5(out)	NA	7.3*	20/68(LE)	0.40	M = 2.4	vsw/high
Northrop F-5E	0	0	3.8	24	0.19	710	ctl/low
Vought A-7E	-5	-1	4	35	0.25	595(5K)	ctl/high
McDONNELL DOUGLAS							
F-4E	0/12	NA	2.8	45(LE)	0.18	1,146	ctl/low
F-15	-1	0	3.0	39	0.25	M =2.5	ctl/high
AV-8B	-12	1.8	4.0	24	0.28	585(0K)	ctl/shldr
GD FB-111A	0	NA	7.6*	16/73(LE)	0.33	1,260	ctl/shldr
GD F-16	0	0	3.0	40(LE)	0.22	495(33K)	ctl/mid
Cessna A37B	3	3.6/1	6.2	0	0.68	455	ctl/low
Aerm. MB339K	2.6	NA	5.3	8.5	0.58	500	ctl/low
Sukhoi Su-7BMK	0	NA	2.6	62(LE)	0.26	730(0K)	ctl/mid

ctl = cantilever shldr = shoulder (30K) = 30,000 ft altitude
* taken at lowest sweep angle

Table 6.10 Military Patrol, Bomb and Transport Airplanes: Wing Geometric Data

Type	Dihedral Angle, Γ_w, deg.	Incidence Angle, i_w, root/tip deg.	Aspect Ratio, A	Sweep Angle, $\Lambda_{c/4}$, deg.	Taper Ratio, λ_w	Max. Speed, V_{max}, kts	Wing Type
Turbopropeller Driven							
Lockh'd C130E	2.5	3/0	10.1	0	0.49	325	ctl/high
Lockheed P3C	6	0/0.5	7.5	0	0.40	411(15K)	ctl/low
Antonov 12BP	-3.8(out)	NA	11.9	7.4	0.34	419	ctl/high
Antonov 22	-3.5	NA	12.0	5	0.36	399	ctl/high
Antonov 26	-2(out)	3	11.7	7	0.34	NA	ctl/high
Grumman E2C	3.1	NA	9.3	5.3	0.34	325	ctl/high
DB Atlantic 2	6 (outer)	3	11.6	9 (LE)	0.39	348	ctl/low
Aerital.G222	2.5 (out)	NA	9.2	2.1	0.50	291	ctl/high
Transall C-160	3.5 (out)	NA	10.0	1.9	0.50	320	ctl/high
Jet Driven							
Lockheed S3A	0	3/-3.5	7.9	15	0.25	450	ctl/high
Lockh'd C-141B	-3.5	NA	7.5	25.5	0.41	492	ctl/high
Lockheed C-5A	-5.1	NA	7.8	25.6	0.34	496(25K)	ctl/high
BAe Nimrod Mk2	2.7	NA	6.2	20	0.23	500	ctl/low
Boeing YC-14	0	NA	9.4	4.6	0.30	438	ctl/high
McDD KC-10A	5/3	+/-	7.5	35	0.25	530(25K)	ctl/low
Tupolev Tu-16	-3.7	NA	6.6	43(LE)	0.44	535(6K)	ctl/high
Tupolev Tu-22	0	NA	4.0	51(LE)	0.31	800(40K)	ctl/mid
Ilyushin Il76T	-3.6	NA	11.7	25	0.37	459	ctl/high

ctl = cantilever shldr = shoulder (30K) = 30,000 ft altitude

Table 6.11 Flying Boats, Amphibious and Float Airplanes: Wing Geometric Data

Type	Dihedral Angle, Γ_w, deg.	Incidence Angle, i_w, root/tip deg.	Aspect Ratio, A	Sweep Angle, $\Lambda_{c/4}$, deg.	Taper Ratio, λ_w	Max. Speed, V_{max}, kts	Wing Type
SHORTS							
Sandringham	2.1	NA	8.6	3.6	0.38	188	ctl/high
Shetland	4.1	NA	8.6	7.7	0.34	232(8K)	ctl/high
DORNIER							semi ctl
Do 24	0	NA	6.8	7	0.36	165	brcd/high
Do 24/72	0	NA	7.5	2	0.71	224	brcd/par.
Do Seastar	0	NA	9.1	0	1.0	220	brcd/par.
Grumman JRF-6B	2	NA	6.4	-1	0.46	175(5K)	ctl/high
Grumman J4F-1	NA	NA	6.5	0	0.48	133	ctl/high
SM S-700	2.1	NA	9.4	0	1.0	180(10K)	ctl/high
Canadair CL215	0	NA	8.2	0	1.0	158	ctl/high
BV-222	3.2	NA	8.0	0	0.72	183	ctl/high
Shin Meiwa US1	2.1	NA	8.0	2.1	0.50	260	ctl/high
Boeing 314-A	5.3	NA	7.7	7.9	0.23	183	ctl/high
Martin PBM-3	19/0	NA	10.1	-1.5	0.33	174	ctl/high
Beriev M-12	26/-2	NA	8.4	6.0	0.41	328	ctl/high
Partenav. P68B*	1	1.5	7.7	0	1.0	173	ctl/high
McKinnon G-21G	2.5	NA	6.1	0	0.50	211	ctl/high

ctl = cantilever shldr = shoulder (30K) = 30,000 ft altitude
par. = parasol * float airplane

Table 6.12 Supersonic Cruise Airplanes: Wing Geometric Data

Type	Dihedral Angle, Γ_w, deg.	Incidence Angle, i_w, root/tip deg.	Aspect Ratio, A	Sweep Angle, $\Lambda_{c/4}$, deg.	Taper Ratio, λ_w	Max. Speed, V_{max}, kts	Wing Type
NORTH AMERICAN AVIATION (ROCKWELL)							
XB-70A	-3	NA	1.8	65.6(LE)	0.02	$M = 2^+$	ctl/low
RA-5C	0	NA	4.0	37.5	0.19	1,204(40K)	ctl/high
B-1B	0	NA	??	??	0.32	$M = 2^+$	ctl/low
BOEING							
SST	NA	NA	3.4*	30-72	0.21	1,565(75K)	ctl/low
AST-100	get data from NASA reports						
NASA							
SSXJet I	0	NA	1.84	72(LE)	0.08	M =	ctl/
SSXJet II	0	NA	1.84	72(LE)	0.08	M =	ctl/
SSXJet III	0	NA	1.84	72(LE)	0.08	M =	ctl/
TUPOLEV							
Tu-144	8.3 (out)	NA	1.9	76/57	0.13	1,350(50K)	ctl/low
Tu-22M	0	NA	8.0*	20-65	0.28	1,446	ctl/mid
Dassault MIVA	-1.5	NA	1.8	60(LE)	0.11	1,261(36K)	ctl/low
GD F-111A	0	NA	7.5*	16-72	0.33	$1,432_+$	ctl/high
GD B-58	0	NA	2.2	59(LE)	0	$M = 2^+$	ctl/low
Aerospatiale/British Aerospace							
Concorde	0	NA	1.7	ogive	0.12	1,259(55K)	ctl/low

ctl = cantilever (30K) = 30,000 ft altitude
* taken at lowest sweep angle

Step 6.4: Select the wing quarter chord sweep angle, $\Lambda_{c/4}$ and the wing thickness ratio, t/c.

The choices for type of sweep were listed in sub-section 3.3.4 as:

1. Zero or negligible sweep
2. Aft sweep (also called positive sweep)
3. Forward sweep (also called negative sweep)
4. Variable sweep (meaning symmetrically variable sweep)
5. Oblique sweep (meaning asymmetrically variable sweep)

Sweep types 4 and 5 are appropriate choices only for missions where there is a combined requirement for supersonic and for subsonic cruise and/or for high 'g' maneuvering. If in addition the mission calls for short field lengths, variable or oblique sweep could be an appropriate choice. Keep in mind that a severe weight penalty is associated with the wing pivot structure needed in the mechanization of variable sweep or oblique sweep wings.

For most airplanes the sweep choice is restricted to items 1-3.

Tables 6.1 through 6.12 provide an initial guide to the selection of sweep angle. For some guidance to the selection of thickness ratio refer to Tables 8.1 through 8.12.

While computing the Class II drag polars of the airplane as part of the work in p.d.sequence II, the reader will discover that sweep angle and thickness ratio have a major influence on the dragrise characteristics of an airplane. For airplanes with a requirement for high subsonic cruise and/or a requirement for supersonic cruise, the trade between thickness ratio and sweep angle turns out to be a deciding factor in the design of the wing.

Figures 6.1 and 6.2 show the effect of sweep angle and thickness ratio on critical Mach number. Note that the cruise lift coefficient $C_{L_{cr}}$ is an important factor.

This cruise lift coefficient may be estimated from:

$$C_{L_{cr}} = (W_{TO} - 0.4W_F)/\bar{q}S \qquad (6.1)$$

In many designs it is possible by sweeping the wing

NOTE: FOR SUPERCRITICAL AIRFOILS USE $\Delta M_{CR} = 0.05$

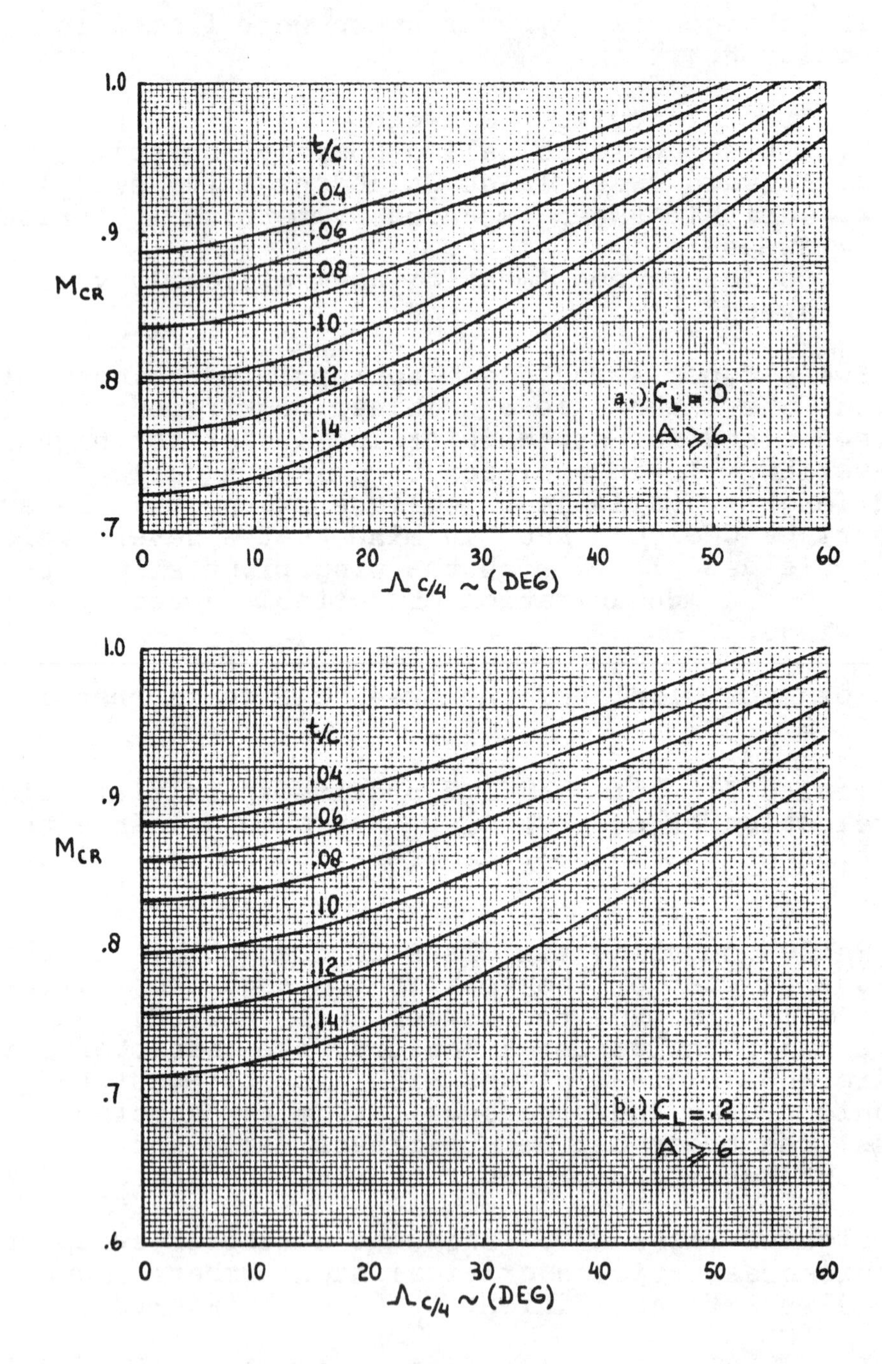

Figure 6.1a Effect of Thickness Ratio and Sweep Angle on Critical Mach Number

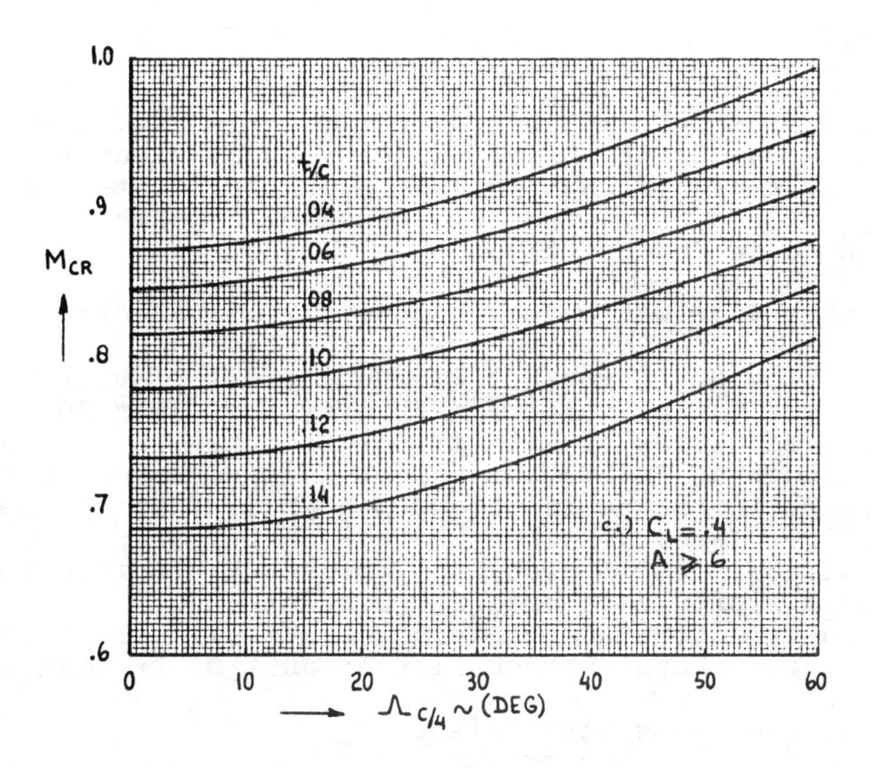

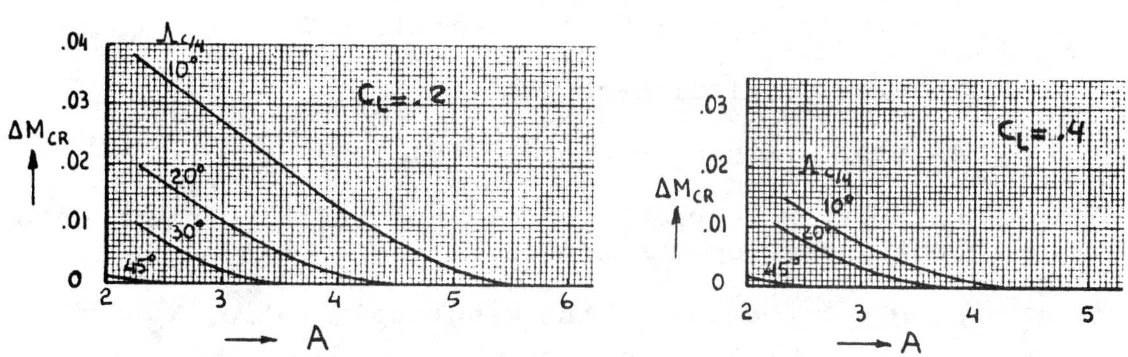

Figure 6.1b Effect of Thickness Ratio and Sweep Angle on Critical Mach Number

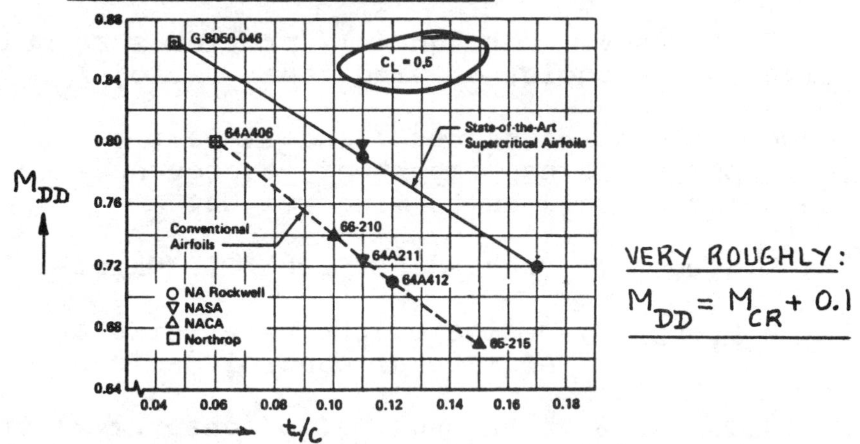

Figure 6.2 Effect of Thickness Ratio on Drag Divergence Mach Number for NACA and Supercrit. Airfoils

forward or aft to achieve a reduction in c.g. travel. In addition, a slight change in sweep angle (away from zero) can have a significant influence on the location of the wing/fuselage a.c. The importance of the latter is discussed in Chapter 11.

Step 6.5: Decide which wing airfoil to use.

Tables 8.1 through 8.12 (Chapter 8) provide an initial guide to the selection of airfoils. Ref.20 contains a detailed review of NACA airfoils. When consulting recent issues of Ref.8, the reader will discover that most airplanes which are in production in 1985 still use NACA airfoils. This, despite the fact that modern computational airfoil design technology makes it possible to tailor airfoils to a specific mission.

In selecting or designing an airfoil, the following important section characteristics must be kept in mind:

section drag coefficient, C_d at the:

section design lift coefficient, $C_{l_{des}}$.

section critical Mach number, M_{crit}

section pitching moment coefficient, $C_{m_{c/4}}$

Part VI, References 16 - 18 and Ref.21 contain data on recently developed airfoils.

Step 6.6: Decide on the wing taper ratio, λ_w and prepare a dimensioned drawing of the wing planform to be used.

Tables 6.1 through 6.12 provide some guidance relative to the choice of wing taper ratio, λ_w. It will become clear in Chapter 7 and in Part V that the choice of taper ratio has important consequences to wing stall behavior as well as to wing weight.

Step 6.7: Proceed to Step 7.1, Chapter 7.

Step 6.8: Decide on the type, size and location of lateral control devices.

Tables 8.1b through 8.12b (chapter 8) provide an initial guide to this decision. Compatibility with the required high lift devices is a major factor in laying out the lateral control surfaces.

Step 6.9: Draw the front and rear spar lines in the wing planform drawing of Step 6.6.

The data developed under Steps 6.7 and 6.8 are required before the spar lines can be located. A clearance of roughly 0.005c should be observed between the spar lines and the outlines of the high lift devices and/or ailerons. Any spoiler hingelines should be just aft of the rear spar line.

Step 6.10: Compute the wing fuel volume.

It will be assumed here that the wing fuel is carried in what is called a 'wet wing'. That means there are no separate fuel tanks. The wing torque box (that is the part of the wing structure between the front and the rear spar) is sealed and forms the fuel tank.

Check in Part IV for rules of where 'dry bays' need to be to suppress fires in the case of a crash. Don't count the 'dry bay' volume as fuel volume.

Assume that no fuel can be carried beyond the 85 percent span point. This is to prevent lightning strikes (which are most likely to hit the airplane extremities) from starting an in-flight fire.

Note: fuel may be carried in wingtips or in tiptanks, provided the skin is locally 'beefed up' to assure that lightning strikes have enough metal to disperse. This solution costs a lot of weight but is sometimes used.

Compare the computed wing fuel volume with the total fuel volume required for the mission. The latter was determined from the preliminary sizing in Part I.

Torenbeek (Ref.17, Eqn.B-12) suggests the following equation for estimating wing fuel volume in preliminary design:

$$V_{WF} =$$

$$0.54(S^2/b)(t/c)_r\{(1 + \lambda_w\tau_w^{1/2} + \lambda_w^2\tau_w)/(1 + \lambda_w)^2\}, \quad (6.2)$$

where:

$$\tau_w = (t/c)_t/(t/c)_r \quad (6.3)$$

This equation is based on statistical data and presumably accounts for any required dry bays as well as for the lightning strike problem.

If there is sufficient fuel volume, proceed to Step 6.11. If not, decide on where to incorporate the additional fuel volume which is required.
Additional fuel volume can sometimes be included in tiptanks, slipper tanks, fuselage tanks and even empennage tanks.
Keep in mind that the accuracy of Eqn.(6.2) is perhaps +/- 10 percent.

In some airplanes, if the fuel volume discrepancy is significant (larger than 20 percent) it may be necessary to enlarge the wing beyond the size determined from the preliminary sizing process of Part I.

Step 6.11: Decide on the wing dihedral angle, Γ_w.

This choice is tied to a trade between lateral stability and dutch roll stability. A detailed discussion of this trade problem is found in Ref.9. Part VI also contains information on this design trade.

Geometric ground clearance (such as for wingtips and wing mounted nacelles and propellers) during flare attitude with a five degree bank angle can also be a deciding factor in selecting wing dihedral.

At this point in the p.d. process it suffices to consult Tables 6.1 through 6.12 for initial guidance to this choice.

Step 6.12: Decide on the wing incidence angle, i_w and on the wing angle, ε_t.

The choice of wing incidence angle has important consequences for:

1. Cruise drag
2. Take-off distance (particularly in the case of airplanes with tandem landing gears)
3. Attitude of the fuselage floor in cruise and the ability of flight attendants to push liqour carts up and down the isles: This is not a trivial requirement!

For specific equations which may be used to determine the wing incidence angle for airplanes dominated by a cruise requirement, the reader is referred to Part VI.

At this stage in the p.d. process, Tables 6.1 through 6.12 should be consulted for the initial choice of wing incidence angle.

Wing twist has important consequences to wing stall characteristics. A method for accounting for this is contained in Part VI.

In terms of wing twist, the following possibilities present themselves:

1. Wash-out (negative twist consisting of decreasing airfoil incidence angles outboard along the span): this tends to suppress tip stall.

2. Wash-in (positive twist: the opposite of 1.): this tends to promote tip stall.

3. Aerodynamic twist (consisting of varying the airfoils along the span): this can suppress or promote tipstall, depending on how the airfoils are changed along the span.

Most airplanes have wash-out. Aerodynamic twist is also found but is more expensive to manufacture.

Some guidance to the selection of twist angles may be found in the second column of Tables 6.1 through 6.12.

Step 6.13: Document the decisions made under Steps 6.1 through 6.12 in a brief, descriptive report including clear dimensioned drawings.

6.2 EXAMPLE APPLICATIONS

The following three example applications will be presented:

6.2.1 Twin Engine Propeller Driven Airplane: Selene
6.2.2 Jet Transport: Ourania
6.2.3 Fighter: Eris

All applications are presented in accordance with Steps 6.1 through 6.12 in Section 6.1.

6.2.1 Twin Engine Propeller Driven Airplane

The following information is already available for the wing of the Selene:

$S = 172\ ft^2$, $A = 8$ and therefore $b = 37.1$ ft. These data follow from the preliminary sizing work of sub-section 3.7.2 in Part I.

Step 6.1: Not applicable: the Selene is not a flying wing.

Step 6.2: The cruise speed of the Selene is required to be 250 kts at 75 percent power at 10,000 ft (Table 2.17, Part I). This speed requirement is consistent only with a cantilever wing.

Step 6.3: In sub-section 3.5.1 it was already decided to go with a high wing. Such a wing configuration does have the appeal of good downward visibility for the passengers.

Step 6.4: In the speed range of the Selene only very low sweep angles are appropriate from an aerodynamic and weight viewpoint. The data of Table 6.3 confirm this. For the Selene a sweep angle of $\Lambda_{c/4} = 0$ deg. is selected.

Selection of thickness ratio for a low speed wing involves a trade-off between clean maximum lift requirement and structural weight. Table 8.3 shows that airplanes in this category have wing root thickness values as high as 18 percent. It is shown in Figure 7.1 (Chapter 7) that values for airfoil maximum lift coefficient deteriorate very rapidly beyond 13 percent thickness. The following airfoil thickness ratios are selected for the Selene:

at the wing centerline: $(t/c)_r = 0.17$

at the wing tip: $(t/c)_t = 0.13$

Step 6.5: Because of its excellent maximum lift characteristic, NASA MS(1)-0317 is selected for the root airfoil. This airfoil is 'thinned out' to NASA(1)-0313 at the tip in a spanwise linear manner. Reference 22 provides the required aerodynamic and geometric data for these airfoils.

Step 6.6: Table 6.3 shows that a wing taper ratio of $\lambda_w = 0.4$ is an appropriate choice. Figure 6.3a shows a dimensioned drawing of the proposed wing planform. The planform is defined by the following parameters:

$S = 172\ ft^2$, $A = 8$, $b = 37.1$ ft

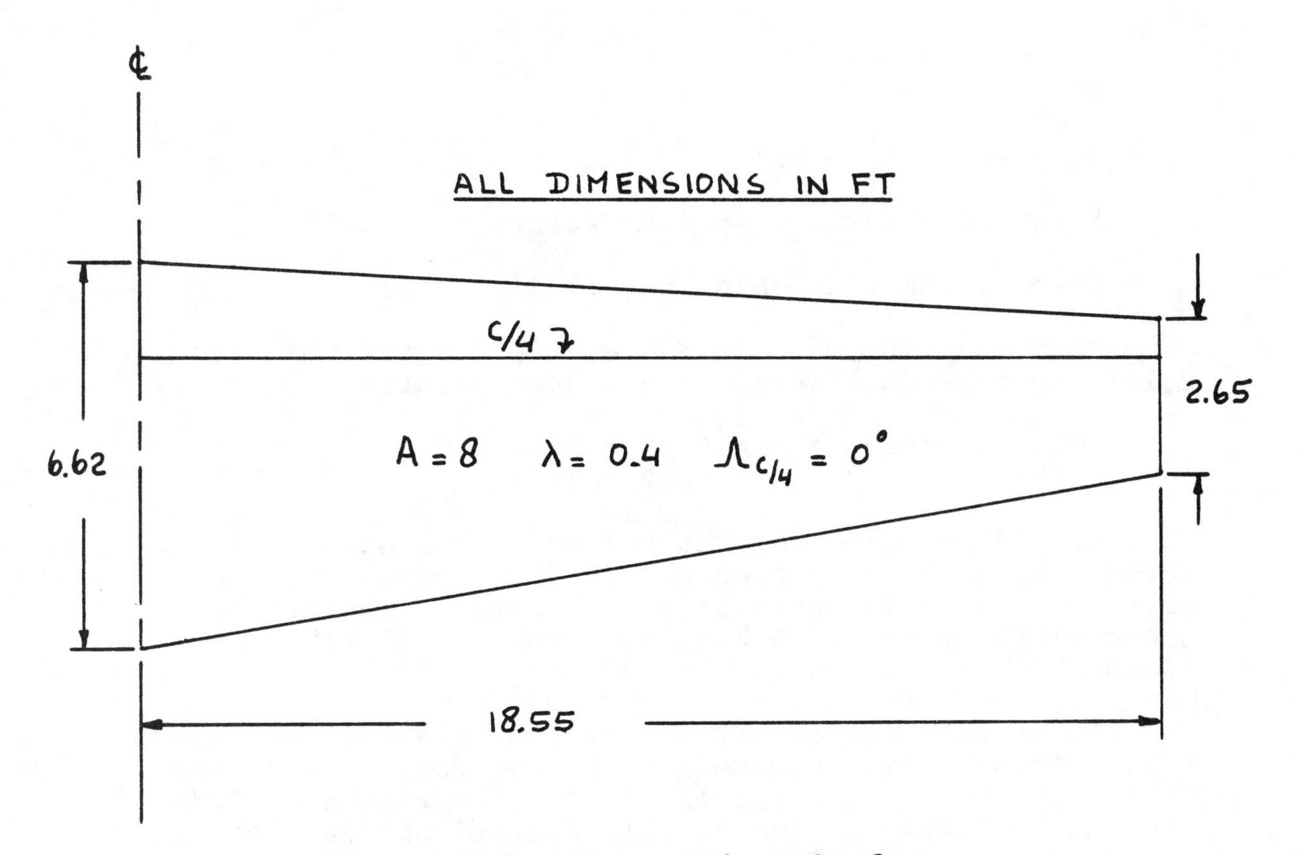

Figure 6.3a Selene: Wing Planform

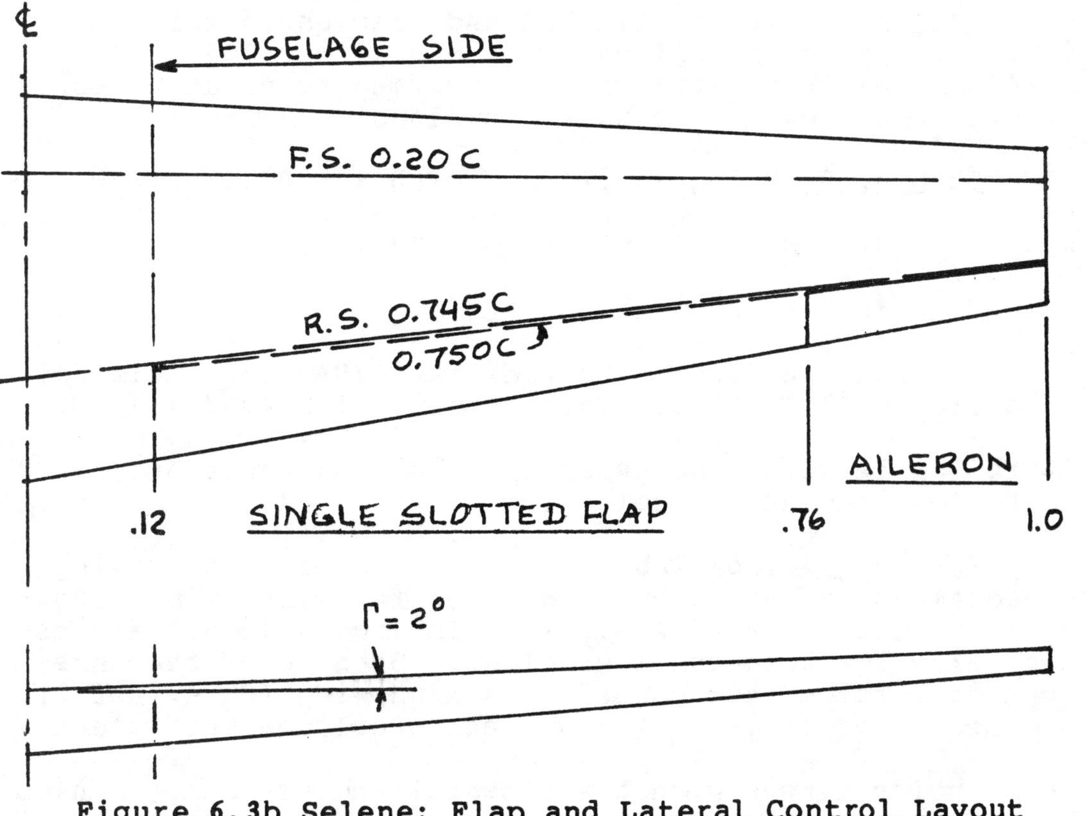

Figure 6.3b Selene: Flap and Lateral Control Layout

$\Lambda_{c/4} = 0^{\circ}$, $\lambda_w = 0.4$

From these data: $c_r = 6.62$ ft and $c_t = 2.65$ ft.

<u>Step 6.7:</u> See sub-section 7.2.1.

<u>Step 6.8:</u> The data in Table 8.3b suggest that the following aileron dimensions are appropriate:

aileron chord ratio: 0.22 - 0.30
aileron span ratio: 0.60 - 1.00

The flap sizing for the Selene in sub-section 7.2.1 shows that an aileron span of 0.76 to 1.00 is available without conflicting with high lift needs. The aileron chord ratio is set at 0.25c to be consistent with the flaps.

These ailerons are drawn into the planform of Figure 6.3b. These ailerons appear to be too small. This can be 'fixed' by using a larger flap chord ratio (say 0.30 instead of 0.25), by adding roll control spoilers or by using smaller span Fowler flaps. To save space, this was not investigated further.

<u>Step 6.9:</u> With an aileron and flap chord ratio of 0.25 the rear spar will be at (1 - 0.25 - 0.005)c = 0.745c. The front spar will be assumed to be at 0.20c. Figure 6.3b shows these spar locations.

<u>Step 6.10:</u> Using Eqn.(6.2), with $\tau = 0.13/0.16 = 0.81$, $\lambda_w = 0.4$, $S = 172\ \text{ft}^2$ and $b = 37.1$ ft:

$V_{WF} = 52.4\ \text{ft}^3$.

The required amount of fuel is 1,706 lbs. This follows from p.53 of Pt.I. This amounts to 1,706/44.9 = 38 ft^3 of required fuel volume. The wing therefore has a sufficient amount of fuel volume.

<u>Step 6.11:</u> From Table 6.3 it is observed that wing dihedral angles are about 6 degrees for most twins. However, except for the P166, all twins in Table 6.3 are essentially low wing configurations. Because of the inherent dihedral effect caused by a high wing (Ch.4, Ref.9), a dihedral angle of $\Gamma_w = 2$ degrees should be sufficient.

This choice agrees with the dihedral angles found in high wing single engine airplanes as shown in Table 6.2.

Step 6.12: From Table 6.3 it is seen that a wing incidence angle of $i_w = 2.5$ degrees with a linear twist of $\varepsilon_t = -3$ degrees toward the tip is fairly common. The NASA MS(1)-0317 airfoil has a value of $C_{l_o} = 0.35$. This compares to a cruise lift coefficient of:

$C_L = 7,100/(172x156) = 0.26$

Therefore an incidence at the root of roughly $i_w=0$ degrees is appropriate. At the wing tip, the effect of lower airfoil thickness is to increase section maximum lift coefficient. However, the smaller tipchord reduces local Reynold's number which offsets this favorable effect. Therefore, a certain amount of twist will probably be required. A value of $\varepsilon_t = -3$ degrees will be used.

Step 6.13: This step has been omitted to save space.

6.2.2 Jet Transport

The following information is already available for the wing of the Ourania:

$S = 1,296 \text{ ft}^2$, $A = 10$ and therefore $b = 113.8$ ft. These data follow from the preliminary sizing work of sub-section 3.7.3 in Part I.

Step 6.1: Not applicable: the Ourania is not a flying wing.

Step 6.2: The cruise speed of the Selene is required to be M = 0.82 at 35,000 ft (Table 2.18, Part I). This speed requirement is consistent only with a cantilever wing.

Step 6.3: A low wing is considered the most appropriate choice for this airplane.

Step 6.4: The sweep angle for the Ourania wing must be selected on the basis of a critical Mach number of at least 0.82. The cruise lift coefficient of the Ourania may be estimated from Eqn.(6.1) as:

$C_{L_{cr}} =$
$(127,000 - 0.4x25,850)/1,482x0.2353x0.82^2x1,296 = 0.38$

If a supercritical airfoil is used, a value of $\Delta M_{crit} = 0.05$ can be used in Figure 6.2. It is seen that with a sweep angle of 35 deg. a thickness ratio of 0.13 is acceptable. Therefore:

$\Lambda_{c/4} = 35$ deg., $(t/c)_r = 0.13$, $(t/c)_t = 0.11$ appear to be reasonable choices at this point.

Step 6.5: A supercritical derivative of NACA 64A413/411 will be used. The airfoil geometry would have to be derived with the help of a transonic airfoil code.

Step 6.6: Table 6.7 shows that a wing taper ratio of $\lambda_w = 0.32$ is an appropriate choice. Figure 6.4a shows a dimensioned drawing of the proposed wing planform. The planform is defined by the following parameters:

$S = 1{,}296\ ft^2$, $A = 10$, $b = 113.8$ ft

$\Lambda_{c/4} = 35^\circ$, $\lambda_w = 0.32$

From these data: $c_r = 17.4$ ft and $c_t = 5.6$ ft.

Step 6.7: See sub-section 7.2.2.

Step 6.8: Tables 8.7b and c provide typical aileron dimensions for jet transports.

The inboard ailerons for the Ourania will run from 0.23b/2 to 0.34b/2 along the wing span. This takes care of the required flap cut-out because of the engine exhaust. A chord ratio of 0.30 will be selected for the inboard ailerons. The inboard ailerons are used for trim and by the autopilot.

The flap sizing data of sub-section 7.2.2 suggest that the flaps need to be full span. Therefore spoilers will be used for additional lateral control. Table 8.7c shows that the following spoiler geometry is a reasonable choice:

inb'd span fraction: 0.50, inb'd chord fraction 0.20
outb'd span fraction: 0.80, outb'd chord fraction 0.20

The spoiler hinge line will be placed at 0.70c.

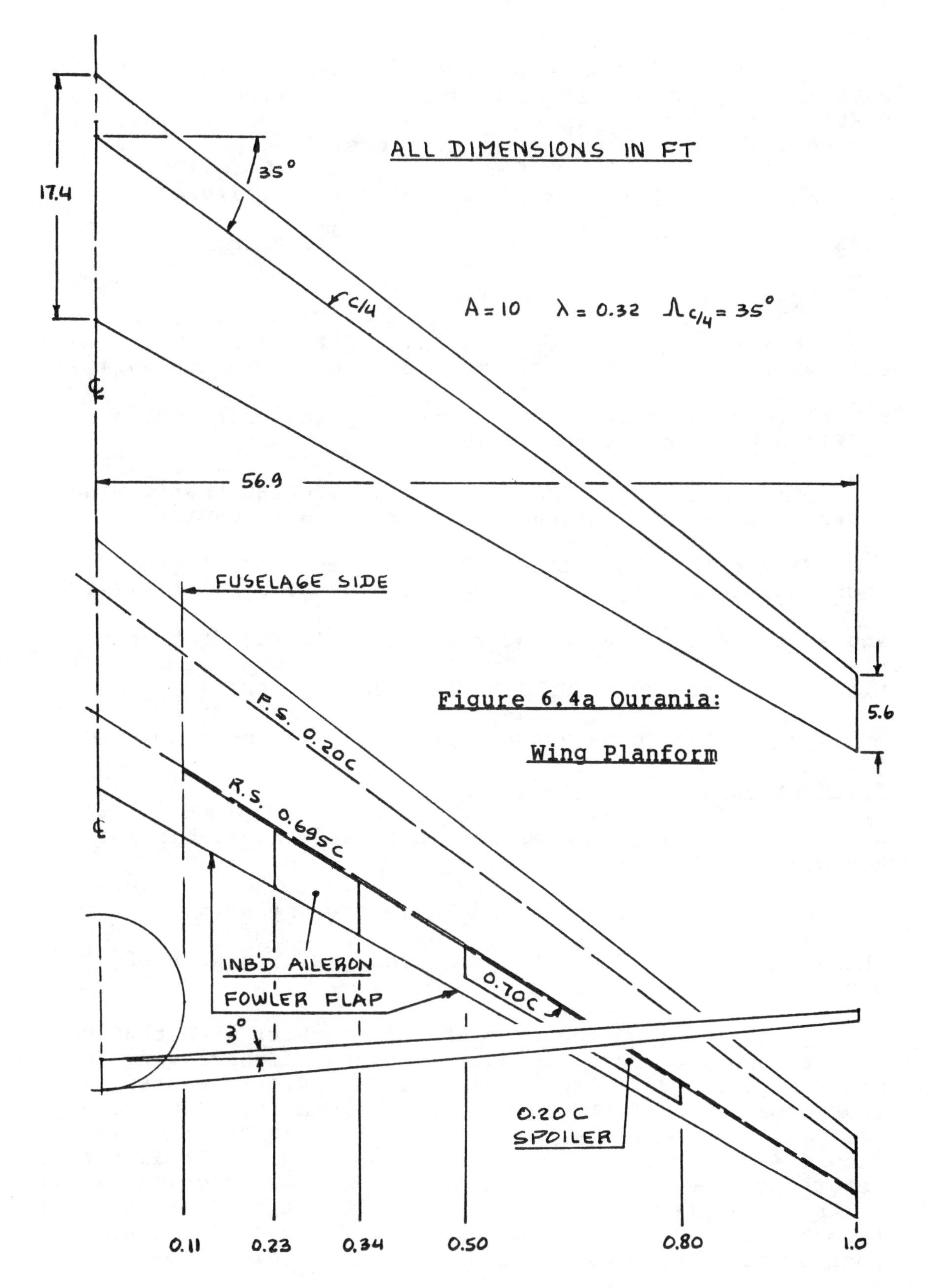

Figure 6.4a Ourania: Wing Planform

Figure 6.4b Ourania: Flap and Lateral Control Layout

Step 6.9: With an aileron and flap chord ratio of 0.30 the rear spar will be at (1 - 0.30 - 0.005)c = 0.695c. The front spar will be assumed to be at 0.20c. Figure 6.4b shows these spar locations.

Step 6.10: Using Eqn.(6.1), with τ = 0.11/0.13 = 0.85, λ_w = 0.32, S = 1,296 ft^2 and b = 113.8 ft:

V_{WF} = 821 ft^3.

The required amount of fuel is 25,850 lbs. This follows from p.59 of Pt.I. This amounts to 25,850/50.4 = ft^3 of required fuel volume. The wing therefore has a sufficient amount of fuel volume.

Step 6.11: From Table 6.7 it is observed that a wing dihedral angle of 3 degrees is an acceptable choice.

Step 6.12: From Table 6.7 it is seen that a wing incidence angle of i_w = 1.5 degrees may be o.k. A twist angle of ε_t = -2 deg. at the tip with a linear distribution from root to tip will be assumed for now.

Step 6.13: To save space this step has been omitted.

6.2.3 Fighter

The following information is already available for the wing of the Eris:

S = 1,173 ft^2, A = 4 and therefore b = 68.5 ft.

These data follow from the preliminary sizing work of sub-section 3.7.4 in Part I.

Comparing the wing area of this fighter with that of the transport example indicates that the fighter wing is very large indeed. If a taper ratio of 0.4 were used, a root chord of 24.5 ft would result. This represents almost the length of the fuselage of the Eris as drawn in Figure 4.9! This is probably not acceptable. It is therefore proposed to take another look at the matching results of Figure 3.36 in Part I(p.187). It is observed from Figure 3.36 that higher wing loadings could be accepted, provided higher values of $C_{L_{max_{TO}}}$ are allowable. Extrapolating to $C_{L_{max_{TO}}} = 2.8$ while maintaining the same value of $(T/W)_{TO} = 0.46$ yields a wing loading of 84 psf. This in turn leads to the much more reasonable value for wing area of 787 ft^2.

While reexamining the wing geometry it becomes evident that the previously selected value for aspect ratio of 4 is probably too low for this type of fighter. Table 6.9 shows that A = 6 is a more reasonable choice when compared to similar attack fighters.

The reader should redo the performance sizing calculations of sub-section 3.7.4 (pt.I) with A = 6 to verify that this is indeed a better choice.

The Eris wing geometry is now defined by:

$S = 787\ ft^2$, $A = 6$, and therefore $b = 68.7$ ft.

Step 6.1: Not applicable: the Eris is not a flying wing.

Step 6.2: The cruise speed of the Eris is required to be M = 0.85 at 40,000 ft (Table 2.19, Part I). This speed requirement is consistent only with a cantilever wing.

Step 6.3: A high wing was already decided on in the selection of the overall configuration in sub-section 3.5.3.

Step 6.4: The sweep angle for the Eris wing must be selected on the basis of a critical Mach number of at least 0.85. The cruise lift coefficient of the Eris may be estimated from Eqn.(6.1) as:

At 40,000 ft: $C_{L_{cr}} =$

$$(54,500 - 0.4x18,500)/1,482x0.1851x0.85^2x0.185x787 = 0.30$$

At sealevel:

$$C_{L_{cr}} = (54,500 - 0.4x18,500)/1,482x(450/662)^2x787 = 0.09$$

Figures 6.1 and 6.2 show that with (t/c) = 0.10 and no sweep, a critical Mach number of 0.83 may be achievable. Since the wing will actually be thinner at the wing/fuselage intersection, this choice may be acceptable.

The following choices are therefore made:

$\Lambda_{c/4}$ = 0 deg., $(t/c)_r$ = 0.10, $(t/c)_t$ = 0.08

There exists a trade between wing critical Mach number, wing weight, wing sweep and wing thickness ratio. A more detailed study of this trade relation will be required before making a final choice.

Step 6.5: A supercritical derivative of NACA 64A210/208 will be used. The airfoil geometry would have to be derived with the help of a transonic airfoil code.

Step 6.6: Table 6.8 shows that a wing taper ratio of λ_w = 0.50 is an appropriate choice. Figure 6.5a shows a dimensioned drawing of the proposed wing planform. The planform is defined by the following parameters:

$S = 787\ ft^2$, $A = 6$, $b = 68.7$ ft

$\Lambda_{c/4} = 0^{\circ}$, $\lambda_w = 0.50$

From these data: c_r = 15.3 ft and c_t = 7.6 ft.

Step 6.7: See sub-section 7.2.3.

Step 6.8: The flap sizing analysis of sub-section 7.2.3 shows that a full span flap is needed. That means no aileron can be used. Therefore spoilers will have to be employed. The following spoiler geometry is guessed at for now:

inb'd spoiler span fraction: 0.40, chord fraction: 0.20
outb'd spoiler span fraction: 1.00, chord fraction: 0.20

The spoiler hingeline will be placed at 0.70c.

Step 6.9: With a spoiler and flap chord ratio of 0.30 the rear spar will be at (1 - 0.30 - 0.005)c = 0.695c. The front spar will be assumed to be at 0.20c. Figure 6.5b shows these spar locations.

Step 6.10: Using Eqn.(6.1), with τ = 0.08/0.10 = 0.80, λ_w = 0.50, $S = 787\ ft^2$ and b = 68.7 ft:

$V_{WF} = 357\ ft^3$.

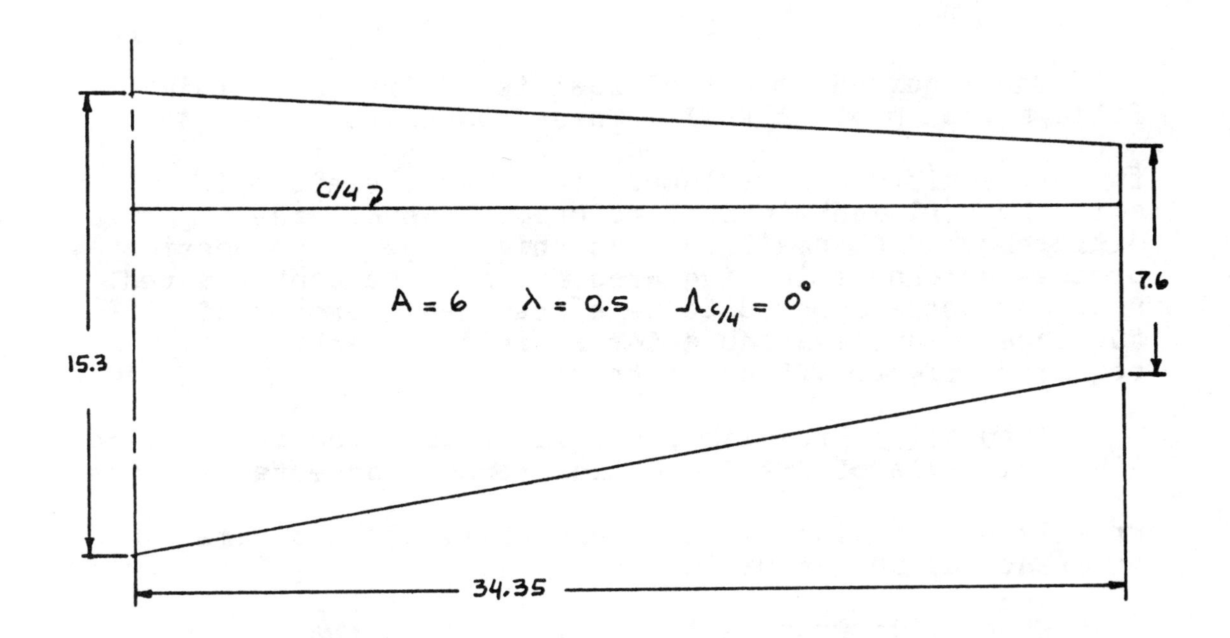

Figure 6.5a Eris: Wing Planform

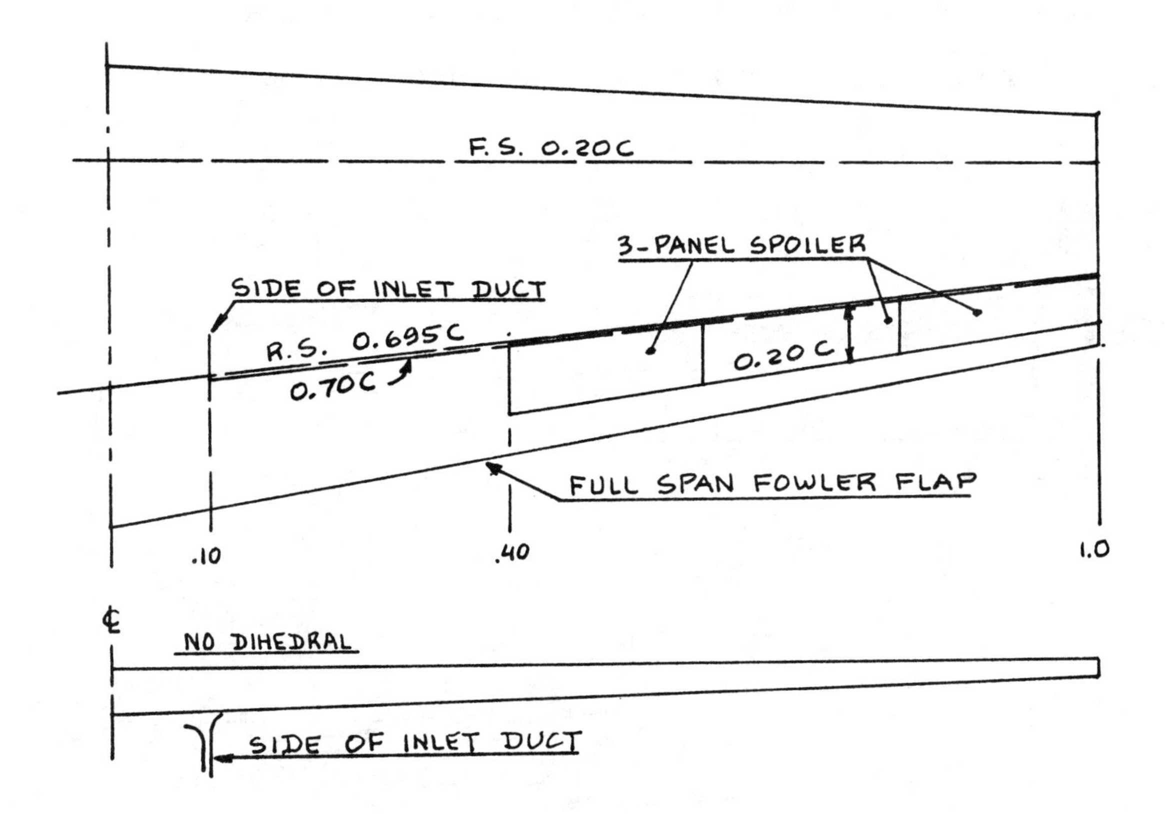

Figure 6.5b Eris: Flap and Lateral Control Layout

The required amount of fuel is 18,500 lbs. This follows from p.67 of Pt.I. This amounts to 18,500/49 =

ft^3 of required fuel volume. The wing therefore is slightly deficient in fuel volume. However, the difference is so small that at this stage in the design process no change in wing area needs to be contemplated. Besides, there appears to be a reasonable amount of fuselage volume available for additional tankage if required: Figure 4.9 shows this.

Step 6.11: From Table 6.9 it is observed that a wing dihedral angle of $\Gamma_w = 0$ deg. is probably acceptable. The Eris is a high wing airplane and therefore has some inherent lateral stability.

Step 6.12: From Table 6.7 it is seen that a wing incidence angle of $i_w = 0$ degrees may be o.k. A twist angle of $\varepsilon_t = -2$ deg. at the tip with a linear distribution from root to tip will be assumed for now.

Step 6.13: To save space this step has been omitted.

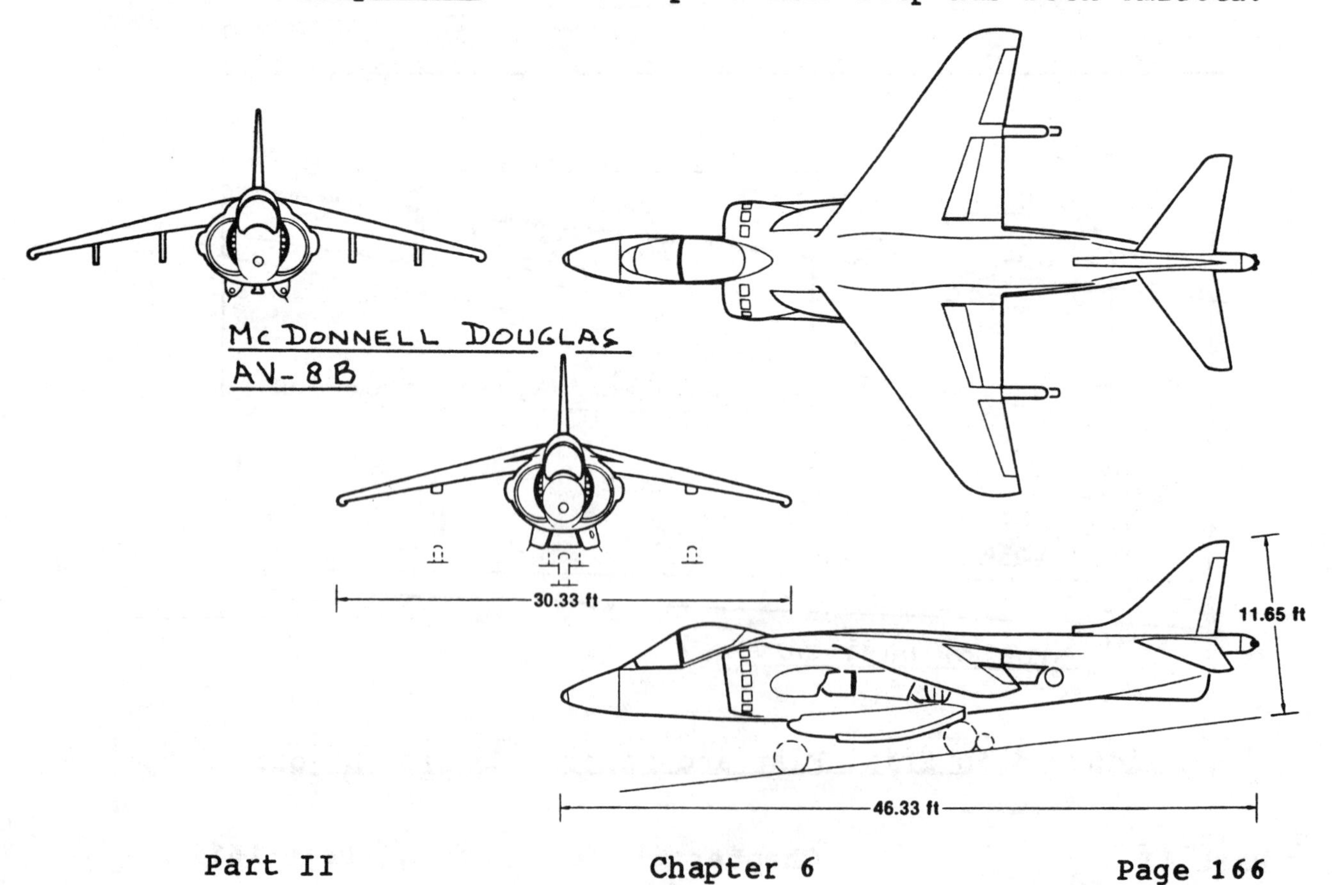

7. CLASS I METHOD FOR VERIFYING CLEAN AIRPLANE $C_{L_{max}}$ AND FOR SIZING HIGH LIFT DEVICES

The purpose of this chapter is to present a Class I methodology for determining:

1. Whether or not the wing geometry selected in Chapter 6 is consistent with the required value of clean airplane $C_{L_{max}}$.

2. The type and size of high lift devices needed by the airplane to meet the requirements for $C_{L_{max_{TO}}}$ and for $C_{L_{max_L}}$.

The method presented is part of Step 7 in p.d. sequence I as outlined in Chapter 2.
Section 7.1 contains the method as an 8-step procedure. Example applications to three types of airplanes are contained in Section 7.2.

7.1 A PROCEDURE FOR DETERMINING CLEAN AIRPLANE $C_{L_{max}}$ AND FOR SIZING HIGH LIFT DEVICES

Important note: The method presented here should not be used for wing sweep angles larger than about +/- 35 degrees. For larger sweep angles the reader should refer to Part VI(Ref.5).

Step 7.1: List the values for the following maximum lift coefficients:

Clean: $C_{L_{max}}$ Take-off: $C_{L_{max_{TO}}}$ Landing: $C_{L_{max_L}}$

The reader will recall that these values followed from the preliminary sizing process of Part I.

Step 7.2: Verify that the existing wing planform can produce a value of $C_{L_{max_w}}$, which is consistent with the required value of clean airplane $C_{L_{max}}$.

First it must be realized that any value for total airplane $C_{L_{max}}$ must be assumed to be a 'trimmed' value.

For most airplane configurations (conventional as well as canard) it is conservative in the early phases of preliminary design to assume:

$$C_{L_{max_W}} = 1.05 \text{ to } 1.1 C_{L_{max}} \tag{7.1}$$

The factor 1.05 to 1.1 accounts for the 'tail down-load to trim' or for the interference of the 'canard up-load to trim' on the wing. For 'short-coupled' airplanes, use 1.1. For 'long-coupled' airplanes use 1.05.

A 'short-coupled' airplane is one with $l_h/\bar{c} < 3.0$.

A 'long-coupled' airplane is one with $l_h/\bar{c} > 5.0$.

If the wing sweep angle is between 0 and 35 degrees it will be necessary to 'correct' for the effect of sweep by using the so-called cosine-rule:

$$C_{L_{max_W}}{}_{\text{unswept}} = C_{L_{max_W}}{}_{\text{swept}} / \cos\Lambda_{c/4} \tag{7.2}$$

To verify whether or not the wing can produce its required value of unswept $C_{L_{max_W}}$ as determined from Eqn.(7.2) the following approximation may be used:

$$C_{L_{max_W}} = k_\lambda (c_{l_{max_r}} + c_{l_{max_t}})/2 \tag{7.3}$$

where: $k_\lambda = 0.88$ for $\lambda = 1.0$

and: $k_\lambda = 0.95$ for $\lambda = 0.4$

NOTE: Eqn.(7.3) does not account for wing twist!

Values for section maximum lift coefficients may be determined from Ref.20 and from Ref.23. In the absence of these references, values for section maximum lift coefficients at the root and at the tip may be determined from Figure 7.1. Note that before Fig. 7.1 can be used, the Reynolds numbers for the root and tip sections must be computed. This can be done with Equations (7.4) and (7.5):

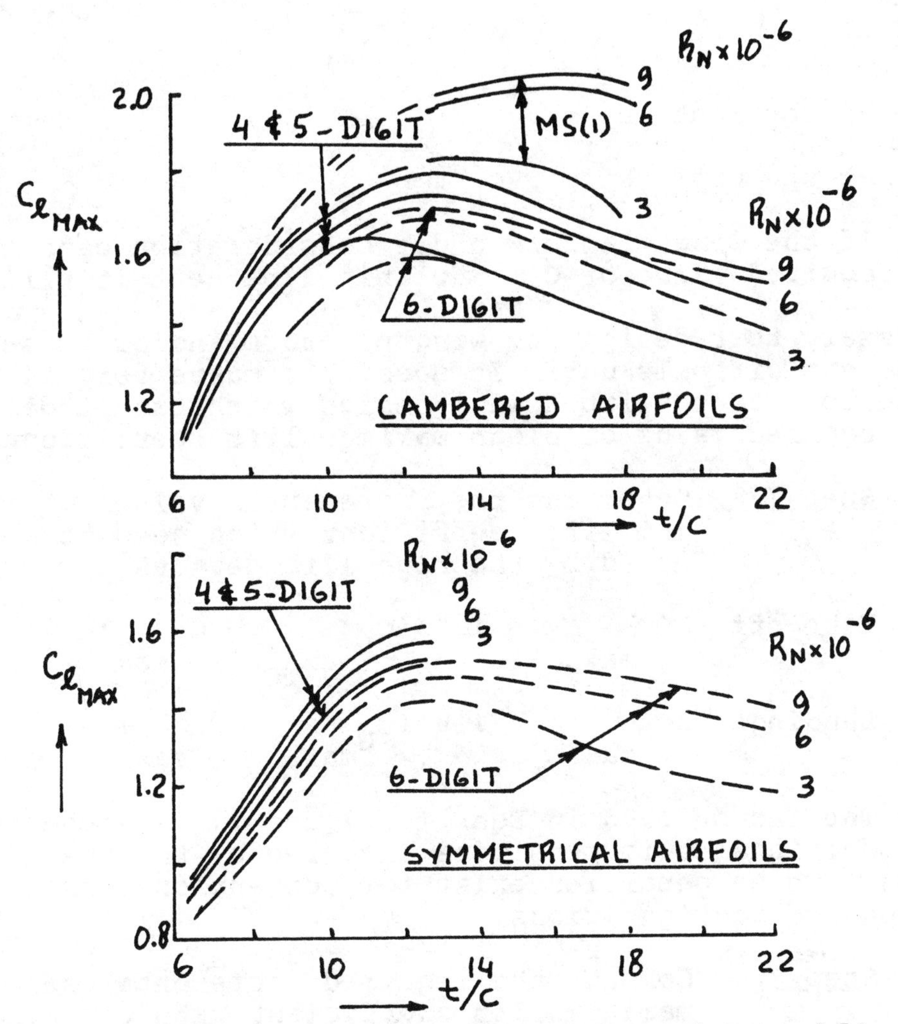

Figure 7.1 Effect of Thickness Ratio and Reynold's Number on Section Maximum Lift Coefficient

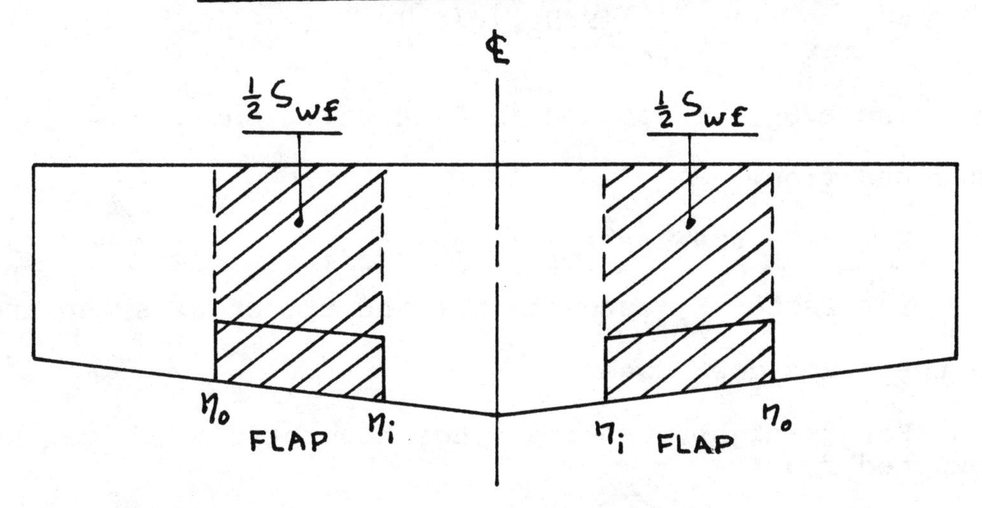

Figure 7.2 Definition of Flapped Wing Area

at the root: $R_{n_r} = \rho V c_r/\mu$ (7.4)

at the tip: $R_{n_t} = \rho V c_t/\mu$ (7.5)

If the wing planform under consideration cannot meet the required value of $C_{L_{max}}$ within 5 percent it will be necessary to redesign the wing planform and/or to select different airfoils until it does. It makes very little sense to proceed with a wing design which cannot deliver the required value of clean maximum lift coefficient.

Step 7.3: Determine the incremental values of maximum lift coefficient which need to be produced by the high lift devices:

Take-off: $\Delta C_{L_{max_{TO}}} = 1.05(C_{L_{max_{TO}}} - C_{L_{max}})$ (7.6)

Landing: $\Delta C_{L_{max_L}} = 1.05(C_{L_{max_L}} - C_{L_{max}})$ (7.7)

The factor 1.05 in Eqns.(7.6) and (7.7) accounts for the additional trim penalties incurred by the use of flaps. These penalties exist for conventional as well as for canard configurations.

Step 7.4: Compute the required incremental section maximum lift coefficient with the flaps down from:

$\Delta c_{l_{max}} = (\Delta C_{L_{max}})(S/S_{wf})/(K_{\Lambda})$, (7.8)

where S_{wf} is defined in Figure 7.2 and where K_{Λ} is found from:

$K_{\Lambda} = (1 - 0.08\cos^2\Lambda_{c/4})\cos^{3/4}\Lambda_{c/4}$ (7.9)

The factor K_{Λ} accounts for the effect of sweep angle in the flaps down case.

For straight, tapered wings the ratio S_{wf}/S can be computed from:

$S_{wf}/S = (\eta_o - \eta_i)\{2 - (1 - \lambda)(\eta_i + \eta_o)\}/(1 + \lambda)$, (7.10)

where the span stations η_i and η_o are defined in Fig.7.2.

Step 7.5: Compute the required value of incremental section lift coefficient, Δc_l, which the flaps must generate and relate this value to flap type, flap angle and flap chord.

The incremental section lift coefficient due to flaps, Δc_l is related to its counterpart $\Delta c_{l_{max}}$ as defined in Figure 7.3.

In preliminary design it is conservative to use:

$$\Delta c_l = (1/K)\Delta c_{l_{max}} , \qquad (7.11)$$

where the factor K is found from Figure 7.4.

The magnitude of incremental section lift coefficient due to flaps depends on the following factors:

1. the flap-to-chord ratio c_f/c of the flaps
2. the type of flaps used
3. the flap deflection angle used

Equations for computing obtainable values for Δc_l are now given for four types of flaps:

Plain flaps: $\Delta c_l = c_{l_{\delta_f}} \delta_f K' ,$ (7.12)

where $c_{l_{\delta_f}}$ and K' may be found from Figure 7.5 and from Figure 7.6 respectively.

Split flaps: $\Delta c_l = k_f (\Delta c_l)_{c_f/c\, =\, 0.2} ,$ (7.13)

where k_f and $(\Delta c_l)_{c_f/c\, =\, 0.2}$ can be found from Fig.7.7.

Single slotted flaps: $\Delta c_l = c_{l_\alpha} \alpha_{\delta_f} \delta_f ,$ (7.14)

where α_{δ_f} may be found from Figure 7.8.

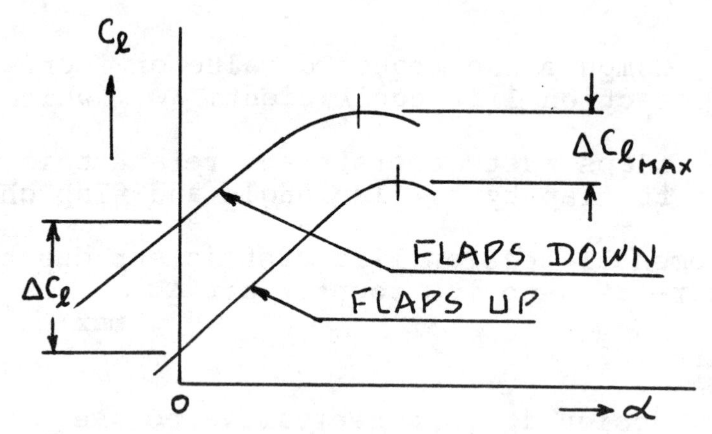

Figure 7.3 Relation Between ΔC_l and $\Delta C_{l_{max}}$

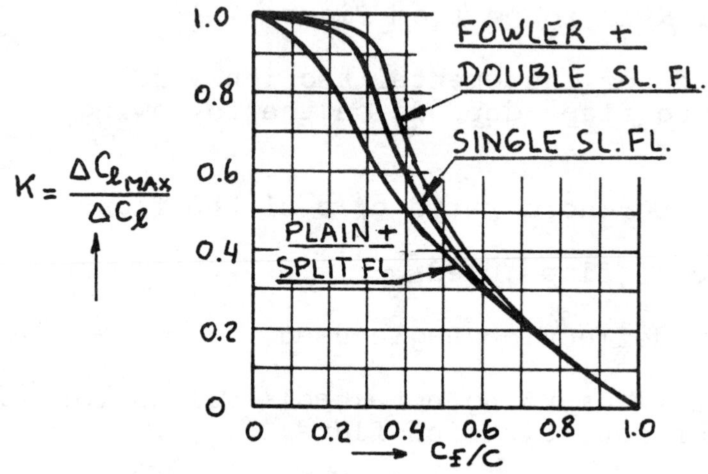

Figure 7.4 Effect of Flap Chord Ratio and Flap Type on $K = \Delta C_{l_{max}} / \Delta C_l$

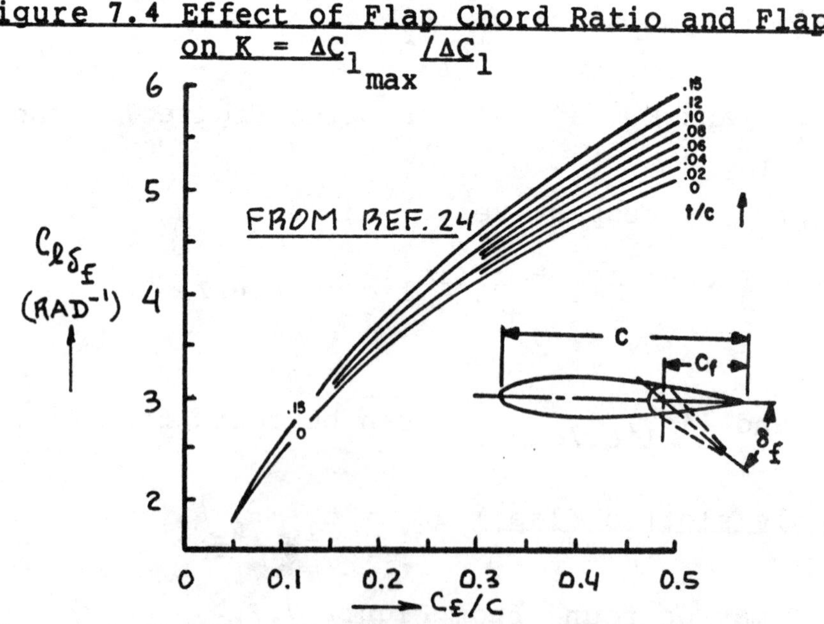

Figure 7.5 Effect of Thickness Ratio and Flap Chord Ratio on $C_{l_{\delta_f}}$

Figure 7.6 Effect of Flap Chord Ratio and Flap Deflection on K'

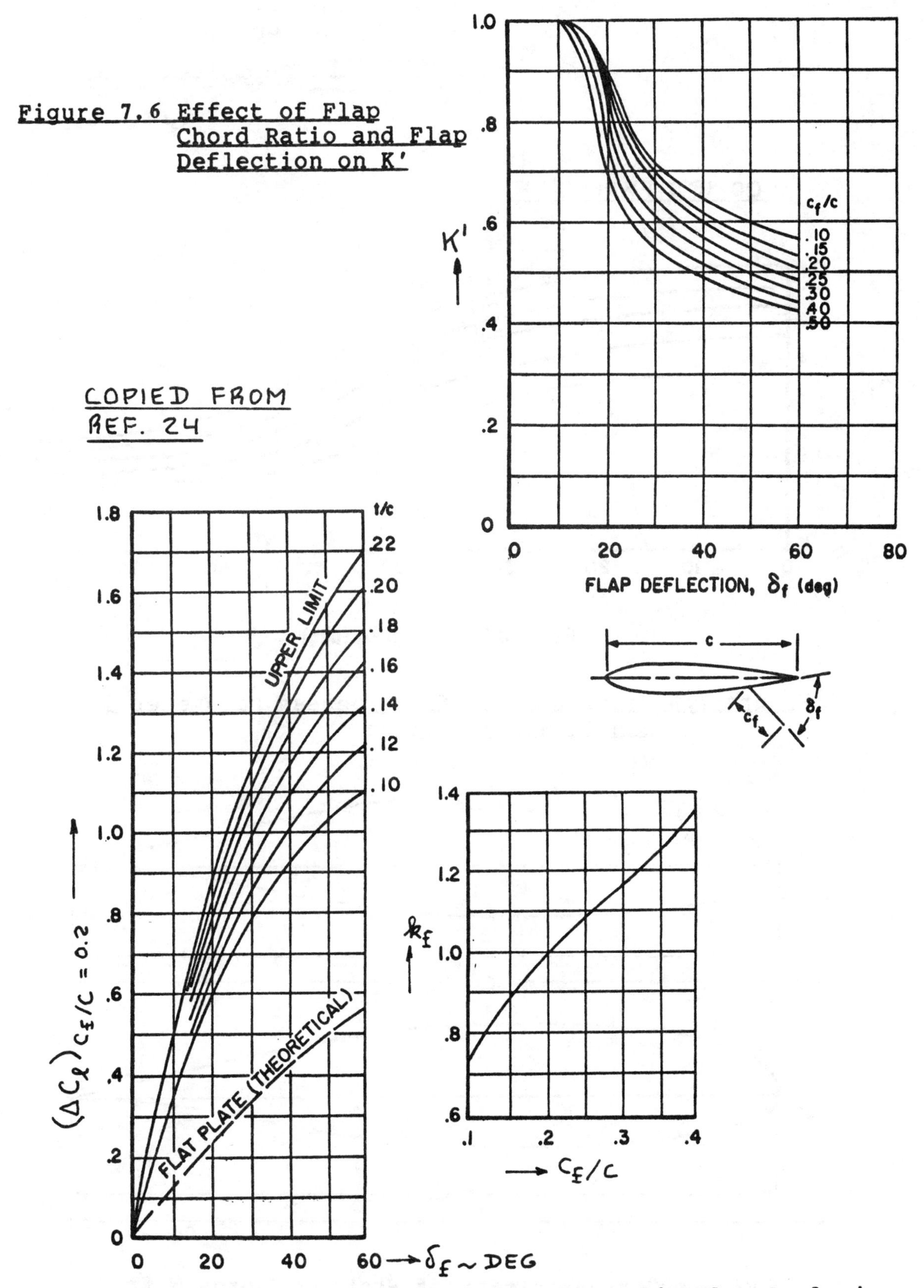

Figure 7.7 Empirical Constants for Split Flap Analysis

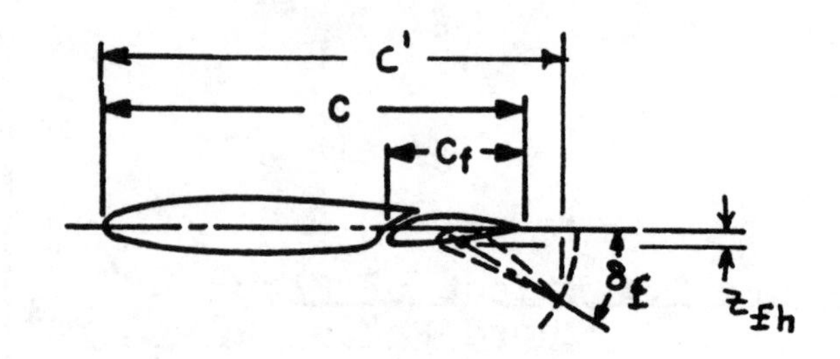

COPIED FROM REF. 24

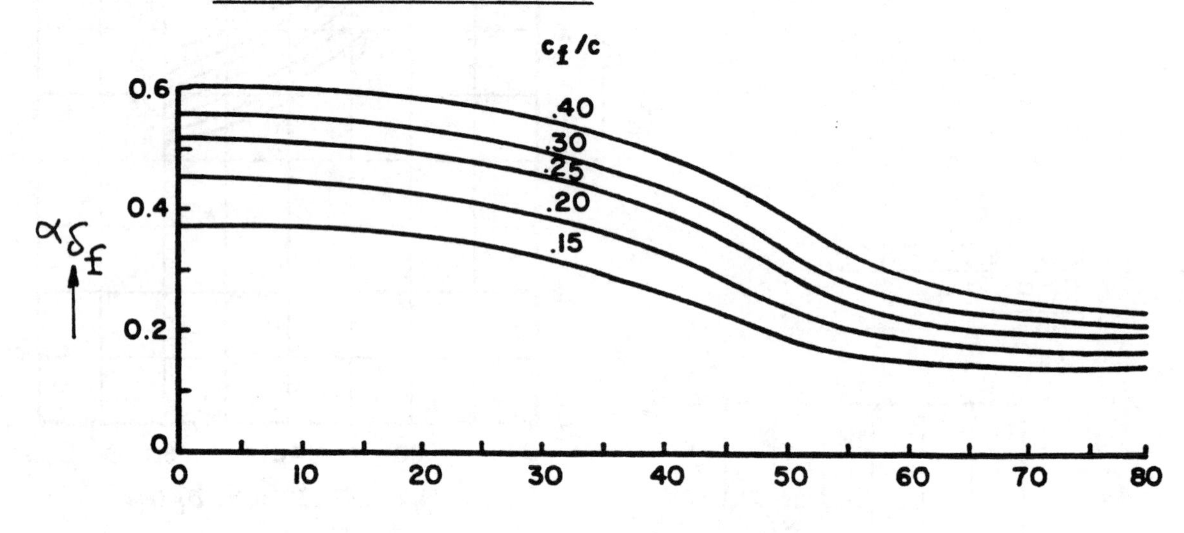

Figure 7.8 Section Lift Effectiveness Parameter for Single Slotted Flaps

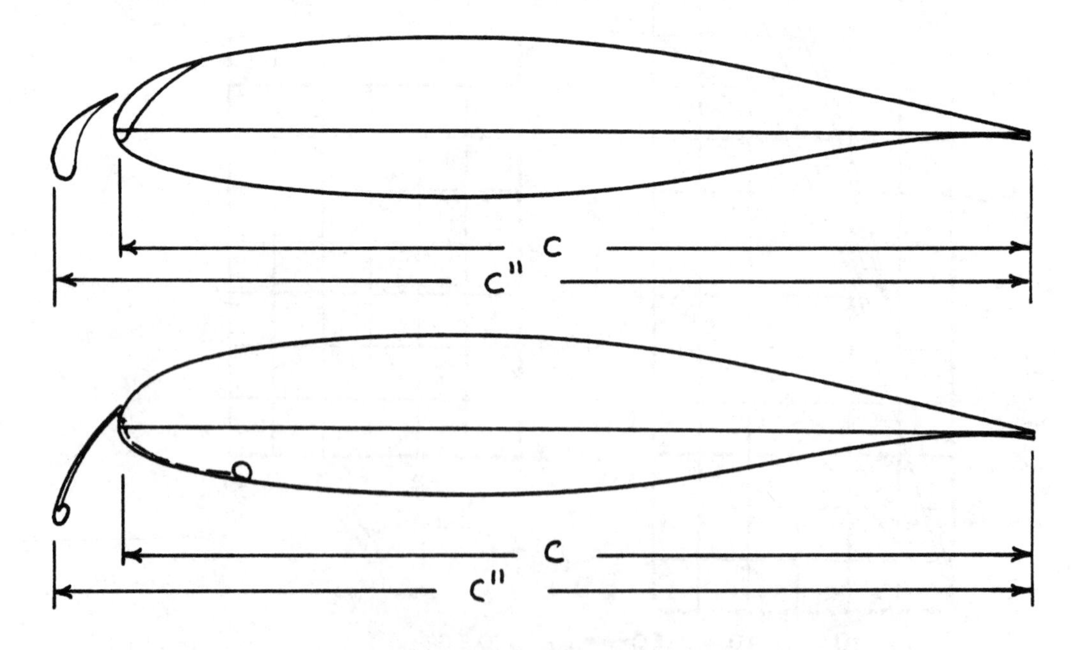

Figure 7.9 Definition of Section Chords With Deployed Leading Edge Devices

The flapped section lift curve slope can be obtained from:

$$c_{l_{\alpha_f}} = c_{l_\alpha}(c'/c) \qquad (7.15)$$

with: $c'/c = 1 + 2(z_{fh}/c)\tan(\delta_f/2)$ (7.16)

Geometric definitions for c' and for z_{fh} are given in Figure 7.8.

The value of unflapped section lift curve slope, c_{l_α} in Eqn.(7.14) may be found from section data as in Ref.20 or may be assumed to be 2π.

<u>Fowler flaps:</u>

$$\Delta c_l = c_{l_\alpha} \alpha_{\delta_f} \delta_f, \qquad (7.17)$$

which applies to a fully aft translating Fowler flap.

The four flap types discussed so far are all trailing edge devices.
In many cases it will be necessary to also employ leading edge devices. The reader should preferably use experimental data to estimate the effect of leading edge devices on maximum section lift. In the absence of such data the following equation may be used in the early phase of preliminary design:

$$c_{l_{max_{\text{with l.e. flap}}}} = c_{l_{max_{\text{no l.e. flap}}}} (c''/c), \qquad (7.18)$$

where c'' is defined in Figure 7.9 for slats and for Krueger flaps.

References 20 and 23 contain a significant amount of data on maximum lift coefficient capability for a wide variety of high lift devices.

With the methods of Step 7.5 it is possible to determine that combination of items 1 through 4:

1. Flap angle δ_f
2. Flap chord ratio c_f/c
3. S_{wf}/S and thus flap span ratio b_f/b
4. Flap type (trailing and leading edge)

which satisfies the flaps down lift coefficient requirements as listed in Step 7.1.

Step 7.6: Draw the required flap geometries in the wing planform drawing of Step 6, Ch.6.

Make sure that the required flaps are compatible with:

1. required lateral controls (as defined in Step 6.7 in Chapter 6).
2. fuselage width at the inboard flap station.
3. engine nacelles placed on the wing: it is not desirable to have hot exhaust gasses impinge on the flaps unless these are made of steel or titanium.

Step 7.7: Document the decisions made under Steps 7.1 - 7.6 in a brief, descriptive report including clear dimensioned drawings.

Step 7.8: Return to Step 6.9 in Chapter 6.

7.2 EXAMPLE APPLICATIONS

The following three example applications will be presented:

7.2.1 Twin Engine Propeller Driven Airplane: Selene
7.2.2 Jet Transport: Ourania
7.2.3 Fighter: Eris

7.2.1 Twin Engine Propeller Driven Airplane

Step 7.1: The values of the required maximum lift coefficients are found from Part I, p.178 as:

$$C_{L_{max}} = 1.7 \quad C_{L_{max_{TO}}} = 1.85 \quad C_{L_{max_L}} = 2.3$$

Step 7.2: The wing planform selected for this airplane is described in Chapter 6, sub-section 6.2.1. It was found that:

$$A = 8,\ S = 172\ \text{ft}^2,\ b = 37.1\ \text{ft},\ \Lambda_{c/4} = 0\ \text{deg.}$$

$$\lambda = 0.4,\ c_r = 6.62\ \text{ft and } c_t = 2.65\ \text{ft.}$$

It may be judged from the fuselage arrangement drawing of Figure 4.2b that the Selene is a moderately short-coupled airplane. Therefore, from Eqn.(7.1):

$$C_{L_{max_w}} = 1.06x1.7 = 1.80.$$

Because the Selene has no sweep, it follows from Eqn.(7.3) that: $(C_{l_{max_r}} + C_{l_{max_t}}) = 2x1.80/0.95 = 3.79.$

Section maximum lift coefficients of the order of 2.0 are therefore required. Consultation of Figure 7.1 shows that NACA airfoils are not able to deliver the required section maximum lift coefficients. The data in Ref.22, on the NASA MS(1)-0317/0313 airfoils suggest that these airfoils may meet the required maximum lift value. To check this, the Reynold's numbers of root and tip are computed from Eqns.(7.4) and (7.5):

$$R_{n_r} = (0.002378x151x6.62)/3.737x10^{-7} = 6.4x10^6$$

$$R_{n_t} = 0.4x6.4x10^6 = 2.5x10^6$$

From Figure 6 of Ref.22 it follows that for this airfoil:

$C_{l_{max_r}} + C_{l_{max_t}} = 2.0 + 1.7 = 3.7$, which is close

enough to the required value of 3.79.

The selected wing geometry will therefore result in the required value of clean airplane maximum lift coefficient as long as NASA MS(1)-0317/0313 are used.

Step 7.3: From Step 7.1 and with Eqn.(7.6) and with Eqn.(7.7):

$$\Delta C_{L_{max_{TO}}} = 1.07(1.85 - 1.7) = 0.16.$$

$$\Delta C_{L_{max_L}} = 1.07(2.3 - 1.7) = 0.64.$$

It is observed that the required flap lift increments are not very high. It is therefore conjectured that a relatively small single slotted flap will probably be sufficient.

Step 7.4: Equation (7.8) which depends on the flap size parameter S_{wf}/S will be used. This flap size parameter is not yet known.

At this point it is possible to proceed with two or three arbitrary values for S_{wf}/S. Example values selected are: 0.3 and 0.6.

The sweep correction factor K_{Λ} from Eqn.(7.9) is 0.92. Eqn.(7.8) now yields:

		Landing flaps		Take-off flaps	
S_{wf}/S	=	0.3	0.6	0.3	0.6
$\Delta c_{l_{max}}$	=	2.32	1.16	0.58	0.29

<u>Step 7.5:</u> It was observed earlier that a simple single slotted flap might be sufficient for this airplane. The following 'educated' guesses are made for the flap geometry:

$\frac{Z_{fh}}{c} = 0.1$ $\quad c_f/c = 0.25 \quad \delta_{f_{TO}} = 15$ deg. $\quad \delta_{f_L} = 48$ deg.

<u>Take-off:</u> From Eqn.(7.16): $c'/c = 1.03$

From Eqn.(7.15): $c_{l_{\alpha_f}} = 1.03 \times 2 \times 3.14 = 6.45$

From Eqn.(7.14) and from Figure 7.8:

$\Delta c_l = 6.28 \times (15/57.3) \times 0.5 = 0.82$

The factor K from Figure 7.4 is: K = 0.93 and thus:

From Eqn.(7.11): $\Delta c_{l_{max}} = (0.93) \times 0.82 = 0.76$

It is seen that this is much more than needed with the previously assumed values of S_{wf}/s. The take-off flaps are thus not critical.

<u>Landing:</u> From Eqn.(7.16): $c'/c = 1.06$

From Eqn.(7.15): $c_{l_{\alpha_f}} = 1.06 \times 2 \times 3.14 = 6.66$

From Eqn.(7.14) and from Figure 7.8:

$\Delta c_l = 6.28 \times (48/57.3) \times 0.43 = 2.26$

From Eqn.(7.11): $\Delta c_{l_{max}} = (0.93) \times 2.26 = 2.10$

From Eqn. (7.8):

$S_{wf}/S = 0.33$

<u>Step 7.6:</u> The following summarizes the flap geometry:

$S_{wf}/S = 0.33$	$c_f/c = 0.25$	Single slotted flap with hinge at:
Take-off $\delta_f = 10$ deg.		$z_{fh}/c = 0.10$
Landing $\delta_f = 48$ deg.		

The ratio of flapped wing area to wing area, $S_{wf}/S = 0.33$ needs to be translated into the required spanwise flap stations. This is done with the help of Eqn.7.10. For the Selene, the value of $\eta_i = 4.5/37.1 = 0.12$.

It follows that: $\eta_o = 0.76$

The take-off flap deflection of 10 deg. is an arbitrary choice at this point.

Figure 6.3b shows a dimensioned sketch of the proposed flap, spar and aileron layout. The body width of 4.5 ft was selected in sub-section 4.2.1, the aileron geometry required in subsection 6.2.1.

Since it was decided in sub-section 3.6.1 to retract the landing gear into the fuselage, the flap/spar geometry has no effect on the landing gear.

The flaps are seen to be compatible with the lateral control size requirement described in sub-section 6.2.1.

<u>Step 6.7:</u> To save space, this step is omitted.

7.2.2 Jet Transport

<u>Step 7.1:</u> The values of the required maximum lift coefficients are found from Part I, p.184 as:

$C_{L_{max}} = 1.4$* $C_{L_{max_{TO}}} = 2.8$ $C_{L_{max_L}} = 3.2$

* This value was assumed for purposes of climb sizing calculations only. It is not essential that this value be met.

Step 7.2: The wing planform selected for this airplane is described in Chapter 6, sub-section 6.2.2. It was found that:

$A = 10$, $S = 1{,}296\ \text{ft}^2$, $b = 113.8$ ft, $\Lambda_{c/4} = 35$ deg.

$\lambda = 0.32$, $c_r = 17.4$ ft and $c_t = 5.60$ ft.

To determine the maximum lift coefficient capability of the Ourania wing, the Reynold's numbers of root and tip are computed from Eqns.(7.4) and (7.5):

$$R_{n_r} = (0.002378 \text{x} 243 \text{x} 17.4)/3.737 \text{x} 10^{-7} = 26.9 \text{x} 10^6$$

$$R_{n_t} = 0.32 \text{x} 26.9 \text{x} 10^6 = 8.6 \text{x} 10^6$$

The speed of 243 fps was computed for the take-off weight and by assuming the clean maximum lift coefficient to be 1.4.

From Figure 7.1 it is seen that the root airfoil with $t/c = 0.13$ could yield a section maximum lift coefficient of 1.9. For the tip airfoil with $t/c = 0.11$ the corresponding value is 1.7. Therefore, with Eqn.(7.3):

$$C_{L_{max_w}} = 0.95(1.9 + 1.7)/2 = 1.71.$$

This in turn yields with Eqn.(7.2):

$$C_{L_{max_w}} = 1.71\cos 35 = 1.4.$$

Since the Ourania is seen from Fig.4.7 to be a moderately short coupled airplane, Eqn.(7.1) yields:

$$C_{L_{max}} = 1.4/1.06 = 1.32.$$

This is judged to be close enough to the assumed value of 1.4. The latter will be used in the flap sizing calculations.

Step 7.3: From Step 7.1 and with Eqns.(7.6) and (7.7):

$$\Delta C_{L_{max_{TO}}} = 1.05(2.8 - 1.4) = 1.47.$$

$$\Delta C_{L_{max_L}} = 1.05(3.2 - 1.4) = 1.89.$$

It is observed that the required flap lift increments are high. It is therefore conjectured that Fowler flaps will be needed to meet the required lift increments. This is entirely in line with the type of flaps employed on existing Boeing transports.

Step 7.4: Equation (7.8) which depends on the flap size parameter S_{wf}/S will be used. This flap size parameter is not yet known.

At this point it is possible to proceed with two or three arbitrary values for S_{wf}/S. Example values selected are: 0.6 and 0.8.

The sweep correction factor K_{Λ} from Eqn.(7.9) is 0.82. Eqn.(7.8) now yields:

		Take-off flaps		Landing flaps	
S_{wf}/S	=	0.6	0.8	0.6	0.8
$\Delta c_{l_{max}}$	=	3.00	2.24	3.84	2.88

Step 7.5: It was observed earlier that a Fowler flap will probably be required. The following 'educated' guesses are made for the flap geometry:

$c_f/c = 0.30$ $\quad \delta_{f_{TO}} = 35$ deg. $\quad \delta_{f_L} = 40$ deg.

The necessary values of Δc_l are found from Eqn.(7.11) and with Figure 7.4 (K = 0.94) as follows:

		Take-off flaps		Landing flaps	
S_{wf}/S	=	0.6	0.8	0.6	0.8
Δc_l	=	3.19	2.38	4.09	3.06

Take-off: From Eqn.(7.15): $c_{l_{\alpha_f}} = 2\pi x1.3 = 8.17$

From Eqn.(7.14) and from Figure 7.8:

$\Delta c_l = 6.28x0.53x(35/57.3) = 2.03$

It is seen that leading edge devices will be needed to produce the required lift increments or that the flap span will have to be carried all the way to the tip. Assuming that the flaps run from the fuselage side (at η_i = 0.11) to the tip (η_o = 1.0), a value of S_{wf}/s = 0.84 is found with Eqn.7.10.

The reader should note that the interruption of the flap span by the high speed aileron has been ignored in this calculation. That interruption will cause some loss in flap lift but not as much as a linear analysis would predict. For purposes of preliminary design it will therefore be assumed that full span Fowler flaps with a chord ratio of 0.30 are required. Instead of outboard ailerons, there will have to be outboard spoilers.

Step 7.6: The following summarizes the flap geometry:

S_{wf}/S = 0.84 c_f/c = 0.30 Fowler flap.

Take-off δ_f= 35 deg.

Landing δ_f= 40 deg.

The take-off flap deflection of 35 deg. is an arbitrary choice at this point.

Figure 6.4b shows a dimensioned sketch of the proposed flap, spar and aileron layout. The body width of 13.2 ft was selected in sub-section 4.2.2, the lateral control geometry required in subsection 6.2.2.

Since it was decided in sub-section 3.6.2 to retract the landing gear into the fuselage, the flap/spar geometry has no effect on the landing gear.

Step 6.7: To save space, this step is omitted.

7.2.3 Fighter

Step 7.1: The values of the required maximum lift coefficients are found from Part I, p.184 as:

$C_{L_{max}}$ and $C_{L_{max_L}}$ are not critical, $C_{L_{max_{TO}}}$ = 2.8

Step 7.2: The wing planform selected for this airplane is described in Chapter 6, sub-section 6.2.3. It was found that:

$A = 6$, $S = 787\ ft^2$, $b = 68.7\ ft$, $\Lambda_{c/4} = 0$ deg.

$\lambda_w = 0.50$, $c_r = 15.3$ ft and $c_t = 7.6$ ft.

To determine the maximum lift coefficient capability of the Eris wing, the Reynold's numbers of root and tip are computed from Eqns.(7.4) and (7.5):

$$R_{n_r} = (0.002378x157x15.3)/3.737x10^{-7} = 15.3x10^6$$

$$R_{n_t} = 0.50x15.3x10^6 = 7.7x10^6$$

The speed of 157 fps was computed for the take-off weight and by assuming the clean maximum lift coefficient to be 2.8.

From Figure 7.1 it is seen that the root airfoil with t/c = 0.10 could yield a section maximum lift coefficient of 1.65. For the tip airfoil with t/c = 0.08 the corresponding value is 1.55. Therefore, with Eqn.(7.3):

$$C_{L_{max_w}} = 0.95(1.65 + 1.55)/2 = 1.52.$$

This in turn yields with Eqn.(7.2):

$$C_{L_{max_w}} = 1.52\cos 0 = 1.52$$

Since the Eris is seen from Fig.4.7 to be a short coupled airplane, Eqn.(7.1) yields:

$$C_{L_{max}} = 1.52/1.10 = 1.38.$$

This is judged to be close enough to the assumed value of 1.4. The latter will be used in the flap sizing calculations.

Step 7.3: From Step 7.1 and with Eqns.(7.6) and (7.7):

$$\Delta C_{L_{max_{TO}}} = 1.05(2.8 - 1.4) = 1.47.$$

It is observed that the required flap lift increments are high. It is therefore conjectured that Fowler flaps will be needed to meet the required lift increments.

Step 7.4: Equation (7.8) which depends on the flap size parameter S_{wf}/S will be used. This flap size parameter is not yet known.

At this point it is possible to proceed with two or three arbitrary values for S_{wf}/S. Example values selected are: 0.4, 0.8 and 1.0

The sweep correction factor K_{Λ} from Eqn.(7.9) is 0.92. Eqn.(7.8) now yields:

Take-off flaps

S_{wf}/S	=	0.4	0.8	1.0
$\Delta c_{l_{max}}$	=	4.00	2.00	1.60

Step 7.5: It was observed earlier that a Fowler flap will probably be required. The following 'educated' guesses are made for the flap geometry:

$c_f/c = 0.30 \quad \delta_{f_{TO}} = 25$ deg.

The necessary values of Δc_l are found from Eqn.(7.11) and with Figure 7.4 (K = 0.94) as follows:

Take-off flaps

S_{wf}/S	=	0.4	0.8	1.0
Δc_l	=	4.25	2.12	1.70

From Eqn.(7.17): $c_{l_{\alpha_f}} = 2\pi x1.3 = 8.17$

From Eqn.(7.14) and from Figure 7.8:

$\Delta c_l = 6.28x0.53x(25/57.3) = 1.45$

It is seen that a full span Fowler flap will be required. This in turn makes it necessary to use spoilers for lateral control. Since a fighter is operated without an autopilot, an aileron surface is not really needed.

Step 7.6: The following summarizes the flap geometry:

$S_{wf}/S = 1.0$ $c_f/c = 0.30$ Fowler flap.

Take-off δ_f = 25 deg.

Landing δ_f = 40 deg.

The landing flap deflection of 40 deg. is an arbitrary choice at this point.

Figure 6.5b shows a dimensioned sketch of the proposed flap, spar and spoiler layout. The body width of 8 ft was selected in sub-section 4.2.3, the lateral control geometry required in subsection 6.2.3.

Since it was decided in sub-section 3.6.2 to retract the landing gear into the fuselage, the flap/spar geometry has no effect on the landing gear.

Step 6.7: To save space, this step is omitted.

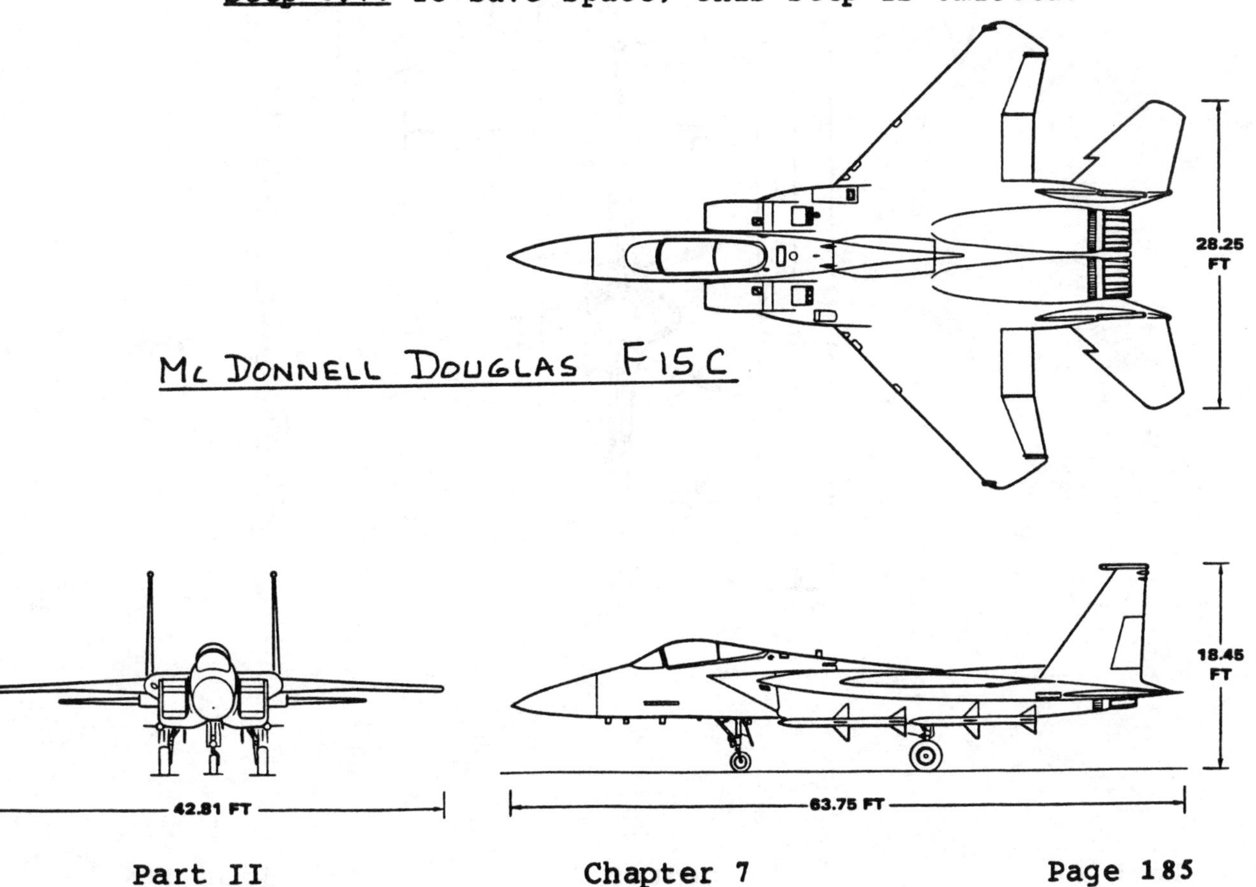

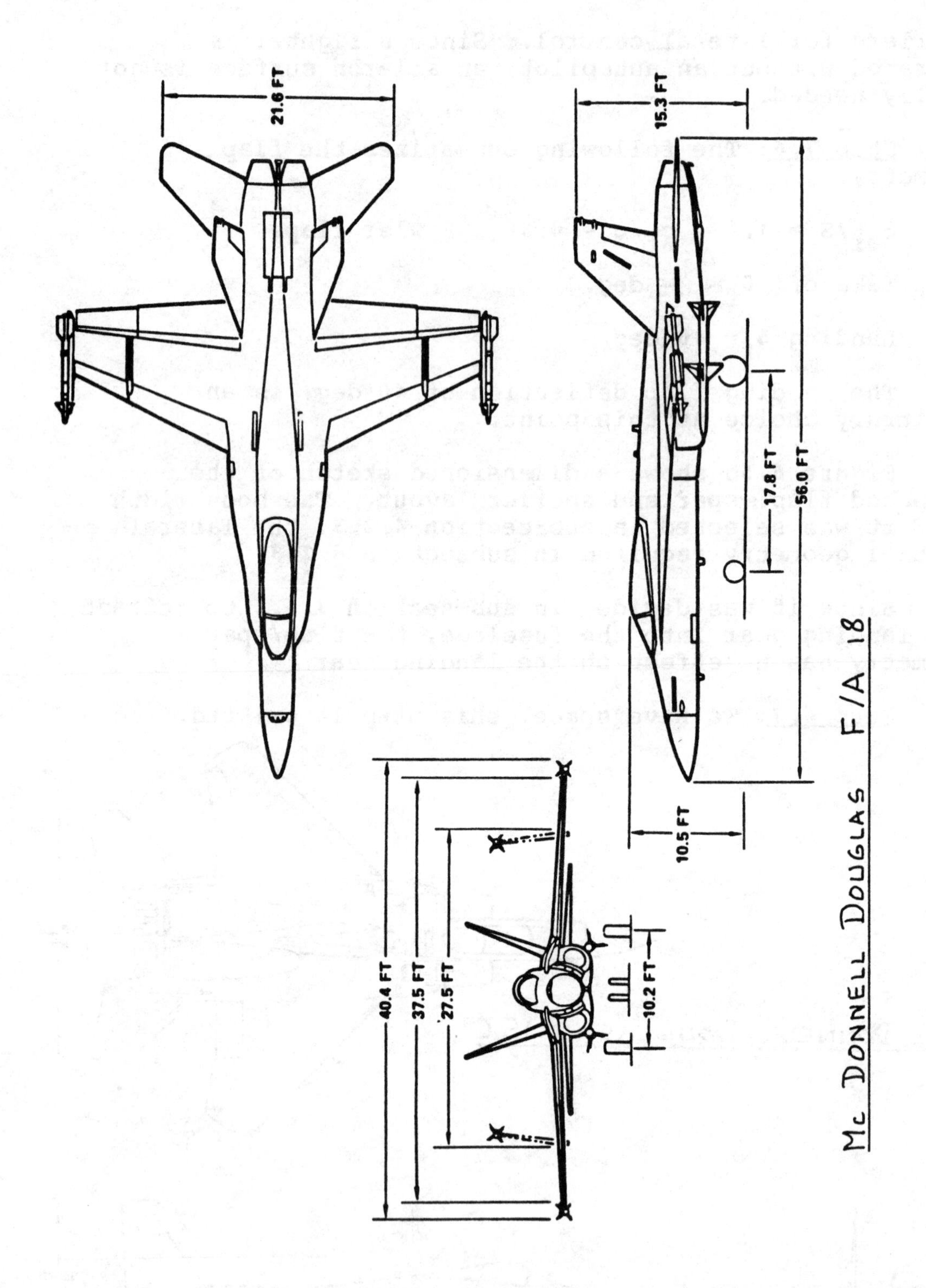
21.6 FT
15.3 FT
56.0 FT
17.8 FT
10.5 FT
40.4 FT
37.5 FT
27.5 FT
10.2 FT
Mc Donnell Douglas F/A 18

8. CLASS I METHOD FOR EMPENNAGE SIZING AND DISPOSITION AND FOR CONTROL SURFACE SIZING AND DISPOSITION

The purpose of this chapter is to present a step-by-step method for deciding on the size and disposition of the empennage as well as on the size and disposition of the longitudinal and directional control surfaces. The method is presented as part of Step 8 in p.d. sequence I as outlined in Chapter 2.

Section 8.1 presents the method while Section 8.2 contains three example applications.

8.1 STEP-BY-STEP METHOD FOR EMPENNAGE SIZING AND DISPOSITION AND FOR CONTROL SURFACE SIZING AND DISPOSITION

Step 8.1: Decide on the overall empennage configuration to be used.

The possibilities which present themselves were already discussed in sub-section 3.3.5. The reader should consult that sub-section and make a decision.

As a general rule, the horizontal tail should not be placed directly in the propeller slipstream. By referring to section 3.1 the reader will observe that many airplanes in fact do have the horizontal tail in the slipstream. The reasons against this arrangement are:

a.) The slipstream will usually cause the tail to buffet which leads to structure-borne cabin noise. Tail buffet can also lead to early structural fatigue.

b.) Rapid power increases or decreases called for by the pilot can result in undesirably large trim changes.

These comments also apply to canards. There is not usually a problem with a vertical tail mounted in the slipstream at the aft end of a fuselage.

Note: Single engine propeller driven airplanes usually do have the empennage mounted in the slipstream. This does enhance elevator effectiveness and rudder effectiveness during the take-off roll. On the other hand, it also causes considerable tail buffet during the take-off roll in some airplanes.

Step 8.2: Determine the disposition of the empennage.

Having decided on the overall empennage configuration in Step 8.1 the location of the empennage components on the airplane should now be decided. This amounts to deciding on the empennage moment arms x_h, x_v and x_c as defined in Figure 8.1. These empennage moment arms can be determined from the general arrangement drawing of the fuselage which was prepared in Chapter 4.

To keep the airplane weight and drag down as much as possible it is obviously desirable to keep the empennage area as small as possible. This in turn can be achieved by locating the empennage components at as large a moment arm as possible relative to the critical center of gravity (aft c.g. for conventional layouts and forward c.g. for a canard).

Note: in some airplanes (carrier based airplanes are one example) severe restrictions are place on the allowable length, height and width!

Step 8.3: Determine the size of the empennage.

Three types of configurations will be considered:

a. Conventional configurations

b. Canard configurations

c. Three-surface configurations

d. Butterfly empennage configurations

a. Conventional configurations.

Sizing the empennage for a conventional configuration means deciding on the magnitude of S_h and S_v.

For a first 'cut' at the size of either the vertical or the horizontal tail, the so-called $\bar{V}$-method is often used. The tail volume coefficients are defined as follows:

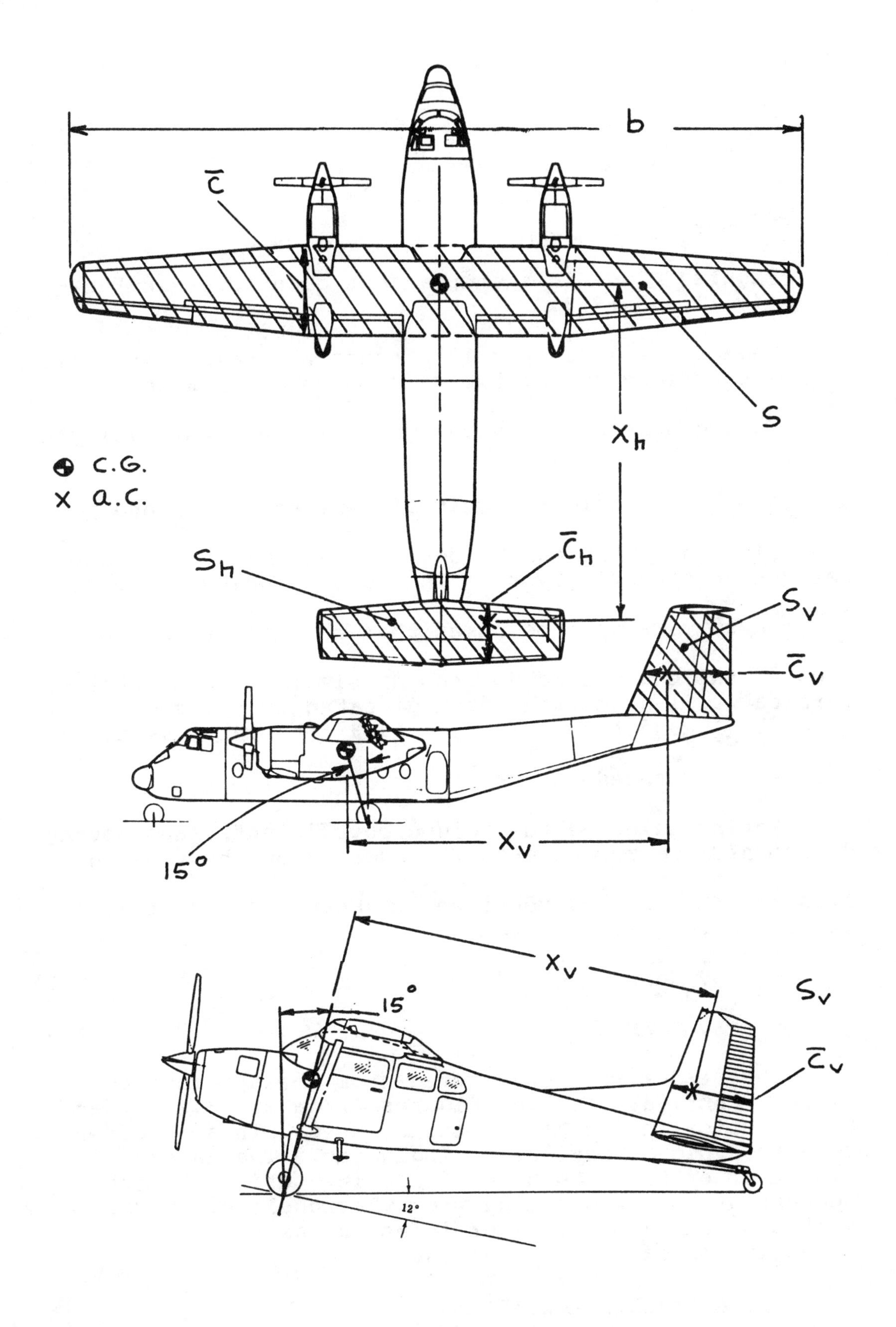

Figure 8.1 Definition of Volume Coefficient Quantities

$$\bar{V}_h = x_h S_h / S\bar{c} \quad (8.1)$$

$$\bar{V}_v = x_v S_v / Sb \quad (8.2)$$

Figure 8.1 defines the various quantities in Equations (8.1) and (8.2).

Tables 8.1 through 8.12 present the values of tail volume coefficients for twelve types of airplanes.

Having determined which type airplane best fits the airplane being designed, suitable values for $\bar{V}_h$ and $\bar{V}_v$ are selected. This can be done by averaging or by comparison to specific types. In deciding which value for $\bar{V}_v$ to use, care must be taken that the lateral disposition of the engines is not too dissimilar. Note that vertical tail sizes are often dictated by the engine-out (i.e. V_{mc}) condition. Section 11.3 contains a vertical tail sizing procedure for V_{mc}.

Having selected the volume coefficients, and having determined the moment arms x_h and x_v from the fuselage arrangement sketches mentioned in Step 8.2, the tail areas can be computed from:

$$S_h = \bar{V}_h S\bar{c} / x_h \quad (8.3)$$

$$S_v = \bar{V}_v Sb / x_v \quad (8.4)$$

The reader will have noted from the supersonic fighter configurations of Figures 3.25a and 3.27b that twin vertical tails are sometimes used. This is often done to avoid a very large single fin. The lateral placement of these twin verticals is a critical problem because of vortex shedding from the fuselage. These vortices can cause structural fatigue as well as a reduction in tail effectiveness.

b. Canard configurations.

The concept of volume coefficients can in principle be extended to a canard configuration. The problem is

Table 8.1a) Homebuilt Airplanes: Horizontal Tail Volume and Elevator Data

Type	Wing Area S (ft^2)	Wing mgc $\bar{c}$ (ft)	Wing Airfoil root/tip (NACA*)	Hor. Tail Area S_h (ft^2)	S_e/S_h	x_h (ft)	$\bar{V}_h$	Elevator Chord root/tip ($fr.c_h$)
PIK-21	76.4	4.50	64212	10.4	0.45	10.1	0.30	0.45
Durable RD-03C	119	4.30	23018/23012	22.2	0.33	11.3	0.49	.47/.32
PIEL CP-750	118	3.82	23012	23.5	0.51	12.6	0.66	.55/.47
CP-90	104	3.81	NA	22.3	0.50	11.8	0.66	.56/.38
POTTIER P-50R	80.7	3.74	23015/23012	13.4	0.52	10.6	0.47	.50/.55
P-70S	77.5	4.10	4415	14.5	0.60	9.68	0.44	0.60
O-O Aerosport	80.7	3.77	23012	15.4	0.48	10.6	0.54	0.48
Aerocar Micro-Imp	81.0	3.00	GA(Pc)-1	11.7	0.25	6.27	0.30	.28/.33
Coats SA-III	112	4.50	63415	16.5	0.46	10.9	0.36	0.46
Sequoia 300	130	4.37	64_2A215/64A210	25.5	0.43	13.2	0.59	0.43
Ord-Hume OH-4B	125	5.25	RAF48	25.4	0.49	11.1	0.43	0.49
Procter Petrel	135	4.54	3415	26.0	0.52	12.2	0.52	0.52
Bede BD-8	96.7	5.0	$63_2$015	19.4	0.14	7.64	0.31	0.17

* Unless otherwise indicated.

Table 8.1b) Homebuilt Airplanes: Vertical Tail Volume, Rudder and Aileron Data

Type	Wing Area S (ft^2)	Wing Span b (ft)	Vert. Tail Area S_v (ft^2)	S_r/S_v	x_v (ft)	$\bar{V}_v$	Rudder Chord root/tip ($fr.c_v$)	S_a/S	Ail. Span Loc. in/out ($fr.b/2$)	Ail. Chord in/out ($fr.c_w$)
PIK-21	76.4	17.0	3.49	0.33	10.5	0.028	.24/.49	0.130	0/1.0	0.13
Durable RD-03C	119	28.7	8.35	0.30	12.5	0.031	.38/.32	0.063	.63/.93	.22/.24
PIEL CP-750	118	26.4	9.49	0.55	12.9	0.039	.50/.64	0.077	.44/.96	.19/.14
CP-90	104	23.6	7.64	0.50	11.9	0.037	.47/.54	0.092	.42/.91	.22/.18
POTTIER P-50R	80.7	20.3	11.3	0.42	10.4	0.072	.34/.61	0.067	.60/.98	.24/.22
P-70S	77.5	19.4	4.36	0.67	10.5	0.031	.59/.76	0.082	.52/.88	0.20
O-O Aerosport	80.7	21.3	6.86	0.38	10.0	0.040	.34/.44	0.080	.54/.97	0.19
Aerocar Micro-Imp	81.0	27.0	7.15	0.31	6.27	0.020	.33/.43	0.140	.07/.95	0.16
Coats SA-III	112	25.0	7.53	0.44	10.6	0.028	.35/.68	0.130	.55/1.0	0.26
Sequoia 300	130	30.0	16.5	0.31	13.2	0.055	.27/.43	0.085	.60/.95	0.29
Ord-Hume OH-4B	125	25.0	6.73	0.71	12.5	0.027	.57/1.0	0.110	.35/.91	0.20
Procter Petrel	135	30.0	11.7	0.35	11.4	0.033	.31/.57	0.097	.62/.98	0.26
Bede BD-8	96.7	19.3	6.89	0.24	8.65	0.032	.20/.34	0.083	.53/.92	0.22

Table 8.2a) Single Engine Propeller Driven Airplanes: Horizontal Tail Volume and Elevator Data

Type	Wing Area S ft^2	Wing mgc $\bar{c}$ ft	Wing Airfoil root/tip NACA*	Hor. Tail Area S_h ft^2	S_e/S_h	x_h ft	$\bar{V}_h$	Elevator Chord root/tip $fr.c_h$
CESSNA								
Skywagon 207	174	4.55	2412	44.9	0.45	16.2	0.92	.48/.47
Cardinal RG	174	4.79	64A215/64A412	35.0	1.00	14.3	0.60	stabilator
Skylane RG	174	4.52	2412	38.8	0.41	14.3	0.71	.47/.39
PIPER								
Cherokee Lance	175	5.25	65_2415	34.6	1.00	16.1	0.61	stabilator
Warrior	170	4.44	65_2415	26.5	1.00	13.5	0.48	stabilator
Turbo Saratoga SP	178	4.71	NA	36.2	1.00	16.2	0.70	stabilator
Bellanca Skyrocket	183	5.30	63_2215	42.6	0.38	13.8	0.61	.36/.42
Grumman Tiger	140	4.44	NA	37.6	0.28	12.6	0.76	0.39
Rockwell Commander	152	4.58	63415	31.2	0.34	10.9	0.49	.33/.44
Trago Mills SAH-1	120	3.94	2413.6	22.0	0.46	17.8	0.83	0.46
Scottish Aviation Bullfinch	129	3.97	63_2615	27.5	0.58	11.9	0.63	0.45

* Unless otherwise indicated.

Table 8.2b) Single Engine Propeller Driven Airplanes: Vertical Tail Volume, Rudder and Aileron Data

Type	Wing Area S ft^2	Wing Span b ft	Vert. Tail Area S_v ft^2	S_r/S_v	x_v ft	$\bar{V}_v$	Rudder Chord root/tip $fr.c_v$	S_a/S	Ail. Span Loc. in/out $fr.b/2$	Ail. Chord in/out $fr.c_w$
CESSNA										
Skywagon 207	174	35.8	16.0	0.44	18.0	0.046	.46/.46	0.10	.61/.94	.25/.22
Cardinal RG	174	35.5	17.4	0.37	13.5	0.038	.35/.43	0.11	.65/.97	.38/.37
Skylane RG	174	35.8	18.6	0.37	15.8	0.047	.41/.42	0.11	.47/.96	.17/.24
PIPER										
Cherokee Lance	175	32.8	13.8	0.31	15.3	0.037	.26/.50	0.064	.56/.88	0.20
Warrior	170	35.0	11.5	0.36	13.2	0.026	.29/.52	0.078	.48/.96	.27/.24
Turbo Saratoga SP	178	36.2	15.9	0.29	15.2	0.038	.23/.58	0.057	.52/.84	0.19
Bellanca Skyrocket	183	35.0	18.1	0.33	13.2	0.037	.28/.40	0.076	.60/1.0	.25/.22
Grumman Tiger	140	31.5	8.4	0.43	12.6	0.024	.36/.46	0.055	.56/.92	0.24
Rockwell Commander	152	32.8	17.0	0.28	11.4	0.039	.30/.46	0.072	.64/.97	.27/.36
Trago Mills SAH-1	120	30.7	17.1	0.40	18.6	0.086	.35/.54	0.080	.58/.97	.25/.29
Scottish Aviation Bullfinch	129	33.8	22.7	0.39	11.9	0.062	.35/.56	0.073	.61/.95	.23/.30

Table 8.3a) Twin Engine Propeller Driven Airplanes: Horizontal Tail Volume and Elevator Data

Type	Wing Area S ft^2	Wing mgc $\bar{c}$ ft	Wing Airfoil root/tip NACA*	Hor. Tail Area S_h ft^2	S_e/S_h	x_h ft	$\bar{V}_h$	Elevator Chord root/tip $fr.c_h$
CESSNA								
310R	179	4.77	23018/23009	54.3	0.41	14.9	0.95	.42/.39
402B	196	4.77	23018/23009	60.7	0.29	16.5	1.07	.41/.39
414A	226	4.73	23018/23009	60.7	0.27	16.4	0.93	.37/.38
T303	189	4.9	23017/23012	48.1	0.42	14.9	0.78	.41/.44
PIPER								
PA-31P	229	5.79	$63_2$415/$63_2$212	68.7	0.44	16.2	0.84	.41/.51
PA-44-180T	184	4.34	NA	23.4	1.0	15.7	0.46	stabilator
Chieftain	229	6.00	63_2A415/63_2A212	61.4	0.38	16.1	0.72	0.38
Cheyenne I	229	5.69	63_2A415/63_2A212	70.5	0.40	15.7	0.85	.40/.41
Cheyen.III	293	7.33	63_2A415/63_2A212	61.8	0.39	23.7	0.68	.35/.44
BEECH								
Duchess	181	5.08	63_2A415	39.4	0.35	15.6	0.67	0.40
Duke B60	213	6.60	23016.5/23010.5	62.0	0.27	14.5	0.64	0.39
Lear Fan 2100	163	4.36	NA	55.0	0.23	13.1	1.01	.36/.31
Rockwell Comdr 700	200	5.28	NA	55.4	0.37	19.7	1.03	0.37
Piaggio P166-DL3	286	6.06	230 series	51.6	0.27	17.2	0.51	.40/.50
EMB-121	296	6.62	NA	62.9	0.43	20.3	0.65	.39/.46

* Unless otherwise indicated

Table 8.3b) Twin Engine Propeller Driven Airplanes: Vertical Tail, Rudder and Aileron Data

Type	Wing Area S ft^2	Wing Span b ft	Vert. Tail Area S_v ft^2	S_r/S_v	x_v ft	$\bar{V}_v$	Rudder Chord root/tip $fr.c_v$	S_a/S	Ail. Span Loc. in/out fr.b/2	Ail. Chord in/out $fr.c_w$
CESSNA										
310R	179	36.9	26.1	0.45	15.9	0.063	.48/.41	0.064	.60/.90	.30/.29
402B	196	39.9	37.9	0.47	16.5	0.080	.48/.40	0.058	.64/.91	.29/.27
414A	226	44.1	41.3	0.38	17.0	0.071	.49/.37	0.061	.62/.87	.30/.28
T303	189	39.0	23.2	0.44	16.5	0.052	.46/.39	0.087	.64/.97	.31/.30
ConquestI	225	44.1	41.3	0.38	17.1	0.071	.47/.34	0.060	.61/.86	0.29
PIPER										
PA-31P	229	40.7	30.1	0.38	17.2	0.056	.37/.40	0.056	.59/.97	.24/.29
PA44-180T	184	38.6	21.5	0.37	14.4	0.044	.30/.50	0.077	.45/.90	.19/.18
Chieftain	229	40.7	29.5	0.40	17.3	0.055	.40/.38	0.060	.66/.98	.24/.30
Cheyen. I	229	42.7	26.5	0.40	16.5	0.045	.37/.42	0.057	.62/.93	.24/.29
Cheye.III	293	47.7	43.6	0.46	20.8	0.065	0.33	0.046	.66/.94	.23/.26
BEECH										
Duchess	181	38.0	25.6	0.29	14.2	0.053	.34/.42	0.059	.67/.97	0.28
Duke B60	213	39.3	28.8	0.43	17.4	0.060	.44/.46	0.054	.50/.84	.24/.26
Lear Fan 2100	163	39.3	44.4	0.17	14.0	0.097	.32/.34	0.044	.72/.98	.31/.24
Rockwell Comdr 700	200	42.5	39.9	0.38	20.5	0.096	.37/.38	0.087	.58/.99	.28/.24
Piaggio P166-DL3	286	48.2	30.7	0.43	18.3	0.041	.38/.43	0.073	.61/.94	.19/.22
EMB-121	296	46.4	42.6	0.45	17.8	0.055	.42/.41	0.052	.71/.97	0.22

Table 8.4a) Agricultural Airplanes: Horizontal Tail Volume and Elevator Data

Type	Wing Area S ft^2	Wing mgc $\bar{c}$ ft	Wing Airfoil root/tip NACA*	Hor. Tail Area S_h ft^2	S_e/S_h	x_h ft	$\bar{V}_h$	Elevator Chord root/tip fr.c_h
PZL-104	167	4.60	2415	34.0	0.60	17.3	0.77	0.51
PZL-106A	306	6.23	Clark Y	81.4	0.56	18.6	0.79	.30/.50
PZL-M18	431	7.50	4416/4412	70.0	0.49	17.4	0.38	0.49
NDN-6	338	6.71	NA	60.4	0.36	17.4	0.46	0.36
EMB201A	215	5.63	23015	50.3	0.32	13.6	0.56	0.56
Cessna Ag Husky	205	4.55	2412	40.7	0.41	15.6	0.68	.43/.37
Schweizer Ag-Cat B	392	4.83	4412	45.0	0.49	12.9	0.31	.38/.60
Aero Boero 260Ag	189	5.29	23012	25.5	0.41	14.1	0.36	0.44
Let Z-37A	256	5.91	33015/43012A	54.1	0.41	16.8	0.60	.44/.42
Hal HA-31	251	6.54	USA35B	45.6	0.43	17.9	0.50	0.46
IAR-822	280	6.90	23014	48.4	0.44	17.4	0.44	0.46
Piper PA-36	226	6.22	$63_{2}618$	43.3	0.48	15.0	0.46	.38/.62

* Unless otherwise indicated.

Table 8.4b) Agricultural Airplanes: Vertical Tail Volume, Rudder and Aileron Data

Type	Wing Area S ft^2	Wing Span b ft	Vert. Tail Area S_v ft^2	S_r/S_v	x_v ft	$\bar{V}_v$	Rudder Chord root/tip fr.c_v	S_a/S	Ail. Span Loc. in/out fr.b/2	Ail. Chord in/out fr.c_w
PZL-104	167	36.5	20.3	0.49	16.1	0.054	.41/.50	0.10	.58/.94	0.25
PZL-106A	306	48.5	31.0	0.56	17.1	0.036	.45/.51	0.087	.53/.96	0.22
PZL-M18	431	58.1	28.5	0.65	18.5	0.021	.50/.46	0.11	.59/.92	0.32
NDN-6	338	50.3	31.0	0.54	18.4	0.034	.50/.64	0.047	.73/1.0	.19/.14
EMB201A	215	38.4	13.0	0.52	14.1	0.022	.39/.36	0.08	.57/.90	0.19
Cessna Ag Husky	205	41.7	18.0	0.38	16.2	0.034	.32/.39	0.11	.53/.94	.27/.28
Schweizer Ag-Cat B	392	42.3	30.0	0.40	13.5	0.024	.25/.31	0.08	.53/.86	0.29
Aero Boero 260Ag	189	35.8	9.94	0.39	15.1	0.022	.32/.51	0.11	.52/.94	.20/.19
Let Z-37A	256	40.1	22.1	0.52	15.3	0.033	.59/.65	0.086	.64/1.0	0.32
HAL HA-31	251	39.4	20.7	0.45	16.6	0.035	.50/.46	0.092	.55/.89	0.28
IAR-822	280	42.0	22.9	0.69	17.9	0.035	.56/.64	0.11	.63/.98	0.27
Piper PA-36	226	38.8	19.9	0.49	16.5	0.038	.59/.21	0.096	.52/.92	0.28

Table 8.5a) Business Jets: Horizontal Tail Volume and Elevator Data

Type	Wing Area	Wing mgc	Wing Airfoil	Hor. Tail Area	S_e/S_h	x_h	$\bar{V}_h$	Elevator Chord
	S	$\bar{c}$	root/tip	S_h				root/tip
	ft^2	ft	NACA*	ft^2		ft		$fr.c_h$
DASSAULT-BREGUET								
Falcon 10	259	6.71	NA	72.7	0.20	16.5	0.69	.31/.29
Falcon 20	440	9.33	NA	122	0.22	21.9	0.65	.28/.31
Falcon 50	495	9.31	NA	144	0.23	21.7	0.68	.31/.34
CESSNA CITATION								
500	260	6.44	23014/23012	70.6	0.29	17.3	0.73	.32/.23
II	323	6.77	NA	73.1	0.36	19.2	0.64	.37/.35
III	312	6.07	NASA Sprcrt	69.6	0.34	26.9	0.99	.39/.42
GATES LEARJET								
24	232	7.03	64A109	54.0	0.26	20.2	0.67	.36/.26
35A	253	7.22	64A109	54.0	0.33	21.9	0.65	.33
55	265	6.88	NA	57.8	0.32	23.8	0.76	.31/.35
Canadair Challenger								
CL-601	450	11.3	NA	105	0.28	32.2	0.67	.30/.31
Aerospatiale								
SN-601	237	5.60	NA	58.9	0.42	16.7	0.74	.40/.44
ISRAEL AIRCRAFT IND.								
Astra	317	5.62	Sigma 2	77.1	0.25	22.8	0.99	.30/.32
Westwind	308	7.58	64A212	70.1	0.25	19.8	0.59	.29/.26
British Aerospace HS								
125-700	353	7.52	NA	100	0.48	19.1	0.72	.37/.67
G.A.-III	935	13.8	NA	184	0.33	35.6	0.51	0.33
MU Diam.I	241	6.23	NA	57.2	0.37	22.4	0.85	0.37

* Unless otherwise indicated.

Table 8.5b) Business Jets: Vertical Tail Volume, Rudder and Aileron Data

Type	Wing Area	Wing Span	Vert. Tail Area	S_r/S_v	x_v	$\bar{V}_v$	Rudder Chord	S_a/S	Ail. Span Loc.	Ail. Chord
	S	b	S_v				root/tip		in/out	in/out
	ft^2	ft	ft^2		ft		$fr.c_v$		fr.b/2	$fr.c_w$
DASSAULT BREGUET										
Falcon 10	259	42.9	48.9	0.32	14.4	0.063	.34/.49	0.051	.67/.95	.27/.31
Falcon 20	440	53.5	81.8	0.23	18.1	0.063	.25/.39	0.057	.62/.92	0.25
Falcon 50	495	61.9	106	0.12	18.7	0.064	.21/.32	0.049	.68/.97	0.27
CESSNA CITATION										
500	260	43.9	50.9	0.36	18.2	0.081	0.36	0.096	.55/.94	.32/.30
II	323	51.7	53.0	0.34	19.36	0.062	.35/.31	0.078	.56/.89	.32/.30
III	312	53.5	70.2	0.30	20.5	0.086	.37/.38	NA*	.70/.86	.21/.17
GATES LEARJET										
24	232	35.6	38.4	0.17	16.6	0.077	.23/.22	0.050	.63/.89	.25/.23
35A	253	38.1	38.4	0.17	16.6	0.066	.26/.25	0.066	.55/.79	.30/.27
55	265	43.8	52.4	0.17	19.2	0.086	.26/.25	0.062	.49/.71	0.30
Can.CL601	450	64.3	96.0	0.26	24.9	0.083	.29/.31	0.033	.73/.91	.23/.26
Aerospatiale										
SN-601	237	42.2	45.4	0.30	15.7	0.071	.36/.32	0.033	.68/.91	.22/.20
ISRAEL AIRCRAFT IND.										
Astra	317	52.7	48.3	0.21	22.0	0.064	.33/.32	0.040	.67/.95	.26/.25
Westwind	308	44.8	59.7	0.18	20.1	0.087	.34/.44	0.050	.59/.90	.21/.31
British Aerospace HS										
125-700	353	47.0	63.8	0.22	15.9	0.061	.31/.37	0.084	.66/1.0	.33/.46
G.A. III	935	77.8	159	0.24	26.9	0.059	0.28	0.038	.66/.86	.24/.27
MU Diam.I	241	43.4	55.9	0.25	17.4	0.093	.33/.28	0.012	.86/.94	.20/.22

* Also uses spoilers for lateral control

Table 8.6a) Regional Turboprop Airplanes: Horizontal Tail Volume and Elevator Data

Type	Wing Area S ft^2	Wing mgc $\bar{c}$ ft	Wing Airfoil root/tip NACA*	Hor. Tail Area S_h ft^2	S_e/S_h	x_h ft	$\bar{V}_h$	Elevator Chord root/tip $fr.c_h$
CASA C-212-200								
	431	6.68	653-218	135	0.35	24.9	1.17	.49/.53
SHORTS								
330	453	6.06	NA	83.6	0.33	27.3	0.83	0.50
360	453	6.06	NA	106	0.39	33.0	1.28	0.48
BEECH								
1900	303	5.35	23018/23015	71.3	0.43	30.3	1.33**	.43/.48
B200	303	5.35	23018.5/23011.3	68.0	0.28	24.6	0.91	0.42
CESSNA CONQUEST			*** I airfoils carry -63 mod.					
I***	225	4.73	23018/23009	62.0	0.33	16.4	0.95	.36/.43
II	254	4.98	23018/23009	63.4	0.29	18.0	0.90	.43/.40
GA Ic	610	8.28	NA	134	0.26	36.5	0.97	.29/.32
GAF N22B	324	5.94	23018	78.0	1.00	20.6	0.83	stabilator
Fokker F27-200								
	754	8.43	64-421/64-415	172	0.27	36.0	0.98	.29/.34
DeHAVILLAND CANADA								
DHC-6-300	420	6.50	NA	100	0.35	24.8	0.91	0.47
DHC-7	860	9.45	63A418/63A415	217	0.46	41.6	1.11	.42/.47
DHC-8	585	6.51	NA	154	0.42	36.3	1.47	.41/.43
EMB-120	409	6.57	23018/23012	108	0.39	31.7	1.27	.38/.44
BAe 31	270	5.27	63A418/63A412	84.0	0.46	20.7	1.22	.43/.48
Metro III	309	6.03	65_2A215/64_2A415	76.0	0.28	26.1	1.07	.31/.48

* Unless otherwise indicated. ** 1900 also has a small fixed stabilizer.

Table 8.6b) Regional Turboprop Airplanes: Vertical Tail Volume, Rudder and Aileron Data

Type	Wing Area S ft^2	Wing Span b ft	Vert. Tail Area S_v ft^2	S_r/S_v	x_v ft	$\bar{V}_v$	Rudder Chord root/tip $fr.c_v$	S_a/S	Ail. Span Loc. in/out $fr.b/2$	Ail. Chord in/out $fr.c_w$
CASA C-212-200										
	431	62.3	77.5	0.41	24.8	0.072	0.41	0.061	.69/1.0	.24/.26
SHORTS										
330	453	74.7	93.1	0.26	27.3	0.075	0.41	0.061	.70/.95	0.27
360	453	74.7	91.4	0.37	33.9	0.091	.39/.36	0.074	.69/.98	0.27
BEECH										
1900*	303	54.5	47.5	0.35	26.5	0.076	.40/.38	0.064	.60/1.0	0.21
B200	303	54.5	52.3	0.29	20.5	0.065	.47/.41	0.059	.60/1.0	0.21
CESSNA CONQUEST										
I	225	44.1	41.3	0.38	17.1	0.071	.46/.38	0.060	.61/.86	.29/.28
II	254	49.3	43.5	0.37	18.7	0.065	.48/.33	0.058	.62/.89	.30/.32
GA Ic	610	78.3	117	0.25	35.4	0.087	.29/.33	0.061	.65/.98	.27/.22
GAF N22B	324	54.2	70.2	0.44	21.6	0.086	.49/.43	0.085	.54/1.0	0.24
Fokker F27-200										
	754	95.2	153	0.30	36.0	0.077	.33/.29	0.050	.69/.98	.31/.29
DeHAVILLAND CANADA										
DHC-6-300	420	65.0	82.0	0.42	25.7	0.077	.35/.44	0.079	.44/.97	0.20
DHC-7	860	93.0	170	0.28	35.7	0.076	.25/.30	0.027	.81/1.0	.27/.31
DHC-8	585	84.0	190	0.26	31.4	0.121	.27/.35	0.031	.80/1.0	.23/.22
EMB-120	409	64.9	74.3	0.38	27.3	0.076	.32/.31	0.084	.63/.97	0.24
BAe 31	270	52.0	83.1	0.26	20.7	0.120	.34/.39	0.061	.59/.97	.28/.30
Metro III	309	57.0	56.0	0.35	27.9	0.089	.37/.56	0.046	.61/.98	.31/.36

* 1900 also has taillets on horizontal tail.

Table 8.7a) Jet Transports: Horizontal Tail Volume and Elevator Data

Type	Wing Area S ft^2	Wing mgc $\bar{c}$ ft	Wing Airfoil root/tip	Hor. Tail Area S_h ft^2	S_e/S_h	x_h ft	$\bar{V}_h$	Elevator Chord root/tip fr.c_h
BOEING								
727-200	1,700	18.0	BAC	376	0.25	67.0	0.82	.29/.31
737-200	980	11.2	BAC	321	0.27	43.8	1.28	.30/.32
737-300	1,117	10.9	BAC	330	0.24	49.7	1.35	.24/.34
747-200B	5,500	38.0	BAC	1,470	0.24	104.5	0.74	0.29
747SP	5,500	38.0	BAC	1,534	0.21	72.9	0.54	.32/.20
757-200	1,951	14.9	BAC	585	0.25	56.9	1.15	.29/.38
767-200	3,050	19.8	BAC	836	0.23	67.6	0.94	.30/.25
McDONNELL-DOUGLAS								
DC-9 S80	1,270	15.7	N.A.	314	0.34	61.4	0.96	.39/.38
DC-9-50	1,001	11.8	N.A.	276	0.38	56.8	1.32	.41/.47
DC-10-30	3,958	24.7	N.A.	1,338	0.22	65.9	0.90	.25/.30
AIRBUS								
A300-B4	2,799	19.2	N.A.	748	0.26	80.4	1.12	0.35
A310	2,357	19.3	N.A.	689	0.26	72.0	1.09	.33/.30
Lockheed L1011					geared elevator			
-500	3,541	24.5	N.A.	1,282	0.19	55.9	0.83	stabilator
Fokker F-28								
-4000	850	10.9	N.A.	210	0.20	47.2	1.07	.34/.33
Rombac/British Aerospace								
1-11 495	1,031	11.8	N.A.	258	0.27	40.7	0.86	.41/.35
British Aerospace								
146-200	832	10.2	N.A.	276	0.39	45.3	1.48	.42/.44
Tu-154	2,169	16.8	N.A.	436	0.18	58.9	0.71	.27/.25

Table 8.7b) Jet Transports: Vert. Tail Volume, Rudder, Aileron and Spoiler Data

Type	Wing Area S ft^2	Wing Span b ft	Vert. Tail Area S_v ft^2	S_r/S_v	x_v ft	$\bar{V}_v$	Rudder Chord root/tip fr.c_v	S_a/S	Inb'd Ail. Span in/out fr.b/2	Inb'd Ail. Chord in/out fr.c_w
BOEING										
727-200	1,700	108	422	0.16	47.4	0.110	.29/.28	0.034	.38/.46	.17/.24
737-200	980	93.0	233	0.24	40.7	0.100	.25/.22	0.024	none	none
737-300	1,117	94.8	239	0.31	45.7	0.100	.26/.50	0.021	none	none
747-200B	5,500	196	830	0.30	102	0.079	0.30	0.040	.38/.44	.17/.25
747-SP	5,500	196	885	0.27	69.5	0.057	.31/.34	0.040	.38/.44	.17/.25
757-200	1,951	125	384	0.34	54.2	0.086	.35/.33	0.027	none	none
767-200	3,050	156	497	0.35	64.6	0.067	.33/.36	0.041	.31/.40	.23/.20
McDONNELL-DOUGLAS										
DC-9 S80	1,270	108	168	0.39	50.5	0.062	.49/.46	0.030	none	none
DC-9-50	1,001	93.4	161	0.41	46.2	0.079	.45/.44	0.038	none	none
DC-10-30	3,958	165	605	0.18	64.6	0.060	0.35	0.047	.32/.39	.20/.25
AIRBUS										
A300-B4	2,799	147	487	0.30	79.5	0.094	.35/.36	0.049	.29/.39	.23/.27
A310	2,357	144	487	0.35	68.5	0.098	.33/.35	0.027	.32/.40	.23/.27
Lockheed L1011										
-500	3,541	164	550	0.23	58.2	0.055	.29/.26	0.051	.40/.49	.22/.23
Fokker F-28										
-4000	850	82.3	157	0.16	37.9	0.085	.29/.31	0.034	none	none
Rombac/British Aerospace										
1-11 495	1,031	93.5	117	0.28	31.6	0.038	.39/.37	0.030	none	none
British Aerospace										
146-200	832	86.4	224	0.44	38.9	0.12	0.29	0.046	none	none
Tu-154	2,169	123	341	0.27	43.3	0.055	0.37	0.036	none	none

Table 8.7c) Jet Transports: Vert. Tail Volume, Rudder, Aileron and Spoiler Data

Type	Outb'd Ail. Span in/out fr.b/2	Outb'd Ail. Chord in/out fr.c_w	Inb'd Spoiler Span Loc. in/out fr.b/2	Inb'd Spoiler Chord in/out fr.c_w	Inb'd Spoiler Hinge Loc. in/out fr.c_w	Outb'd Spoiler Span Loc. in/out fr.c_w	Outb'd Spoiler Chord in/out fr.c_w	Outb'd Spoiler Hinge Loc. in/out fr.c_w
BOEING								
727-200	.76/.93	.23/.30	.14/.37	.09/.14	.79/.69	.48/.72	.16/.20	.65/.63
737-200	.74/.94	.20/.28	.40/.66	.14/.18	.66/.67	none	none	none
737-300	.72/.91	.23/.30	.38/.64	0.14	.64/.70	none	none	none
747-200B	.70/.95	.11/.17	.46/.67	.12/.16	0.71	none	none	none
747-SP	.70/.95	.11/.17	.46/.67	.12/.16	0.71	none	none	none
757-200	.76/.97	.22/.36	.41/.74	.12/.13	.73/.69	none	none	none
767-200	.76/.98	.16/.15	.16/.31	.09/.11	.85/.78	.44/.67	.12/.17	.74/.71
McDONNELL-DOUGLAS								
DC-9 S80	.64/.85	.31/.36	.35/.60	.10/.08	.69/.65	none	none	none
DC-9-50	.78/.95	.30/.35	.35/.60	.10/.08	.69/.65	none	none	none
DC-10-30	.75/.93	.29/.27	.17/.30	.05/.06	.78/.74	.43/.72	.11/.16	.75/.70
AIRBUS								
A300-B4	.83/.99	.32/.30	.57/.79	.16/.22	.73/.72	none	none	none
A310	none	none	.62/.83	.16/.22	.69/.66	none	none	none
Lockheed L1011								
-500	.77/.98	.26/.22	.13/.39	.08/.12	.82/.73	.50/.74	.14/.14	.67/.67
Fokker F-28								
-4000	.66/.91	.29/.28	no lateral control spoilers					
Rombac/British Aerospace								
1-11 495	.72/.92	0.26	.37/.68	.06/.11	.68/.63	none	none	none
British Aerospace								
146-200	.78/1.0	.33/.31	.14/.70	.22/.27	.76/.68	none	none	none
Tu-154	.76/.98	.34/.27	.43/.70	.14/.20	.62/.60	none	none	none

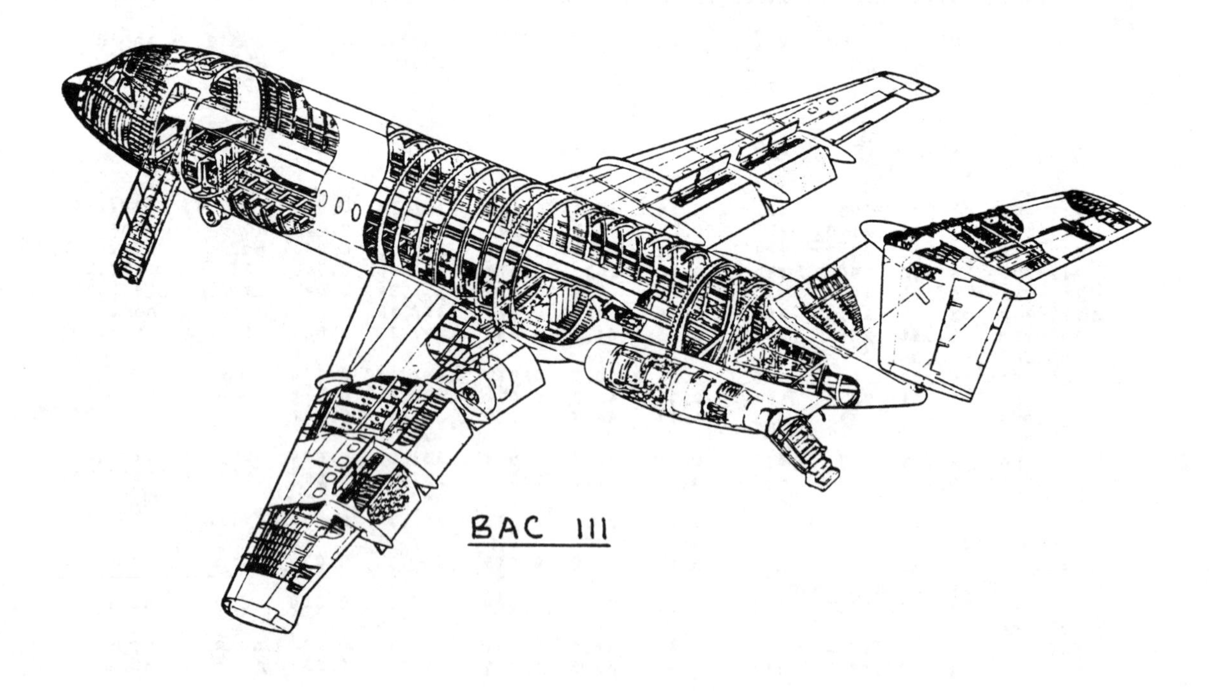

BAC 111

Table 8.8a) Military Trainers: Horizontal Tail Volume and Elevator Data

Type	Wing Area	Wing mgc	Wing Airfoil	Hor. Tail Area	S_e/S_h	x_h	$\bar{V}_h$	Elevator Chord
	S	$\bar{c}$	root/tip	S_h				root/tip
	ft^2	ft	NACA*	ft^2		ft		fr.c_h
Turbopropeller Driven								
EMB-312	209	5.77	63_2A415/63A212	49.2	0.44	16.9	0.69	.42/.44
Pil. PC-7	179	5.23	64_2A415/64_1A612	36.9	0.49	16.2	0.64	.49/.50
NDN 1T	126	5.4	23012	25.8	0.47	14.0	0.53	0.44
T-34C	180	4.01	23016.5/23012	37.2	0.37	14.8	0.76	.43/.44
Epsilon	96.9	3.97	RA1643/RA1243	21.5	0.48	13.8	0.77	.49/.54
SF-260M	109	4.35	$64_1$212/$64_1$210	26.0	0.40	12.7	0.70	.35/.56
Yak-52	162	5.20	Clark YN	30.8	0.54	13.3	0.49	.54/.60
Neiva T25	185	5.19	63_2A315/63_1A212	33.0	0.44	15.0	0.52	.46/.40
Jet Driven								
Aero L39C	202	7.04	64A012	54.6	0.23	15.2	0.58	.35/.44
Microturbo Microjet 200B	65.9	2.79	RA16.3C3	22.9	0.32	8.98	1.12	.37/.34
Dassault-Breguet/Dornier Alphajet	188	7.37	N.A.	42.4	1.0	14.1	0.43	stabilator
Aermacchi MB-339A	208	6.34	64A114/64A212	46.9	0.23	14.6	0.52	.26/.36
SM S-211	136	5.40	KU .17 sprcrt.	36.4	0.40	15.2	0.75	.41/.40
PZL TS-11	188	5.80	64209/64009	38.1	0.33	16.3	0.57	.31/.32
CASA C101	215	6.32	Norcasa 15	47.8	0.23	15.2	0.54	.33/.46
British Aerospace Hawk Mk1	180	6.30	N.A.	46.6	1.0	14.8	0.61	stabilator

* Unless otherwise indicated.

Table 8.8b) Military Trainers: Vertical Tail Volume, Rudder and Aileron Data

Type	Wing Area	Wing Span	Vert. Tail Area	S_r/S_v	x_v	$\bar{V}_v$	Rudder Chord	S_a/S	Ail. Span Loc.	Ail. Chord
	S	b	S_v				root/tip		in/out	in/out
	ft^2	ft	ft^2		ft		fr.c_v		fr.b/2	fr.c_w
Turbopropeller Driven										
EMB-312	209	36.5	22.4	0.70	16.6	0.049	.37/1.0*	0.100	.56/.99	.21/.31
Pil. PC-7	179	34.1	20.2	0.47	14.4	0.048	.52/.49	0.082	.56/.97	.23/.27
NDN 1T	126	26.0	13.5	0.52	11.8	0.049	.38/.57	0.110	.50/.87	0.26
T-34C	180	33.3	19.8	0.35	14.4	0.048	.41/.40	0.063	.55/.95	.22/.23
Epsilon	96.9	26.0	11.0	0.39	13.4	0.058	.48/.45	0.090	.58/.91	.30/.29
SF-260M	109	27.4	16.4	0.40	12.5	0.069	.35/.63	0.075	.61/.92	.23/.30
Yak-52	162	30.5	15.9	0.59	13.9	0.045	.46/.51	0.130	.47/.98	.27/.26
Neiva T25	185	36.1	18.5	0.52	15.7	0.043	.53/.52	0.085	.51/.96	.16/.22
Jet Driven										
Aero L39C	202	31.0	37.8	0.28	13.9	0.083	.36/.33	0.066	.62/.93	.36/.34
Microturbo Microjet 200B	65.9	24.8	14.5	0.39	10.0	0.089	.37/.43	0.073	.64/.96	.29/.32
Dassault-Breguet/Dornier Alphajet	188	29.9	32.0	0.21	14.8	0.084	.32/.36	0.059	.68/1.0	.23/.27
Aermacchi MB-339A	208	35.6	25.5	0.26	12.6	0.043	.30/.38	0.069	.60/.92	0.25
SM S-211	136	27.7	21.6	0.33	13.5	0.078	.37/.36	0.100	.58/.97	.22/.21
PZL TS-11	188	33.0	24.2	0.31	16.8	0.066	.24/.47	0.085	.55/.95	.23/.27
CASA C101	215	34.8	34.4	0.41	15.8	0.072	.37/.36	0.080	.61/.93	.26/.27
British Aerospace Hawk Mk1	180	30.8	27.0	0.23	12.1	0.059	.28/.31	0.063	.65/1.0	.26/.32

* Large hornbalance at tip.

Table 8.9a) Fighters: Horizontal Tail Volume and Elevator Data

Type	Wing Area S ft^2	Wing mgc $\bar{c}$ ft	Wing Airfoil root/tip NACA*	Hor. Tail Area S_h ft^2	S_e/S_h	x_h ft	$\bar{V}_h$	Elevator Chord root/tip $fr.c_h$
DASSAULT-BREGUET								
Mir. IIIE	377	17.7	NA	0	0	0	0	elevons
Mir. F1C	269	10.4	NA	96.9	1.0	14.9	0.51	stabilator
Mir. 2000	441	18.2	NA	0	0	0	0	elevons
Super Et.	306	10.5	NA	59.7	1.0	15.5	0.29	stabilator
FR A-10A	506	8.94	6716/6713	89.4	0.32	20.6	0.41	0.33
Grum.A6A	529	10.9	NA	109.8	1.0	24.2	0.46	stabilator
Grum.F14A	565	10.2	NA	140	1.0	16.4	0.40	stabilator
North.F5E	186	8.05	65A004.8	59.0	1.0	13.0	0.51	stabilator
Vht A7A	375	10.8	65A007	56.2	1.0	16.2	0.22	stabilator
McDONNELL DOUGLAS								
F-4E	530	15.5	64A005.9	96.9	1.0	22.2	0.26	stabilator
F-15	608	17.8	McD .003	104	1.0	20.7	0.20	stabilator
GENERAL DYNAMICS								
FB-111A	476	8.22	63(NA)	168	1.0	17.6	0.75	stabilator
F-16	300	11.4	64A204	66.6	1.0	15.4	0.30	stabilator
Cessna								
A37B	184	5.61	2418/2412	46.7	0.25	15.1	0.68	.34/.31
Aermacchi								
MB339K	208	6.30	64A114/64A212	36.4	0.29	14.5	0.40	.26/.37
MIG-25	612	17.3	NA	236	1.0	16.0	0.36	stabilator
Su-7BMK	329	12.5	0.008 thick	92.7	1.0	17.9	0.40	stabilator

* Unless otherwise indicated.

Table 8.9b) Fighters: Vertical Tail Volume, Rudder and Aileron Data

Type	Wing Area S ft^2	Wing Span b ft	Vert. Tail Area S_v ft^2	S_r/S_v	x_v ft	$\bar{V}_v$	Rudder Chord root/tip $fr.c_v$	S_a/S	Ail. Span Loc. in/out fr.b/2	Ail. Chord in/out $fr.c_w$
DASSAULT BREGUET										
Mir. IIIE	377	27.0	48.4	0.20	13.9	0.066	.22/.29	0.14	.18/1.0	.13/1.0
Mir. F1C	269	27.6	53.9	0.16	13.5	0.098	.21/.35	0.031	.77/1.0	.23/.25
Mir. 2000	441	29.5	71.8	0.16	13.6	0.075	.21/.34	0.13	.19/1.0	.13/1.0
Super Et.	306	31.5	48.3	0.18	12.4	0.062	.25/.49	0.053	.57/.81	.23/.27
FR A-10A	506	57.5	84.0	0.28	20.9	0.060	.31/.34	0.094	.58/.91	.42/.40
Grum.A6A	529	53.0	79.3	0.21	24.6	0.069	.28/.21	see Jane's 81-81		
Grum.F14A	565	64.1	118	0.29	18.4	0.060	.29/.33	see Jane's 81-82		
North.F5E	186	26.7	41.4	0.15	11.7	0.098	.26/.30	0.050	.76/.99	.34/.33
Vht A7A	375	38.8	115	0.13	16.1	0.13	.21/.29	0.053	.59/.90	.20/.24
McDONNELL DOUGLAS										
F-4E	530	38.4	59.6	0.20	18.3	0.054	.20/.29	0.040	.63/.98	.23/.28
F-15	608	42.8	143	0.25	17.8	0.098	.30/.50	0.053	.60/.86	.25/.27
GENERAL DYNAMICS								look under Grumman		
FB-111A	476	63.0	96.1	0.21	17.0	0.054	.25/.26	see Jane's 82-83		
F-16	300	31.8	62.2	0.25	14.4	0.094	.34/.33	0.13*	.30/.73	.21/.23
Cessna										
A37B	184	35.9	17.8	0.35	15.1	0.041	.37/.39	0.061	.56/.91	.27/.32
Aermacchi										
MB339K	208	36.2	25.5	0.26	12.6	0.043	.26/.41	0.069	.58/.90	.24/.26
MIG-25	612	45.8	174	0.15	16.8	0.10	0.24	0.053	.54/.79	.22/.21
Su-7BMK	329	29.3	58.2	0.26	16.9	0.10	.28/.25	0.11	.62/.97	.29/.35

* Flaperon

Table 8.10a) Military Patrol, Bomb and Transport Airplanes: Horizontal Tail Volume and Elevator Data

Type	Wing Area S ft^2	Wing mgc $\bar{c}$ ft	Wing Airfoil root/tip NACA*	Hor. Tail Area S_h ft^2	S_e/S_h	x_h ft	$\bar{V}_h$	Elevator Chord root/tip $fr.c_h$
Turbopropeller Driven								
LOCKHEED								
C-130E	1,745	13.7	64A318/64A412	536	0.29	42.1	0.94	.34/.44
P3C	1,300	14.1	0014/0012	322	0.25	48.5	0.85	.29/.37
ANTONOV								
An-12BP	1,310	11.3	NA	319	0.24	52.5	1.13	.33/.36
An-22	3,713	18.8	NA	846	0.28	87.4	1.06	.34/.53
An-26	807	8.79	NA	213	0.28	43.5	1.31	.34/.38
Grum.E2C	700	9.73	NA	174	0.29	26.9	0.69	.29/.36
D/B Atlant.2	1,295	11.5	NA	355	0.25	43.4	1.04	.35/.36
Aerital.G222	883	8.65	NA	255	0.20	37.0	1.24	.39/.30
Jet Driven								
LOCKHEED								
S-3A Viking	598	9.85	NA	176	0.28	20.0	0.60	.35/.25
C-141B	3,406	21.4	NA	545	0.26	82.5	0.62	.28/.29
C-5A	6,200	32.9	NA	966	0.27	130.4	0.62	0.30
BA Nimrod 2	2,121	20.5	NA	435	0.31	50.5	0.51	.32/.40
Boeing YC-14	1,762	16.8	NA	690	0.40	61.5	1.43	0.46
McDD KC-10A	3,958	24.7	NA	1,338	0.22	65.1	0.89	0.27
Tu-16	1,772	15.9	NA	360	0.27	50.6	0.65	.26/.41
Il-76T	3,229	20.7	NA	639	0.25	71.2	0.68	.31/.30

* Unless otherwise indicated.

Table 8.10b) Military Patrol, Bomb and Transport Airplanes: Vertical Tail Volume, Rudder, Aileron and Spoiler Data

Type	Wing Area S ft^2	Wing Span b ft	Vert. Tail Area S_v ft^2	S_r/S_v	x_v ft	$\bar{V}_v$	Rudder Chord root/tip $fr.c_v$	S_a/S	Inb'd Ail. Span in/out fr.b/2	Inb'd Ail. Chord in/out $fr.c_w$
Turbopropeller Driven										
LOCKHEED										
C-130E	1,745	133	300	0.25	40.5	0.053	.26/.31	0.063	none	none
P3C	1,300	99.7	176	0.34	46.1	0.063	.32/.39	0.069	none	none
ANTONOV										
An-12BP	1,310	125	205	0.28	48.9	0.061	.42/.44	0.064	none	none
An-22	3,713	211	700	0.44	82.6	0.074	.54/.40	0.040	none	none
An-26	807	95.8	171	0.40	39.9	0.088	.41/.43	0.071	none	none
Grum.E2C	700	80.6	199	0.52	27.7	0.098	.44/.64	0.077	none	none
D/B Atl.2	1,295	123	179	0.36	44.3	0.050	.37/.42	0.044	none	none
Aer.G222	883	94.2	207	0.37	36.7	0.091	.39/.47	0.045	none	none
Jet Driven										
LOCKHEED										
S-3A Viking	598	68.7	129	0.29	20.0	0.063	.37/.35	0.022	none	none
C-141B	3,406	160	455	0.21	72.1	0.060	.24/.28	0.056	none	none
C-5A	6,200	223	961	0.24	113	0.079	.27/.31	0.041	none	none
BA Nimr.2	2,121	115	118	0.35	50.4	0.024	.45/.37	0.058	none	none
B. YC-14	1,762	129	650	0.26	55.7	0.160	0.40	0.048	none	none
MDD KC10A	3,958	165	605	0.18	62.9	0.058	.39/.40	0.047	.32/.39	.20/.25
Tu-16	1,772	108	276	0.24	48.5	0.070	.35/.29	0.057	none	none
Il-76T	3,229	166	596	0.26	60.7	0.068	.46/.38	0.040	none	none

Table 8.10c) Military Patrol, Bomb and Transport Airplanes: Vertical Tail Volume, Rudder, Aileron and Spoiler Data

Type	Outb'd Ail. Span in/out fr.b/2	Outb'd Ail. Chord in/out fr.c_w	Inb'd Spoiler Span Loc. in/out fr.b/2	Inb'd Spoiler Chord in/out fr.c_w	Inb'd Spoiler Hinge Loc. in/out fr.c_w	Outb'd Spoiler Span Loc. in/out fr.c_w	Outb'd Spoiler Chord in/out fr.c_w	Outb'd Spoiler Hinge Loc. in/out fr.c_w
<u>Turbopropeller Driven</u>								
LOCKHEED								
C-130E	.70/.99	0.29	no lateral control spoilers					
P3C	.63/.96	.22/.25	no lateral control spoilers					
ANTONOV								
An-12BP	.68/.98	.31/.33	no lateral control spoilers					
An-22	.63/.98	.27/.32	no lateral control spoilers					
An-26	.66/.98	.32/.26	no lateral control spoilers					
Grum.E2C	.57/.98	.22/.33	no lateral control spoilers					
D/B Atl.2	.70/.95	.24/.25	.37/.65	.06/.08	.74/.68	none	none	none
Aer.G222	.72/1.0	.35/.45	.48/.70	.07/.08	.70/.66	none	none	none
<u>Jet Driven</u>								
LOCKHEED								
S-3A Vik.	.79/.96	.23/.25	.24/.79	.12/.15	.67/.56	none	none	none
C-141B	.67/1.0	.26/.23	.15/.41	.09/.12	.85/.80	.43/.66	.10/.13	.83/.83
C-5A	.72/.93	.28/.30	.36/.70	.13/.12	0.80	none	none	none
BA Nimr.2	.61/.96	.26/.27	no lateral control spoilers					
B. YC-14	.78/1.0	.37/.33	none	none	none	.53/.78	0.16	.74/.64
MDD KC10A	.75/.93	.29/.27	.17/.30	.05/.06	.78/.74	.43/.72	.11/.16	.75/.70
Tu-16	.66/.97	.25/.29	no lateral control spoilers					
Il-76T	.74/.98	.25/.26	.17/.71	.10/.13	.80/.69	none	none	none

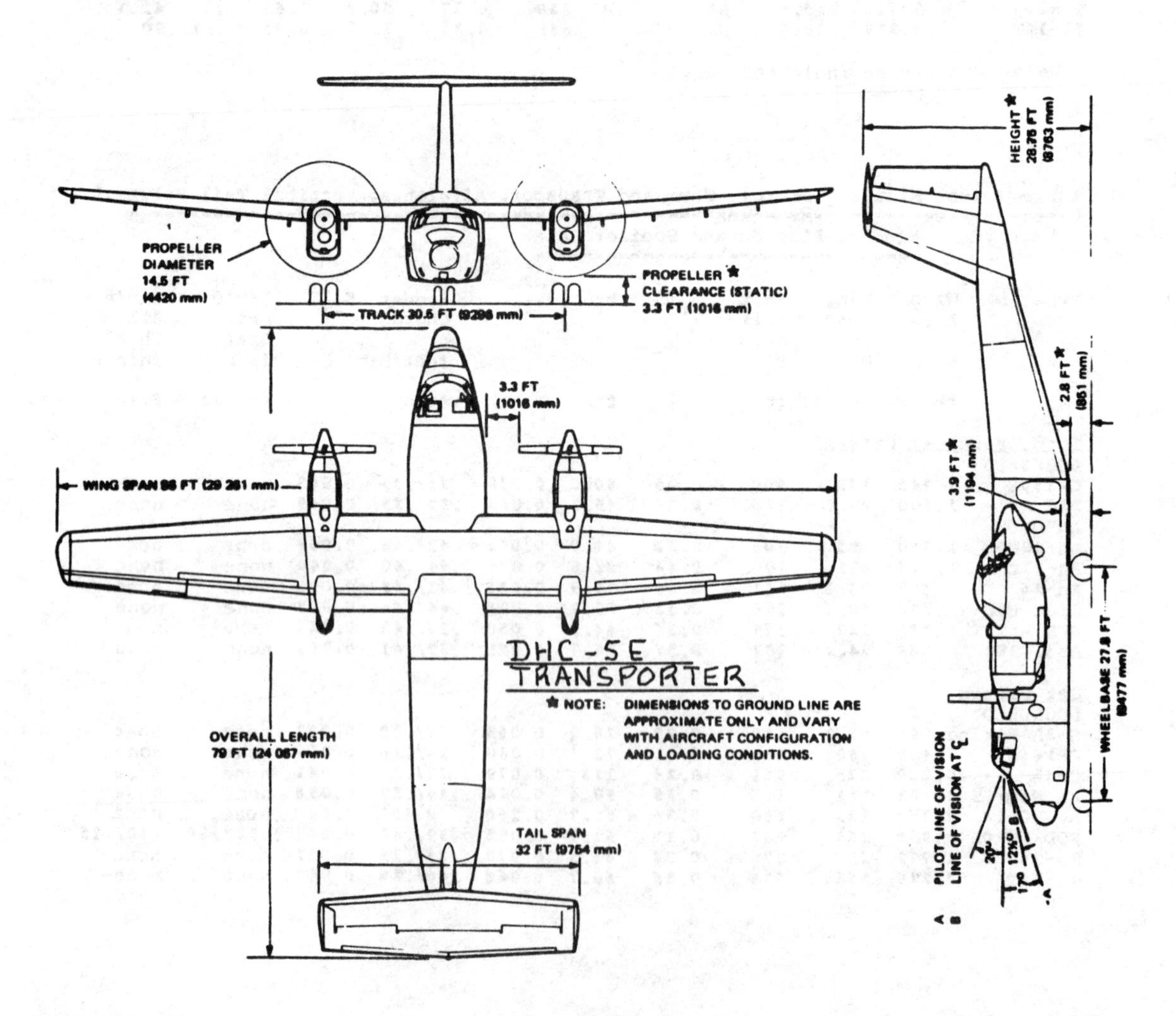

Table 8.11a) Flying Boats, Amphibious and Float Airplanes: Horizontal Tail Volume and Elevator Data (Piston/Prop. Except as Indicated)

Type	Wing Area S ft^2	Wing mgc $\bar{c}$ ft	Wing Airfoil root/tip NACA*	Hor. Tail Area S_h ft^2	S_e/S_h	x_h ft	$\bar{V}_h$	Elevator Chord root/tip $fr.c_h$
SHORTS								
Sandringham	1,487	16.6	NA	259	0.35	44.1	0.46	.53/.35
Shetland	2,773	20.0	Gott. 436	388	0.32	55.8	0.39	.45/.41
DORNIER								
Do 24	1,162	13.8	NA	202	0.35	33.6	0.42	0.42
Do 24/72	1,129	12.4	NA	262	0.25	40.2	0.75	.25/.31
Do Seastar**	258	5.27	23018	52.6	0.41	18.7	0.72	0.41
GRUMMAN								
JRF-6B	375	8.33	NA	79.9	0.38	21.8	0.56	0.42
J4F-1	245	5.85	NA	50.4	0.43	16.8	0.56	.45/.48
SM S-700	258	5.31	NASA GAW-1	76.1	0.47	18.5	1.03	0.47
Can. CL-215	1,080	11.5	NA	306	0.28	28.2	0.70	0.40
BV-222	3,077	18.1	NA	413	0.23	59.0	0.44	.31/.17
SM US-1**	1,462	12.6	NA	343	0.28	51.3	0.95	.33/.34
Boeing 314-A	3,001	22.3	BAC	580	0.26	52.8	0.46	.31/.39
Martin PBM-3	1,385	12.8	NA	257	0.42	39.8	0.58	0.50
Beriev M-12***	1,130	10.2	NA	244	0.40	39.9	0.85	.37/.57
Part.P68B****	200	5.08	NA	47.5	1.00	15.7	0.74	stabilator
McK G-21G	378	7.78	23000	84.5	0.53	22.1	0.64	.49/.69

* Unless otherwise indicated. ** Turbopropeller driven *** Jet Driven
**** Float Airplane

Table 8.11b) Flying Boats, Amphibious and Float Airplanes: Vertical Tail Volume, Rudder and Aileron Data

Type	Wing Area S ft^2	Wing Span b ft	Vert. Tail Area S_v ft^2	S_r/S_v	x_v ft	$\bar{V}_v$	Rudder Chord root/tip $fr.c_v$	S_a/S	Ail. Span Loc. in/out $fr.b/2$	Ail. Chord in/out $fr.c_w$
SHORTS										
Sandr'ham	1,487	113	157	0.31	43.5	0.041	.43/.36	0.089	.52/.93	.26/.20
Shetland	2,773	150	247	0.28	53.6	0.032	.33/.30	0.069	.51/.92	.22/.23
DORNIER										
Do 24	1,162	88.6	98.4	0.46	33.6	0.032	.41/.56	0.090	.32/.94	.15/.21
Do 24/72	1,129	91.8	200	0.38	42.2	0.081	.28/1.0	0.088	.63/.97	.29/.27
Do Seastar*	258	48.6	31.3	0.35	18.5	0.046	.33/.41	0.098	.60/.96	0.28
GRUMMAN										
JRF-6B	375	49.0	45.3	0.44	20.7	0.051	.41/.57	0.077	.56/.92	.27/.21
J4F-1	245	40.0	26.8	0.43	16.5	0.045	.35/.59	0.063	.57/.94	.20/.23
SM S-700	258	49.2	47.8	0.34	17.9	0.067	.29/.44	0.058	.63/.94	0.19
Can.CL215	1,080	93.8	186	0.35	29.2	0.053	.41/.57	0.080	.64/.95	0.26
BV-222	3,077	157	255	0.40	60.6	0.032	.36/.64	0.052	.56/.97	.12/.16
SM US-1*	1,462	109	265	0.29	46.4	0.077	.17/.30	0.047	.72/.98	.23/.21
B 314A	3,001	152	252	0.41	54.8	0.030	0.41	0.033	.58/.95	.09/.23
M PBM-3	1,385	118	196	0.44	39.7	0.048	.48/.39	0.053	.66/.96	.25/.28
Beriev M-12**	1,130	97.5	203	0.38	41.9	0.077	.36/.38	0.076	.58/.98	.29/.30
P68B***	200	39.4	21.9	0.22	15.5	0.043	.36/.40	0.096	.62/.96	0.21
McK G21-G	378	50.8	40.1	0.56	22.3	0.047	.39/.71	0.078	.55/.89	.23/.21

* Turbopropeller driven ** Jet Driven *** Float Airplane

Table 8.12a) Supersonic Cruise Airplanes: Horiz. Tail Volume and Elevator Data

Type	Wing Area	Wing mgc	Wing Airfoil	Hor. Tail Area	S_e/S_h	x_h	$\bar{V}_h$	Elevator Chord
	S	$\bar{c}$	root/tip	S_h				root/tip
	ft^2	ft		ft^2		ft		$fr.c_h$
NORTH AMERICAN AVIATION (Now Rockwell)								
XB-70A	6,297	78.5	NA	delta with elevons and small canard				
RA-5C	700	15.7	NA	356	1.0	17.1	0.56	stabilator
BOEING								
SST*	9,000	29.0**	NA	592	0.16	161	0.36	.24/.74
AST-100*	11,630	96.2	NA	547	1.0	107	0.052	stabilator
NASA*								
SSXjet I	965	30.6	.002/.003	65.0	1.0	47.2	0.10	stabilator
SSXjet II	965	30.6	.002/.003	80.0	1.0	41.2	0.09	stabilator
SSXjet III	1,128	33.1	.002/.003	80.0	1.0	41.9	0.09	stabilator
TUPOLEV								
Tu-144	4,715	58.3		delta with elevons and folding canard				
Tu-22M	1,585	15.4**	NA	727	1.0	37.2	1.11	stabilator
Tu-22	2,062	23.7***	NA	620	0.12	34.7	0.44	.29/.30
Dassault								
Mirage IVA	840	24.7	NA	delta with elevons				
GD F-111A	530	9.12**	NA	352	1.0	17.6	1.28	stabilator
Concorde	3,856	61.7	NA	ogive with elevons				
Rockwell B1B	1,950	15.8**	NA	494	1.0	49.9	0.80	stabilator
Convair B58	1,481	34.6	NA	delta with elevons				

* Study projects only ** Measured at forward sweep *** Fixed sweep airplane
See Refs. xx - yy

Table 8.12b) Supersonic Cruise Airplanes: Vertical Tail Volume, Rudder, Aileron and Spoiler Data

Type	Wing Area	Wing Span	Vert. Tail Area	S_r/S_v	x_v	$\bar{V}_v$	Rudder Chord	S_a/S	Ail. Span Loc.	Ail. Chord
	S	b	S_v				root/tip		in/out	in/out
	ft^2	ft	ft^2		ft		$fr.c_v$		fr.b/2	$fr.c_w$
NORTH AMERICAN AVIATION (Now Rockwell)										
XB-70A	6,297	105	468	0.75	48.5	0.034	****	0.067	.33/.72	.13/.31*
RA-5C	700	53.0	102	1.0**	21.8	0.060	1.0**	no ailerons		
BOEING***										
SST	9,000	174	866	0.26	88.5	0.049	.23/.46	0.014	.78/.96	.32/.43
AST-100	11,630	138	890	1.0**	121	0.067	1.0**	0.017	.72/1.0	.15/.29
NASA***										
SSXjet I	965	42.1	75.0	1.0**	38.3	0.071	1.0**	0.018	.76/1.0	.21/.26
SSXjet II	965	42.1	75.0	1.0**	35.5	0.066	1.0**	0.018	.76/1.0	.21/.26
SSXjt III	1,128	45.6	97.0	1.0**	32.1	0.061	1.0**	0.017	.74/1.0	.19/.26
TUPOLEV										
Tu-144	4,715	94.5	648	0.19	55.6	0.081	.20/.35	0.100	.31/.97	.11/.51*
Tu-22M	1,585	113	437	0.17	35.6	0.087	.39/.36	NA	.80/.95	.24/.28
Tu-22	2,062	90.9	376	0.14	29.6	0.059	.25/.33	0.051	.66/.95	.29/.31
Dassault										
Mirage IVA	840	38.9	129	0.12	14.1	0.056	.14/.24	0.120	.30/.96	.17/.63*
GD F-111A	530	63.0	115	0.25	18.6	0.064	.27/.29	no ailerons		
Concorde	3,856	84.0	477	0.24	54.1	0.080	.18/.47	0.089	.51/1.0	.15/.27*
Rockw.B1B	1,950	137	230	0.30	45.8	0.039	.29/.38	no ailerons		
Conv. B58	1,481	57.0	153	0.24	31.8	0.057	.32/.31	0.120	.18/.69	.16/.28*

* Elevon equipped ** Slab vertical tail ***Study projects only
**** Rudder hingeline skewed

Table 8.12c) Supersonic Cruise Airplanes: Vertical Tail Volume, Rudder, Aileron and Spoiler Data

Type	Inb'd Ail. Span in/out fr.b/2	Inb'd Ail. Chord in/out $fr.c_w$	Inb'd Spoiler Span Loc. in/out fr.b/2	Inb'd Spoiler Chord in/out $fr.c_w$	Inb'd Spoiler Hinge Loc. in/out $fr.c_w$	Outb'd Spoiler Span Loc. in/out $fr.c_w$	Outb'd Spoiler Chord in/out $fr.c_w$	Outb'd Spoiler Hinge Loc. in/out $fr.c_w$
NORTH AMERICAN AVIATION (Now Rockwell)								
XB-70A	none	none	no lateral control spoilers					
RA-5C	none	none	none	none	none	.25/.73	.14/.19	.60/.65
BOEING*								
SST	none	none	none	none	none	.36/.78	.17/.15	.69/.67
AST-100	none	none	none	none	none	.60/.70	.08/.11	.73/.65
NASA*								
SSXjet I	none	none	none	none	none	.38/.75	.04/.07	.88/.78
SSXjet II	none	none	none	none	none	.31/.75	.04/.07	.85/.78
SSXjt III	none	none	none	none	none	.31/.74	.04/.06	.86/.78
TUPOLEV								
Tu-144	none	none	no lateral control spoilers					
Tu-22M	none	none	none	none	none	.32/.80	.08/.13	.69/.66
Dassault								
Mir. IVA	none	none	no lateral control spoilers					
GD F111A	none	none	none	none	none	.25/.79	0.17	.65/.66
Concorde	none	none	no lateral control spoilers					
Rockw.B1B	none	none	none	none	none	.47/.81	.36/.35	.64/.65
Conv. B58	none	none	no lateral control spoilers					

* Study projects only

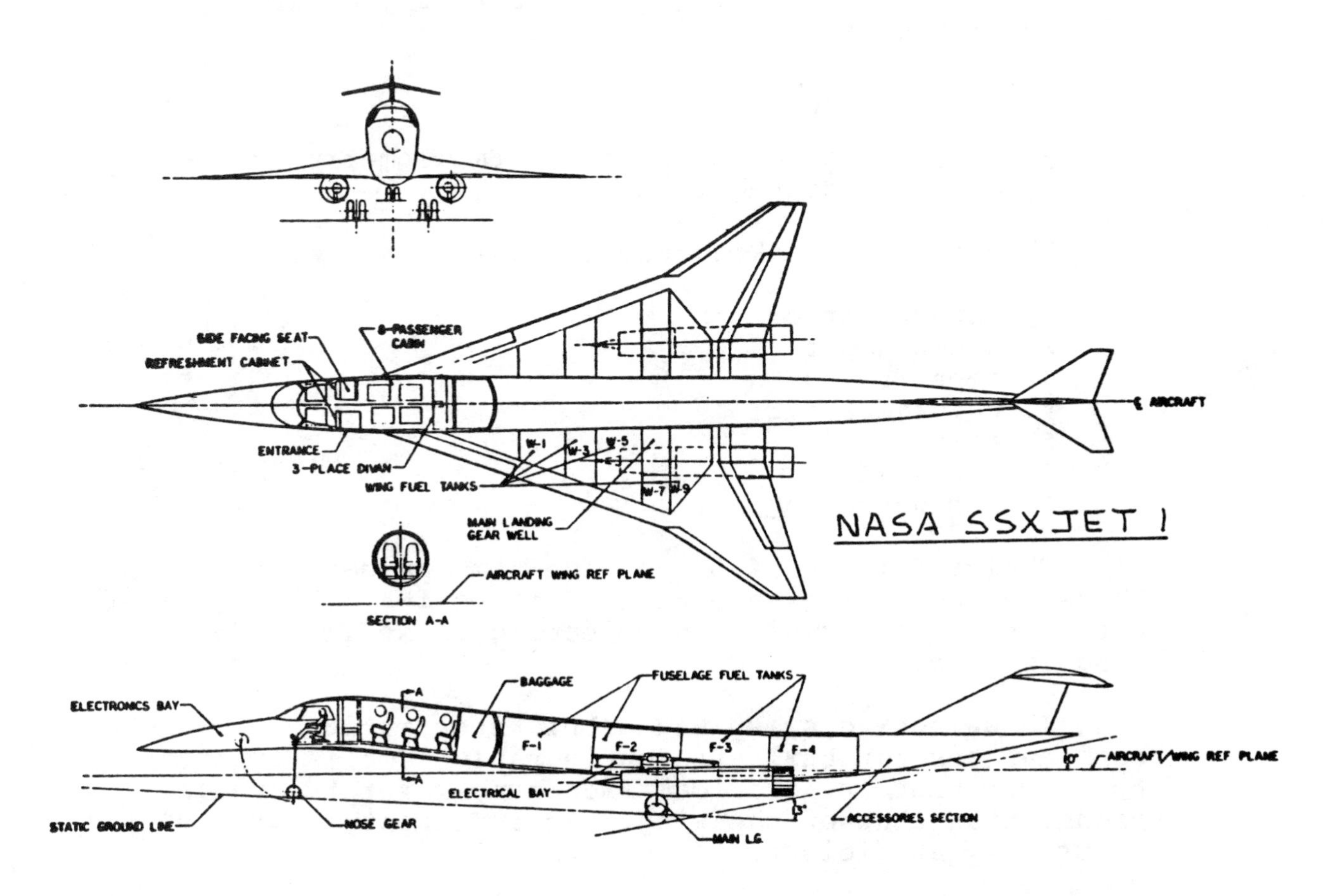

that not enough different canard configurations have been built for a reliable data base.

For this reason it is suggested that the reader use the so-called X-plot method for the sizing of a canard. This method is explained in Chapter 11.

c. Three-surface configurations.

The comments made under b. also apply here. The reader should use the X-plot method of Chapter 11 to size the canard and the horizontal tail of a three-surface airplane.

d. Butterfly empennage configurations.

For a butterfly arrangement, the first step is to apply the sizing method as if the tail were conventional. The surface areas S_h and S_v obtained in this manner must now be considered to be equal to the projections of the butterfly arrangement onto the horizontal and vertical reference planes. The required 'butterfly angle', Γ_h follows from this projection analogy:

$$\Gamma_h = \arctan(S_v/S_h) \quad (8.5)$$

Step 8.4: Decide on the planform geometry of the empennage.

This involves making the following choices:

1. aspect ratio
2. sweep angle
3. taper ratio
4. thickness ratio
5. airfoil
6. dihedral
7. incidence angle

Tables 8.13 and 8.14 provide some guidance in making these choices. The selection of items 1-7 follow some of the same reasoning used in selecting these items for the wing in Chapter 6.

In selecting sweep angle/thickness ratio combinations for tail aft configurations it is important to ensure that the critical Mach number for the tails is higher than that of the wing. An increment of $\Delta M = 0.05$ is usually sufficient.

Table 8.13 Planform Design Parameters for Horizontal Tails

Type	Dihedral Angle, Γ_h deg.	Incidence Angle, i_h deg.	Aspect Ratio, A_h	Sweep Angle, $\Lambda_{c/4_h}$ deg.	Taper Ratio, λ_h
Homebuilts	+5 - -10	0 fixed to variable	1.8 - 4.5	0 - 20	0.29 - 1.0
Single Engine Prop. Driven	0	-5 - 0 or variable	4.0 - 6.3	0 - 10	0.45 - 1.0
Twin Engine Prop Driven	0 - +12	0 fixed to variable	3.7 - 7.7	0 - 17	0.48 - 1.0
Agricultural	0 - +3	0	2.7 - 5.4	0 - 10	0.59 - 1.0
Business Jets	-4 - +9	-3.5 fixed	3.2 - 6.3	0 - 35	0.32 - 0.57
Regional Turbo-Props.	0 - +12	0 - 3 fixed to variable	3.4 - 7.7	0 - 35	0.39 - 1.0
Jet Transports	0 - +11	variable	3.4 - 6.1	18 - 37	0.27 - 0.62
Military Trainers	-11 - +6	0 fixed to	3.0 - 5.1	0 - 30	0.36 - 1.0
Fighters	-23 - +5	0 fixed to variable	2.3 - 5.8	0 - 55	0.16 - 1.0
Mil. Patrol, Bomb and Transports	-5 - +11	0 fixed to variable	1.3 - 6.9	5 - 35	0.31 - 0.8
Flying Boats, Amph. and Float Airplanes	0 - +25	0 fixed	2.2 - 5.1	0 - 17	0.33 - 1.0
Supersonic Cruise Airplanes	-15 - 0	0 fixed to variable	1.8 - 2.6	32 - 60	0.14 - 0.39

Table 8.14 Planform Design Parameters for Vertical Tails

Type	Dihedral Angle, Γ_v deg.	Incidence Angle, i_v deg.	Aspect Ratio, A_v	Sweep Angle, $\Lambda_{c/4_v}$ deg.	Taper Ratio, λ_v
Homebuilts	90	0	0.4 - 1.4	0 - 47	0.26 - 0.71
Single Engine Prop. Driven	90	0	0.9 - 2.2	12 - 42	0.32 - 0.58
Twin Engine Prop Driven	90	0	0.7 - 1.8	18 - 45	0.33 - 0.74
Agricultural	90	0	0.6 - 1.4	0 - 32	0.43 - 0.74
Business Jets	90	0	0.8 - 1.6	28 - 55	0.30 - 0.74
Regional Turbo-Props.	90	0	0.8 - 1.7	0 - 45	0.32 - 1.0
Jet Transports	90	0	0.7 - 2.0	33 - 53	0.26 - 0.73
Military Trainers	90	0	1.0 - 2.9	0 - 45	0.32 - 0.74
Fighters	75 - 90	0	0.4 - 2.0	9 - 60	0.19 - 0.57
Mil. Patrol, Bomb and Transports	90	0	0.9 - 1.9	0 - 37	0.28 - 1.0
Flying Boats, Amph. and Float Airplanes	90	0	1.2 - 2.4	0 - 32	0.37 - 1.0
Supersonic Cruise Airplanes	75 - 90	0	0.5 - 1.8	37 - 65	0.20 - 0.43

For most horizontal tails and vertical tails NACA symmetrical airfoils are in use. Typical of such airfoils are NACA 0009/0018. Ref.20 provides data on these airfoils.

For canards the choice of airfoil is particularly critical. The required maximum lift coeffficient capability at the canard Reynold's number must be determined so that the canard always stalls first. If a laminar flow airfoil is selected for the canard it will be necessary to verify that the canard lift is not altered drastically when the flow becomes turbulent such as may happen when suddenly encountering rain.

Step 8.5: Prepare dimensioned drawings of the selected empennage planforms.

Step 8.6: Decide on the sizes and disposition of the longitudinal and directional control surfaces.

Tables 8.1 through 8.12 provide data for twelve types of airplanes on the size and location of:

1. elevators and stabilators   2. rudders

After deciding which type of airplane best 'fits' the type being designed, initial control surface sizes can be determined directly from Tables 8.1 through 8.12.

The control surfaces should now be sketched into the planform drawings of Step 8.5. Watch out for a possible conflict between rudder and elevator deflections. Such conflicts often arise in conventional arrangements and lead to inboard cut-outs of one of these surfaces. Typical examples are shown in Figures 3.4b and 3.4d.

Step 8.7: Document the decisions made under Steps 8.1 through 8.6 in a brief, descriptive report including clear dimensioned drawings.

8.2 EXAMPLE APPLICATIONS

Three examples applications will now be discussed:

8.2.1 Twin Engine Propeller Driven Airplane: Selene
8.2.2 Jet Transport: Ourania
8.2.3 Fighter: Eris

8.2.1 Twin Engine Propeller Driven Airplane

Step 8.1: It was decided in sub-section 3.5.1 to employ a conventional configuration. That implies a tail aft arrangement.

Step 8.2: From the general arrangement drawing of the fuselage in Figure 4.2b (p.113) the following moment arms are 'guestimated':

x_h = 21.4 ft. and x_v = 16.8 ft.

Step 8.3: The following table summarizes volume coefficient and control surface size data for comparable airplanes. The data are taken from Tables 8.3a and b:

Airplane Type	$\bar{V}_h$	S_e/S_h	$\bar{V}_v$	S_r/S_v
Cessna 310R	0.95	0.41	0.063	0.45
Cessna 402B	1.07	0.29	0.080	0.47
Cessna 414A	0.93	0.27	0.071	0.38
Cessna T303	0.78	0.42	0.052	0.44
Beech Duke B60	0.64	0.27	0.060	0.43
Piaggio P166-DL3	0.51	0.27	0.041	0.43
Averages:	0.81	0.32	0.061	0.43

For the Selene the following values are selected:

$\bar{V}_h = 0.94$, $S_e/S_h = 0.32$, $\bar{V}_v = 0.10$, $S_r/S_v = 0.43$

The reason for selecting higher volume coefficients is the higher wing loading of the Selene. With a relatively smaller wing this could lead to tail surfaces which are too small.

For the Selene, S = 172 ft^2, $\bar{c}$ = 4.92 ft and b = 37.1 ft. With Eqns (8.3) and (8.4) this leads to the following tail sizes:

$S_h = 37\ ft^2$ and $S_v = 38\ ft^2$.

Step 8.4: The following table summarizes the geometric parameters for the horizontal and for the vertical tail of the Selene. These quantities are in overall agreement with those listed in Tables 8.13 and 8.14 for twin engine propeller driven airplanes:

Parameter	Hor. Tail	Vert. Tail
Aspect ratio, A	3.85	1.0
Leading edge sweep angle	30 deg.	50 deg.
Taper ratio	0.40	0.56
Thickness ratio	0.12	0.15
Airfoil	NACA 0012	NACA 0015
Dihedral angle	0 deg.	not appl.
Incidence angle	variable	0 deg.

Step 8.5: Figure 8.2 presents dimensioned drawings of the proposed empennage arrangement for the Selene.

Step 8.6: Using the control surface ratios selected in Step 8.3, the elevator and rudder outlines are drawn into the planforms of Figure 8.2.

Step 8.7: This step has been omitted to save space.

8.2.2 Jet Transport

Step 8.1: It was decided in sub-section 3.5.2 to employ a conventional configuration. That implies a tail aft arrangement.

Step 8.2: From the general arrangement drawing of the fuselage in Figure 4.7 (p.120) the following moment arms are 'guestimated':

$x_h = 51.0$ ft. and $x_v = 54.0$ ft.

Step 8.3: The following table summarizes volume coefficient and control surface size data for comparable airplanes. The data are taken from Tables 8.7a and b:

Airplane Type	$\bar{V}_h$	S_e/S_h	$\bar{V}_v$	S_r/S_v
Boeing 737-200	1.28	0.27	0.100	0.24
Boeing 737-300	1.35	0.24	0.100	0.31
McDD DC-9-S80	0.96	0.34	0.062	0.39
McDD DC-9-50	1.32	0.38	0.079	0.41
Fokker F-28-4000	1.07	0.20	0.085	0.16
Rombac/BAe 1-11-495	0.86	0.27	0.038	0.28
Averages:	1.14	0.28	0.077	0.30

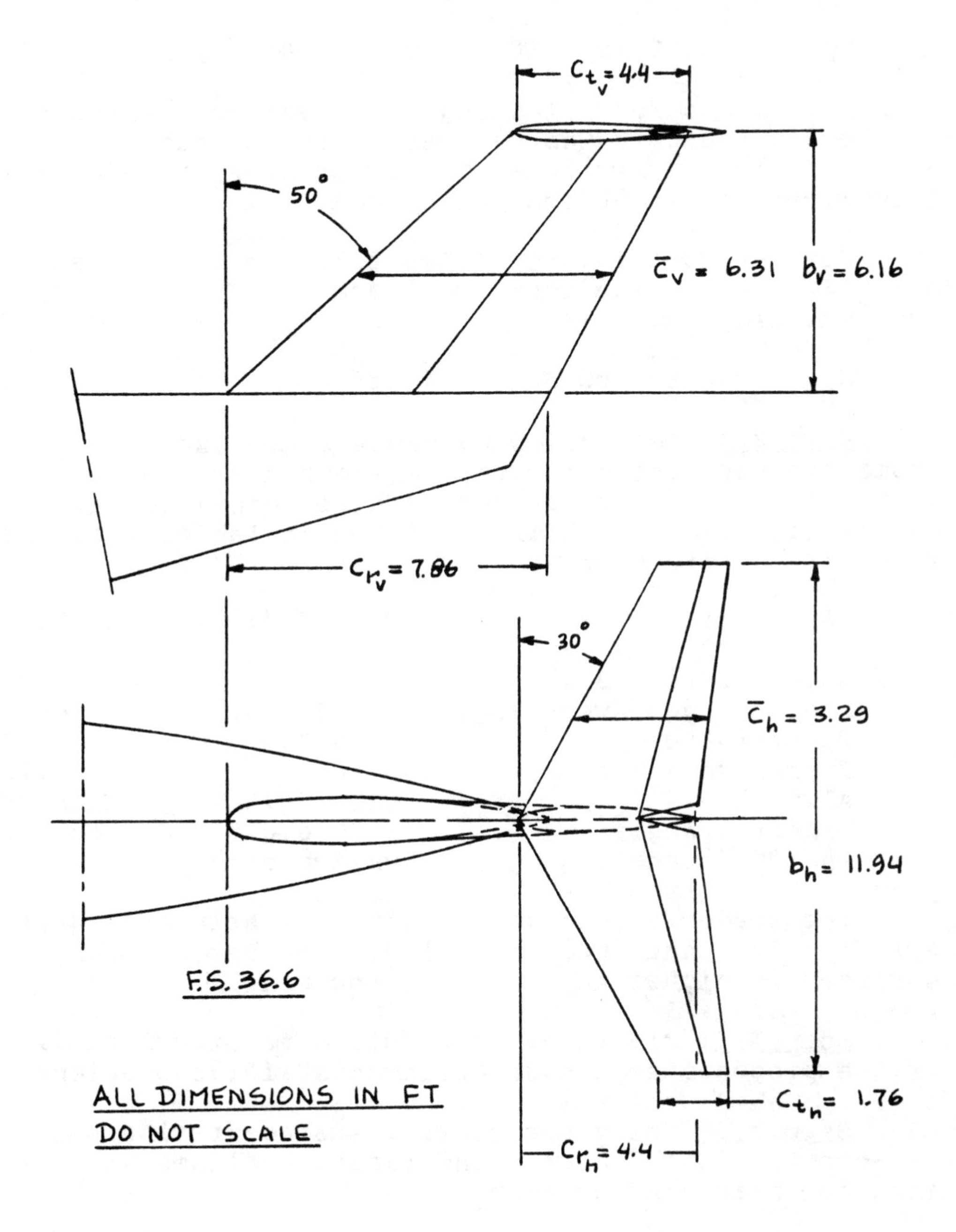

Figure 8.2 Selene: Empennage Configuration

For the Ourania the following values are selected:

$\bar{V}_h = 0.80$, $S_e/S_h = 0.30$, $\bar{V}_v = 0.06$, $S_r/S_v = 0.35$

The reason for selecting lower volume coefficients is the fact that it was decided in sub-section 3.5.2 to employ 'relaxed' static stability combined with a digital 'fly-by-wire' flight control system.

For the Ourania, $S = 1,296$ ft^2, $\bar{c} = 12.5$ ft and $b = 113.8$ ft. Using Eqns (8.3) and (8.4) this leads to the following tail sizes:

$S_h = 254$ ft^2 and $S_v = 164$ ft^2.

<u>Step 8.4:</u> The following table summarizes the geometric parameters for the horizontal and for the vertical tail of the Ourania. These quantities are in overall agreement with those listed in Tables 8.13 and 8.14 for jet transports.

Parameter	Hor. Tail	Vert. Tail
Aspect ratio, A	5.0	1.8
Leading edge sweep angle	35 deg.	45 deg.
Taper ratio	0.32	0.32
Thickness ratio	0.12	0.15
Airfoil	NACA 0012	NACA 0015
Dihedral angle	0 deg.	not appl.
Incidence angle	variable	0 deg.

The reader should verify with the help of Figure 6.1a (p.150) that the critical Mach number of both tail surfaces is higher than that of the wing.

<u>Step 8.5:</u> Figure 8.3 presents dimensioned drawings of the proposed empennage arrangement for the Selene.

<u>Step 8.6:</u> Using the control surface ratios selected in Step 8.3, the elevator and rudder outlines are drawn into the planforms of Figure 8.3.

<u>Step 8.7:</u> This step has been omitted to save space.

<u>8.2.3 Fighter</u>

<u>Step 8.1:</u> It was decided in sub-section 3.5.3 to employ a conventional, twin boom configuration. That implies a tail aft arrangement.

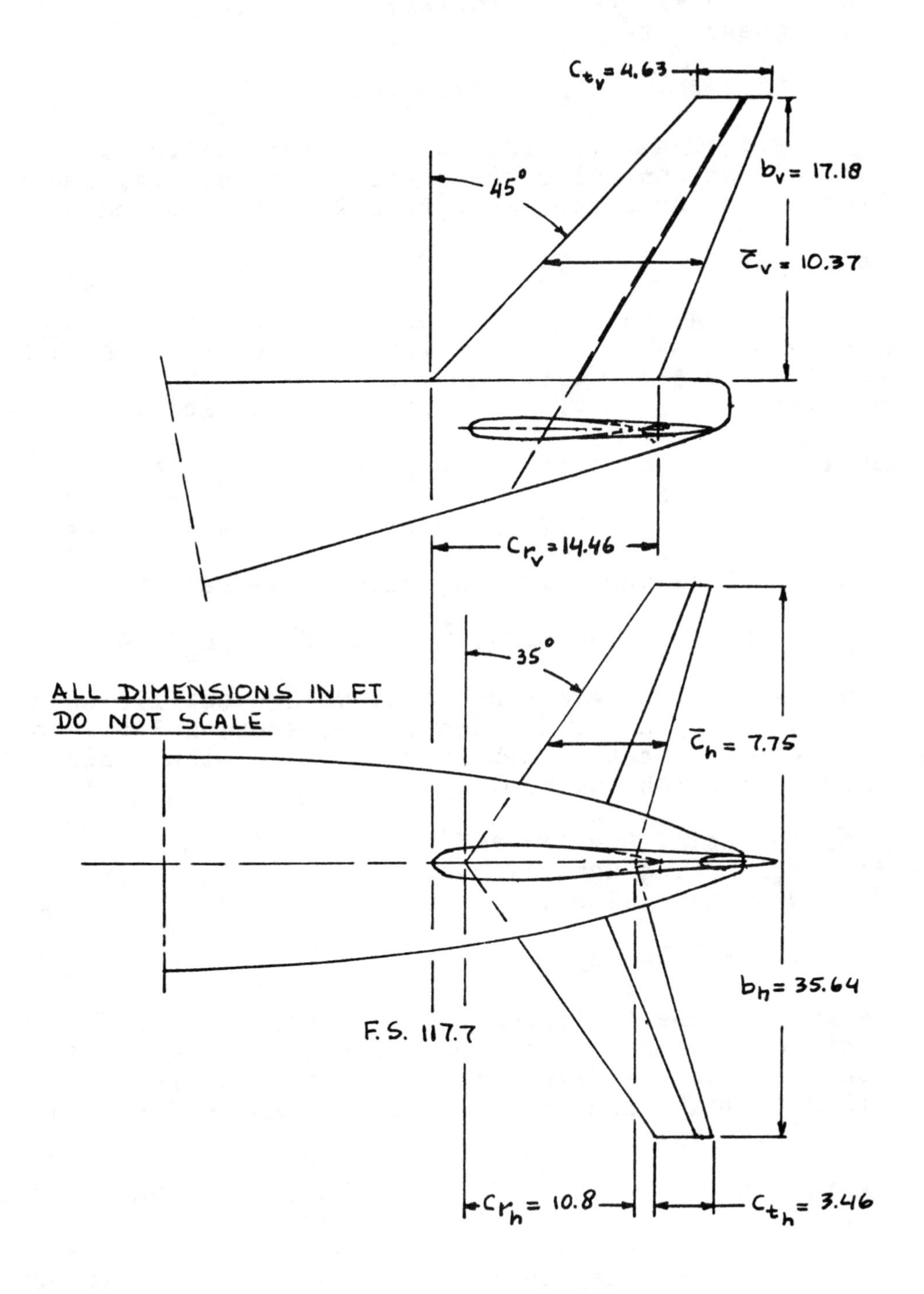

Figure 8.3 Ourania: Empennage Configuration

Step 8.2: From the general arrangement drawing of the fuselage in Figure 4.9 (p.122) the following moment arms are 'guestimated':

$x_h = 25.3$ ft. and $x_v = 22.0$ ft.

Step 8.3: The following table summarizes volume coefficient and control surface size data for comparable airplanes. The data are taken from Tables 8.9a and b:

Airplane Type	$\bar{V}_h$	S_e/S_h	$\bar{V}_v$	S_r/S_v
Fairchild Rep. A-10A	0.41	0.32	0.060	0.28
Grumman A6A	0.46	1.00*	0.069	0.21
Aermacchi MB339K**	0.40	0.29	0.043	0.26
Vought A7A**	0.22	1.00*	0.130	0.13

*stabilator **single engine fighter

Averages:	0.37	0.31	0.076	0.22

For the Eris the following values are selected:

$\bar{V}_h = 0.25$, $S_e/S_h = 0.31$, $\bar{V}_v = 0.06$, $S_r/S_v = 0.22$

The reason for selecting lower volume coefficients is the fact that it was decided in sub-section 3.5.3 to employ 'relaxed' static stability combined with a digital 'fly-by-wire' flight control system.

For the Eris, $S = 787$ ft^2, $\bar{c} = 11.9$ ft and $b = 68.7$ ft. Using Eqns (8.3) and (8.4) this leads to the following tail sizes:

$S_h = 93$ ft^2 and $S_v = 147$ ft^2.

Step 8.4: The following table summarizes the geometric parameters for the horizontal and for the vertical tail of the Eris. These quantities are in overall agreement with those listed in Tables 8.13 and 8.14 for fighters.

Parameter	Hor. Tail	Vert. Tail
Aspect ratio, A	3.6	1.2
Leading edge sweep angle	0 deg.	45 deg.
Taper ratio	1.0	0.55
Thickness ratio	0.10	0.15
Airfoil	NACA 0010	NACA 0015
Dihedral angle	0 deg.	not appl.
Incidence angle	0 deg.	0 deg.

The reader should verify with the help of Figure 6.1a (p.150) that the critical Mach number of both tail surfaces is higher than that of the wing.

Step 8.5: Figure 8.4 presents dimensioned drawings of the proposed empennage arrangement for the Eris.

Step 8.6: Using the control surface ratios selected in Step 8.3, the elevator and rudder outlines are drawn into the planforms of Figure 8.4.

Step 8.7: This step has been omitted to save space.

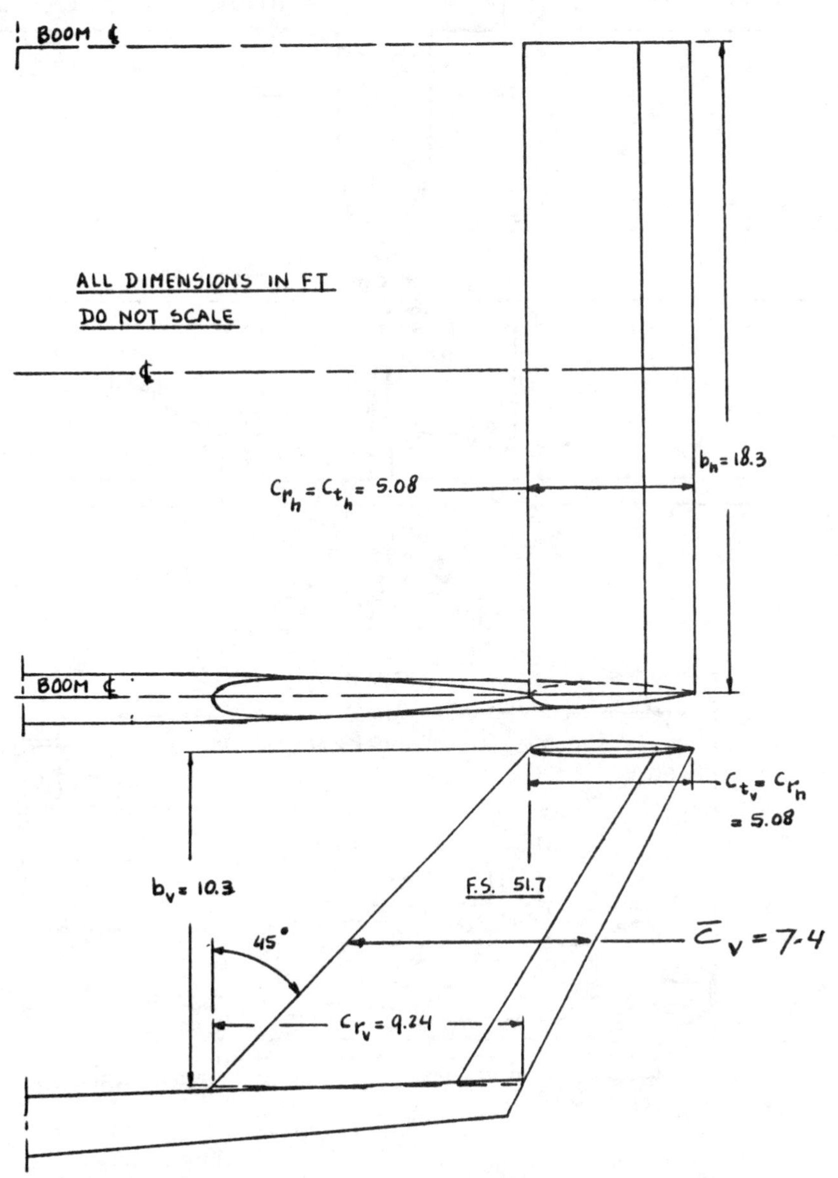

Figure 8.4 Eris: Empennage Configuration

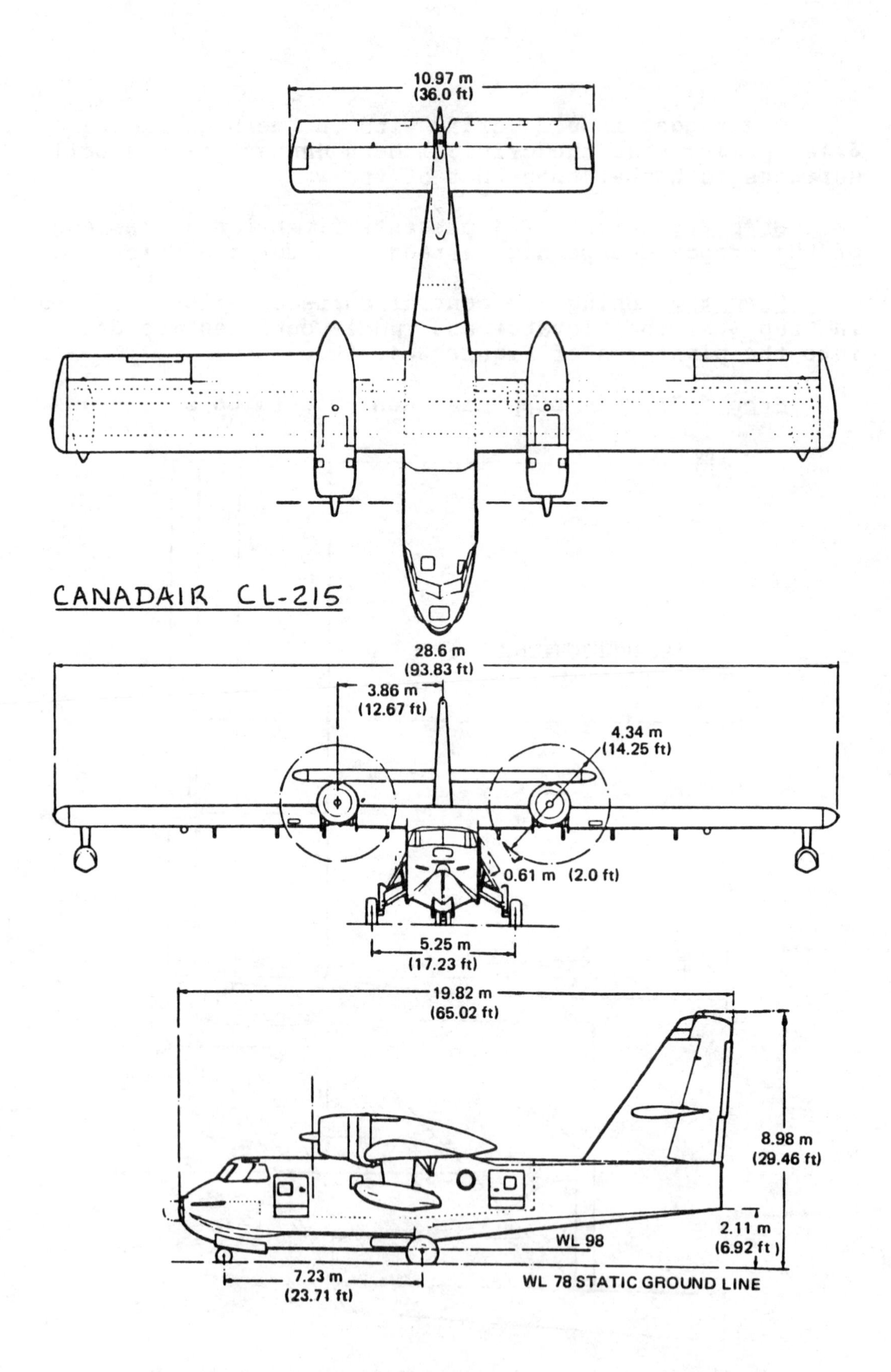
10.97 m
(36.0 ft)
CANADAIR CL-215
28.6 m
(93.83 ft)
3.86 m
(12.67 ft)
4.34 m
(14.25 ft)
0.61 m (2.0 ft)
5.25 m
(17.23 ft)
19.82 m
(65.02 ft)
8.98 m
(29.46 ft)
WL 98
2.11 m
(6.92 ft)
7.23 m
(23.71 ft)
WL 78 STATIC GROUND LINE

9. CLASS I METHOD FOR LANDING GEAR SIZING AND DISPOSITION

The purpose of this chapter is to provide a rapid, step-by-step method to determine the following landing gear characteristics:

1. Number, type and size of tires
2. Length and diameter of strut(s)
3. Preliminary disposition
4. Retraction feasibility

The method is presented as part of Step 9 of p.d. sequence I as outlined in Chapter 2. Section 9.1 presents the step-by-step method. Example applications are given in Section 9.2.

9.1 CLASS I METHOD FOR LANDING GEAR SIZING AND DISPOSITION

Step 9.1: Decide which landing gear system to use.

The choices here are:

1. Fixed or non-retractable
2. Retractable

In the past several airplanes have used droppable and/or skid type landing gears. One such example is the Me163. Such landing gears will not be considered here.

Another type of landing gear is the so-called air-cushion (or ground effect) type gear. This type of gear will not be considered either.

As a general rule, if the cruise speed of the airplane is above 150 kts, a fixed landing gear imposes an unacceptably high drag penalty.

Step 9.2: Decide on the overall landing gear configuration.

The choices here are as follows:

1. Tailwheel or taildragger
2. Conventional (i.e. nosewheel or tricycle)
3. Tandem
4. Outrigger
5. Beaching gear (for flying boats)

Tandem and outrigger gears are often combined: the Boeing B52 (Fig.3.28a) and the McDonnell Douglas AV8B (Page 221) are typical examples.

For ground operations on soft and/or unprepared fields taildraggers offer a minor weight advantage.

From an ease of ground maneuvering viewpoint as well as a groundlooping viewpoint the nosewheel configuration is to be preferred. Most airplanes today are equipped with nosewheel (tricycle) type landing gears.

Part IV contains more detailed discussions of landing gears.

IMPORTANT NOTE: Before embarking on the next steps, it will be necessary to determine the c.g. range of the airplane:

Step 9.3: Proceed to Chapter 10 and prepare a rough weight and balance statement for an assumed disposition of the landing gear.

Step 9.4: Decide on a preliminary landing gear strut disposition and sketch the proposed strut disposition in the general arrangement drawing of Step 10.2, Chapter 10.

There are two geometric criteria which need to be considered in deciding the disposition of the landing gear struts:

1.) Tip-over Criteria.

2.) Ground Clearance Criteria.

1. Tip-over Criteria:

Figure 9.1a presents the tip-over criteria A and B:

A) Longitudinal Tip-over Criterion:

a. For tricycle gears: The main landing gear must be behind the aft c.g. location. The 15 deg. angle shown in Figure 9.1a represents the 'usual' relation between main gear and the aft c.g.

b. For taildraggers: The main landing gear must be forward of the aft c.g. location. The 15 deg. angle shown in Figure 9.1a represents the 'usual' relation between main gear and aft c.g.

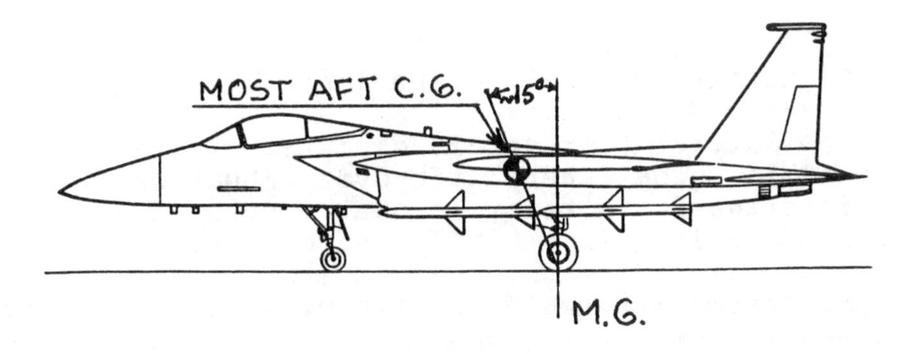

Longitudinal Tip-over Criterion for Tricycle Gears

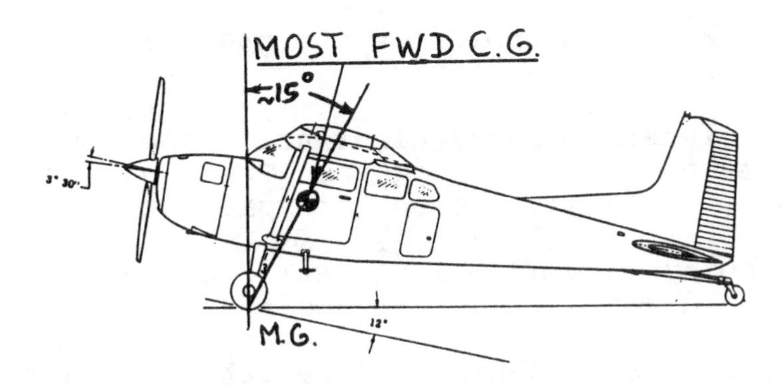

Longitudinal Tip-over Criterion for Taildraggers

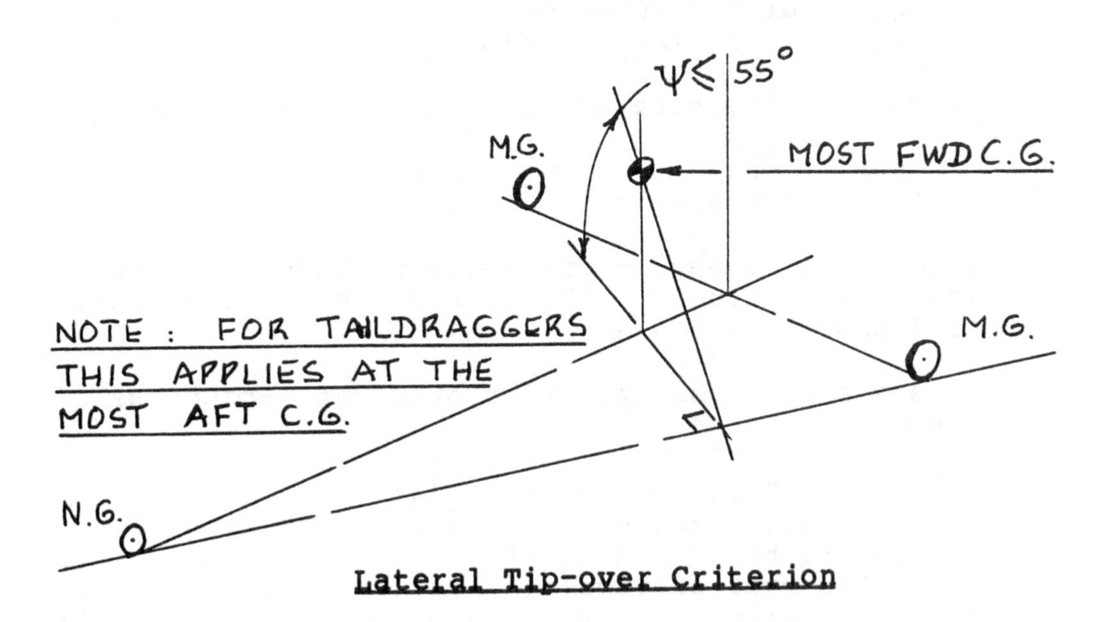

Lateral Tip-over Criterion

Figure 9.1a Tip-over Criteria for Landing Gear Placement

B) Lateral Tip-over Criterion:

The lateral tip-over is dictated by the angle ψ, in Figure 9.1a. The lateral tip-over situation in Figure 9.1a is drawn for a tricycle gear. Note that this criterion applies in a similar fashion to taildraggers.

Approximate forward and aft c.g. locations were be obtained in Step 9.3.

<u>2. Ground Clearance Criteria:</u>

Figure 9.1b summarizes the required ground clearance angles.

The lateral ground clearance angle applies to tricycles and to taildraggers. The longitudinal ground clearance angle applies to tricycles only.

Keeping in mind the geometric criteria, the following decisions must now be made:

1. Number, location and length of main gear struts:

   a.) under the wing
   b.) under the fuselage
   c.) both (as in the 747 and DC 10-30)

2. Number, location and length of nose gear struts:

   usually only one strut, located at the forward end of the fuselage.

This decision should initially be made by referring to competitive concepts. The configurations presented in Chapter 3 should be reviewed.

To summarize, the selection of strut length has a major impact on:

* the weight of the landing gear
* the ground clearance of the airplane with deflated tires and struts
* the tip-over characteristics
* Overall airplane stability during ground operation

Part V (Ref.4) contains detailed discussions on these factors.

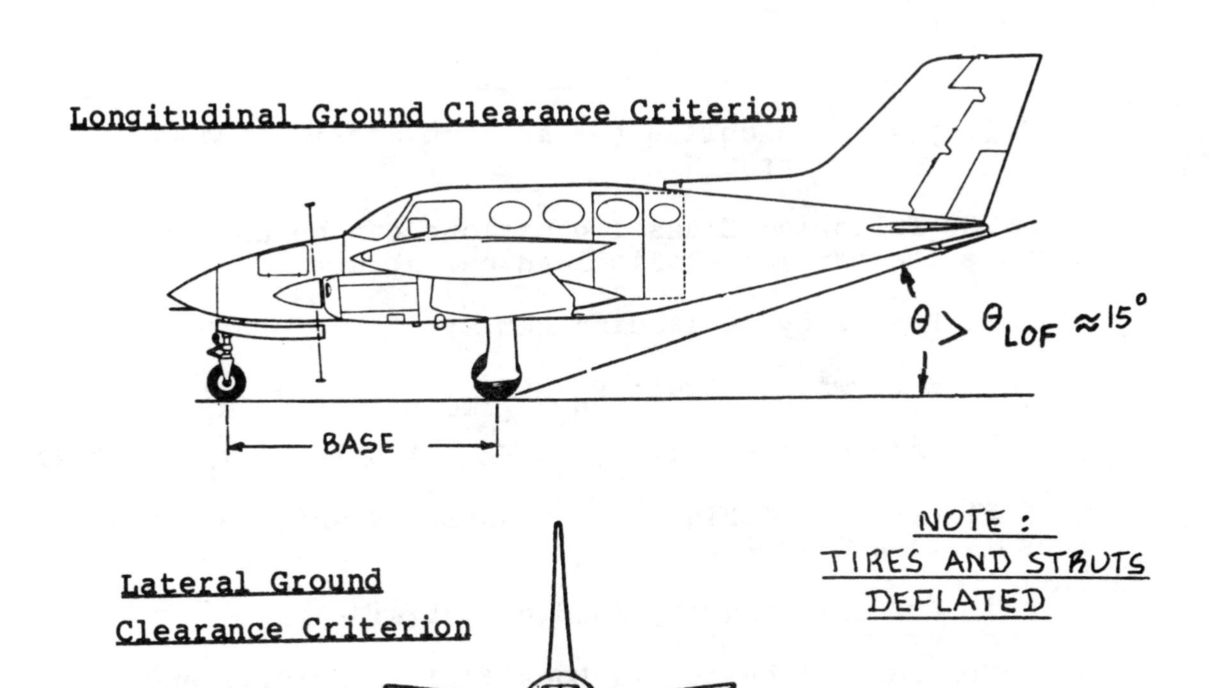

Figure 9.1b Ground Clearance Criteria for Gear Placement

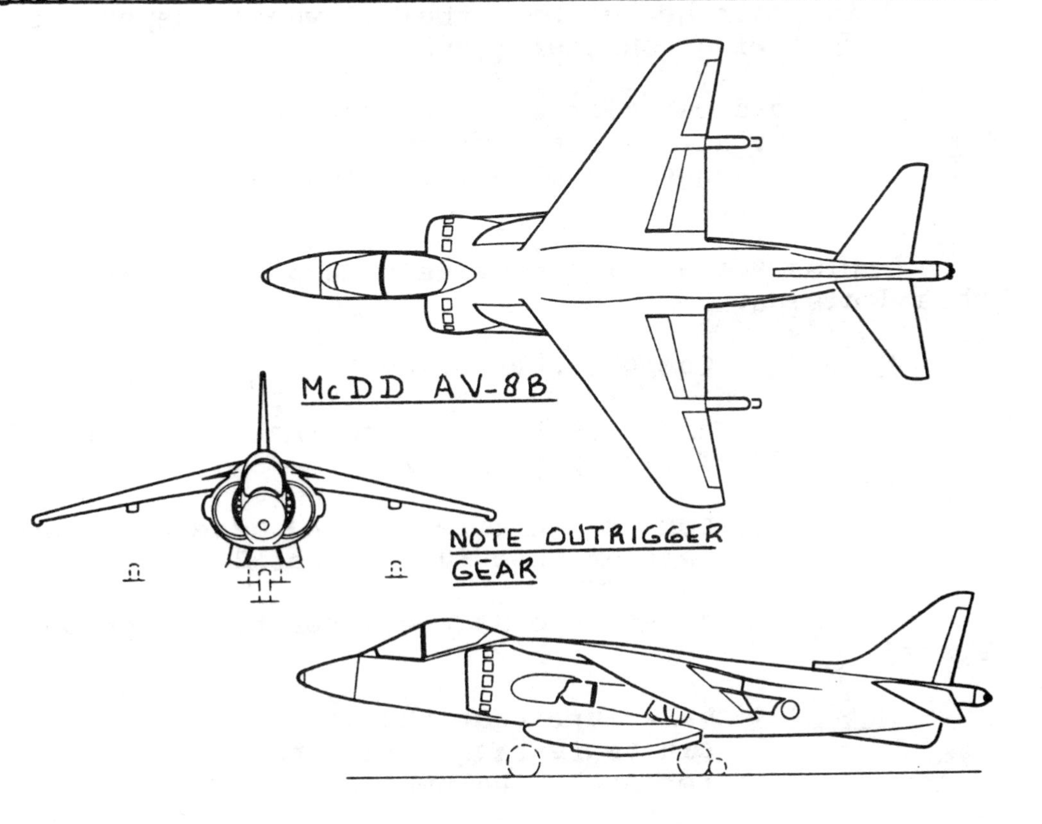

Step 9.5: Calculate the maximum static load per strut.

The following Class I equations can be used to compute the maximum static load per strut:

1. For tricycle landing gears:

Nose wheel strut: $P_n = (W_{TO} l_m)/(l_m + l_n)$ (9.1)

Main gear strut: $P_m = (W_{TO} l_n)/n_s(l_m + l_n)$ (9.2)

Figure 9.2a defines the quantities which are used in Eqns (9.1) and (9.2).

2. For taildragging landing gears:

Replace 'n' by 't' in Eqns (9.1) and (9.2) and refer to Figure 9.2b.

Step 9.6: Decide on the number of wheels to be used.

The usual number of wheels is as follows:

* for tailwheels: one * for nosewheels: one or two

* for main gears the number of wheels depends on the following considerations:

  1. Load per tire and the associated surface bearing strength
  2. Consequences of a tire blow-out
  3. Cost.

Tables 9.1 and 9.2 provide some guidance in making this decision.

Step 9.7: Compute the ratios P_n/W_{TO} and $n_s P_m/W_{TO}$

and select the approximate tire size from Tables 9.1 or 9.2.

Step 9.8: Locate the tires in the general arrangement of Step 10, Chapter 2.

It is important to draw the tires to the proper scale!

Step 9.9: Make sure that the gear as now configured can be retracted into the designated retraction volume(s).

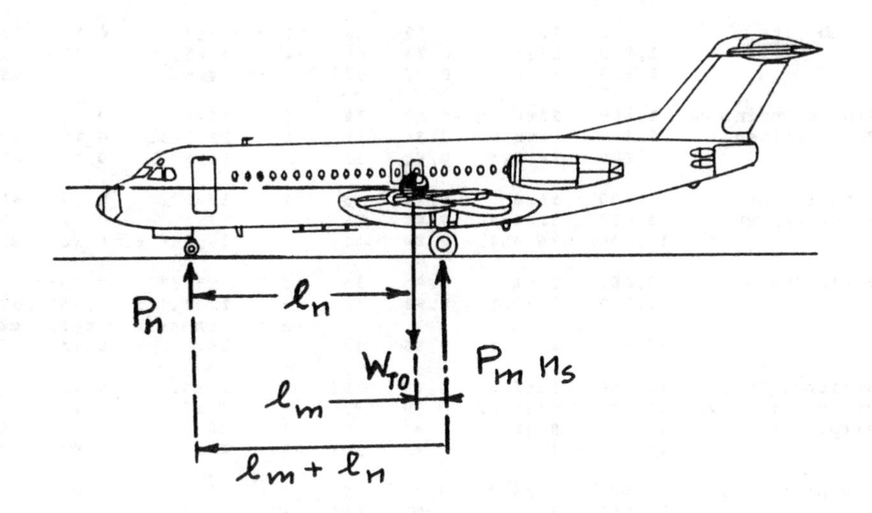

Figure 9.2a Geometry for Static Load Calculation for Tricycle Gears

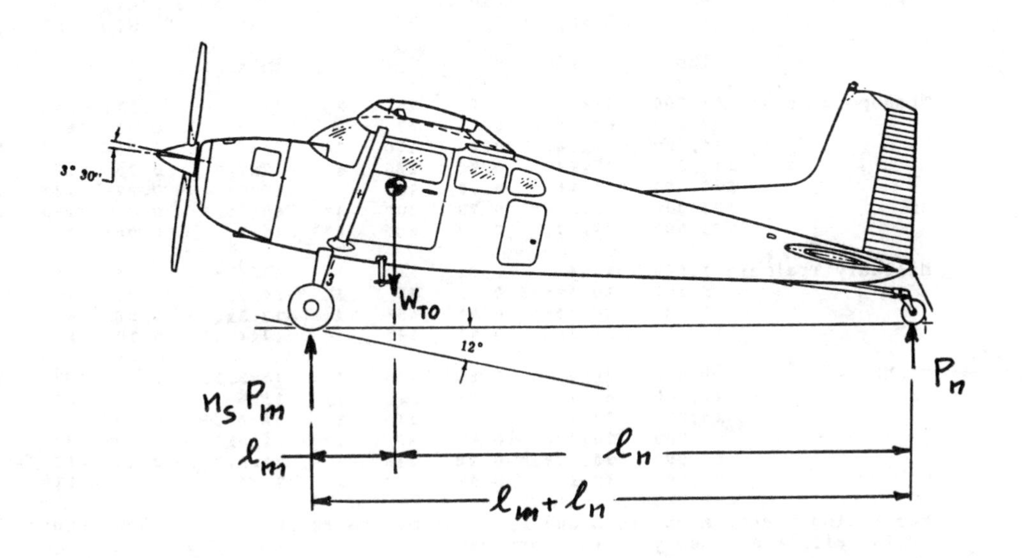

Figure 9.2b Geometry for Static Load Calculation for Taildraggers

Table 9.1 Typical Landing Gear Wheel Data (n_s = 2)

Type	W_{TO}	Main Gear $D_t x b_t$	$2P_m/W_{TO}$	PSI	n_{mt}	Nose Gear $D_t x b_t$	P_n/W_{TO}	PSI	n_{nt}
	lbs	in.xin.				in.xin.			
Homebuilts	600	13x5	0.80	25	1	9x3.4	0.17	25	1
	1,200	12x5	0.78	45	1	12x5	0.22	45	1
	3,300	16x6	0.87	45	1	16x6	0.13	45	1
Single Engine Prop. Driven	1,600	15x6	0.80	18	1	15x5	0.20	28	1
	2,400	17x6	0.84	19	1	12.5x5	0.16	22	1
	3,800	16.5x6	0.84	55	1	14x5	0.16	49	1
Twin Engine Prop. Driven	5,000	16x6	0.83	55	1	16x6	0.17	40	1
	8,000	22x6.5	0.88	75	1	17x6	0.12	40	1
	12,000	26.6x7	0.84	82	1	19.3x6.6	0.16	82	1
Agricultural	3,000	22x8	0.95	35	1	9x3.5*	0.05*	55*	1*
	7,000	24x8.5	0.92	35	1	12.4x4.5*	0.08*	50*	1*
						*Note: these are tailwheel data			
	10,000	29x7.5	0.85	35	1	25x7	0.15	35	1
Regional Turbo-propeller Driven Airplanes	12,500	18x5.5	0.89	105	2	22x6.75	0.11	57	1
	21,000	24x7.25	0.90	85	2	18x5.5	0.10	65	2
	26,000	36x11	0.92	40	1	20x7.5	0.08	40	1
	44,000	30x9	0.93	107	2	23.4x6.5	0.07	77	2
Business Jets	12,000	22x6.3	0.93	90	1	18x5.7	0.07	120	1
	23,000	27.6x9.3	0.95	155	1	17x5.5	0.05	50	2
	39,000	26x6.6	0.92	208	2	14.5x5.5	0.08	130	2
	68,000	34x9.25	0.93	174	2	21x7.25	0.07	113	2

Table 9.2 Typical Landing Gear Wheel Data (n_s = 2 unless otherwise noted)

Type	W_{TO}	Main Gear $D_t x b_t$	$n_s P_m/W_{TO}$	PSI	n_{mt}	Nose Gear $D_t x b_t$	P_n/W_{TO}	PSI	n_{nt}
	lbs	in.xin.				in.xin.			
Transport Jets	44,000	34x12	0.89	75	2	24x7.7	0.11	68	2
	73,000	40x14	0.92	77	2	29.5x6.75	0.08	68	2
	116,000	40x14	0.94	170	2	24x7.7	0.06	150	2
	220,000	40x14	0.94	180	4	29x7.7	0.06	180	2
	330,000	46x16	0.93	206	4	40x14	0.07	131	2
	572,000	52x20.5	0.93	200	4*	40x15.5	0.07	190	2
	775,000	49x17	0.94	205	4**	46x16	0.06	190	2
Military Trainers	2,500	17x6	0.82	36	1	13.5x5	0.18	28	1
	5,500	20.3x6.5	0.91	60	1	14x5	0.09	40	1
	7,500	20.25x6	0.92	65	1	17.2x5.0	0.08	45	1
	11,000	23.3x6.5	0.90	143	1	17x4.4	0.10	120	1
Fighters	9,000	20x5.25	0.86	135	1	17x3.25	0.14	82	1
	14,000	18.5x7	0.87	110	1	18x6	0.13	37	1
	25,000	24x8	0.91	210	1	18x6.5	0.09	120	1
	35,000	24x8	0.90	85	2	21.5x9.8	0.10	57	1
	60,000	35.3x9.3	0.88	210	1	21.6x7.5	0.12	120	2
	92,000	42x13	0.93	150	1	20x6.5	0.07	120	2

For Flying Boats, Amphibious and Float Airplanes as well as for Supersonic cruise airplanes, use jet transport data.

*three main gear struts: n_s = 3 ** four main gear struts: n_s = 4

Note: all other airplanes have n_s = 2: two main gear struts.

At this stage of the preliminary design process it is useful to verify the retraction capability with the help of a so-called 'stick diagram'. Examples of such stick diagrams are given in Figure 9.3.

Step 9.10: With the gear layout defined, proceed to Chapter 10, perform the weight and balance calculations and if necessary, iterate back to Step 9.3 until the gear location satisfies all criteria.

Step 9.11: Document the decisions made under Steps 9.1 through 9.10 in a brief, descriptive report with clear dimensioned drawings.

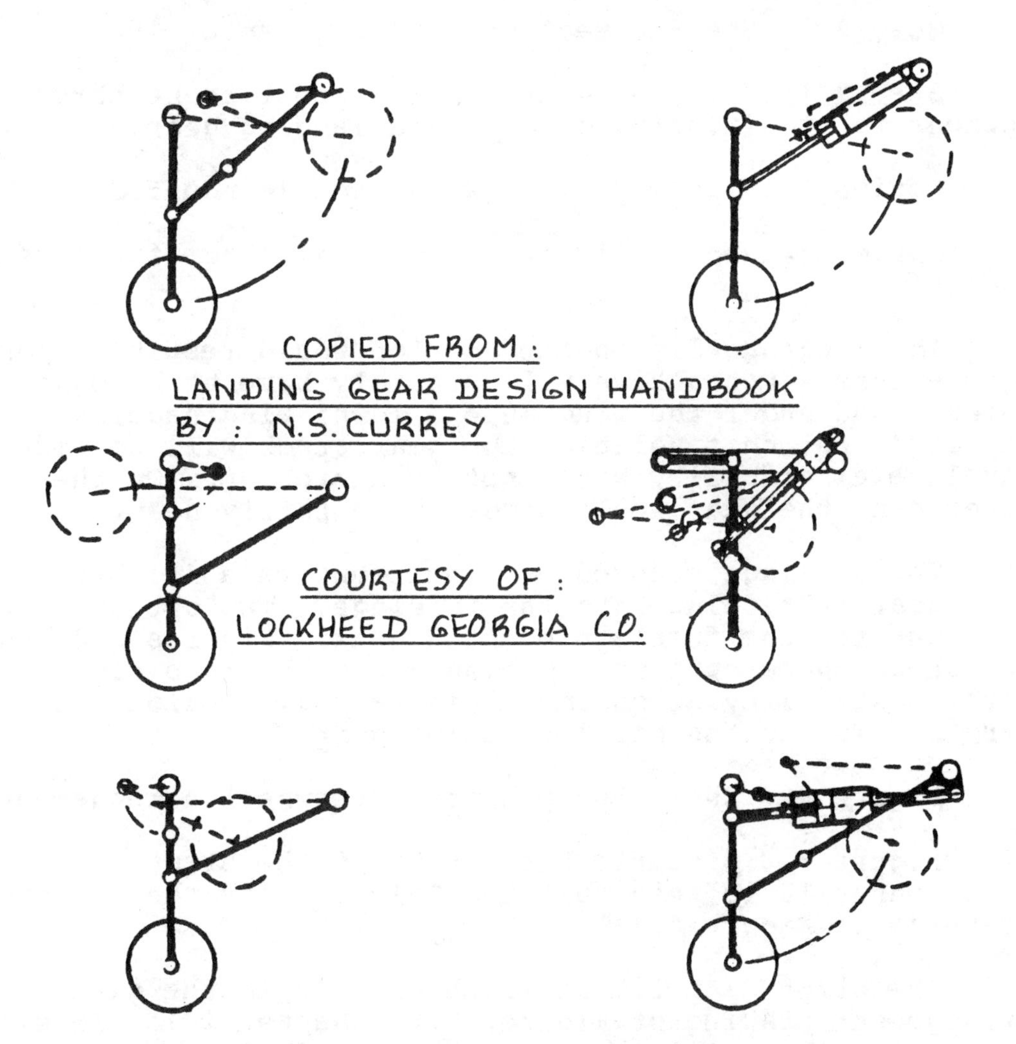

Figure 9.3 Typical Gear Retraction Stick Diagrams

9.2 EXAMPLE APPLICATIONS

Three example applications will now be discussed:

9.2.1 Twin Engine Propeller Driven Airplane: Selene
9.2.2 Jet Transport: Ourania
9.2.3 Fighter: Eris

9.2.1 Twin Engine Propeller Driven Airplane

Step 9.1: Because of the 250 kts cruise speed requirement of Table 2.17 (Part I) a retractable landing gear will be selected.

Step 9.2: A conventional, tricycle type landing gear will be selected.

Step 9.3: See Sub-section 10.2.1, Chapter 10.

Step 9.4: For the Selene there appear to be three options for positioning of the main landing gear:

Option 1 (Figure 9.4) is wing/nacelle mounted.

Options 2 and 3 (Figures 9.5 and 9.6) are fuselage mounted.

The wing/nacelle mounted option would result in long main struts. Retraction will probably have to be done forward and under the wing into a lower wing/nacelle fairing. For this solution the gear track will be wide and lateral stability would not be a problem. On the other hand the gear would probably be fairly heavy.

The fuselage mounted options requires a 'fighter' type gear retracting into the fuselage. Two options were laid out for the fuselage mounted gear. Figures 9.5 and 9.6 shows these options. Option 3 results in better lateral stability as shown by Figure 9.5. Option 3 is very similar to the MiG 23 landing gear.

Figure 9.7 shows the proposed nosewheel arrangement.

Figure 9.8 presents the layout of the strut locations. It is seen that the Selene meets the tip-over criteria of Figure 9.1a.

The strut disposition is shown also in the general arrangement drawing of Figure 10.3 (Chapter 10). It will be seen that the Selene meets the ground clearance criteria of Figure 9.1b.

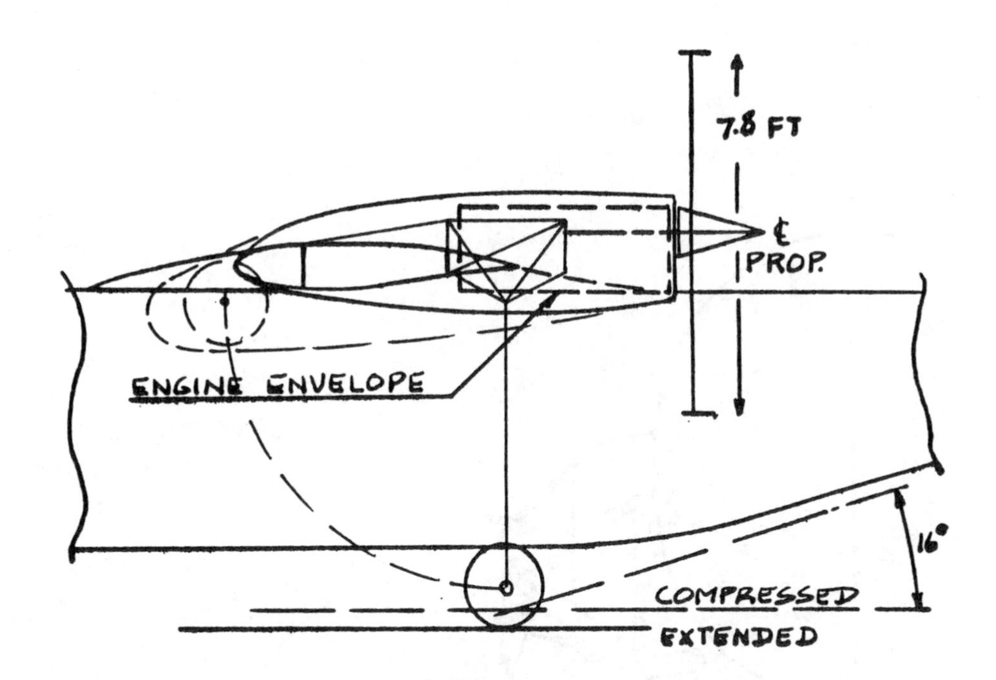

Figure 9.4 Selene: Main Gear Arrangement: Option 1

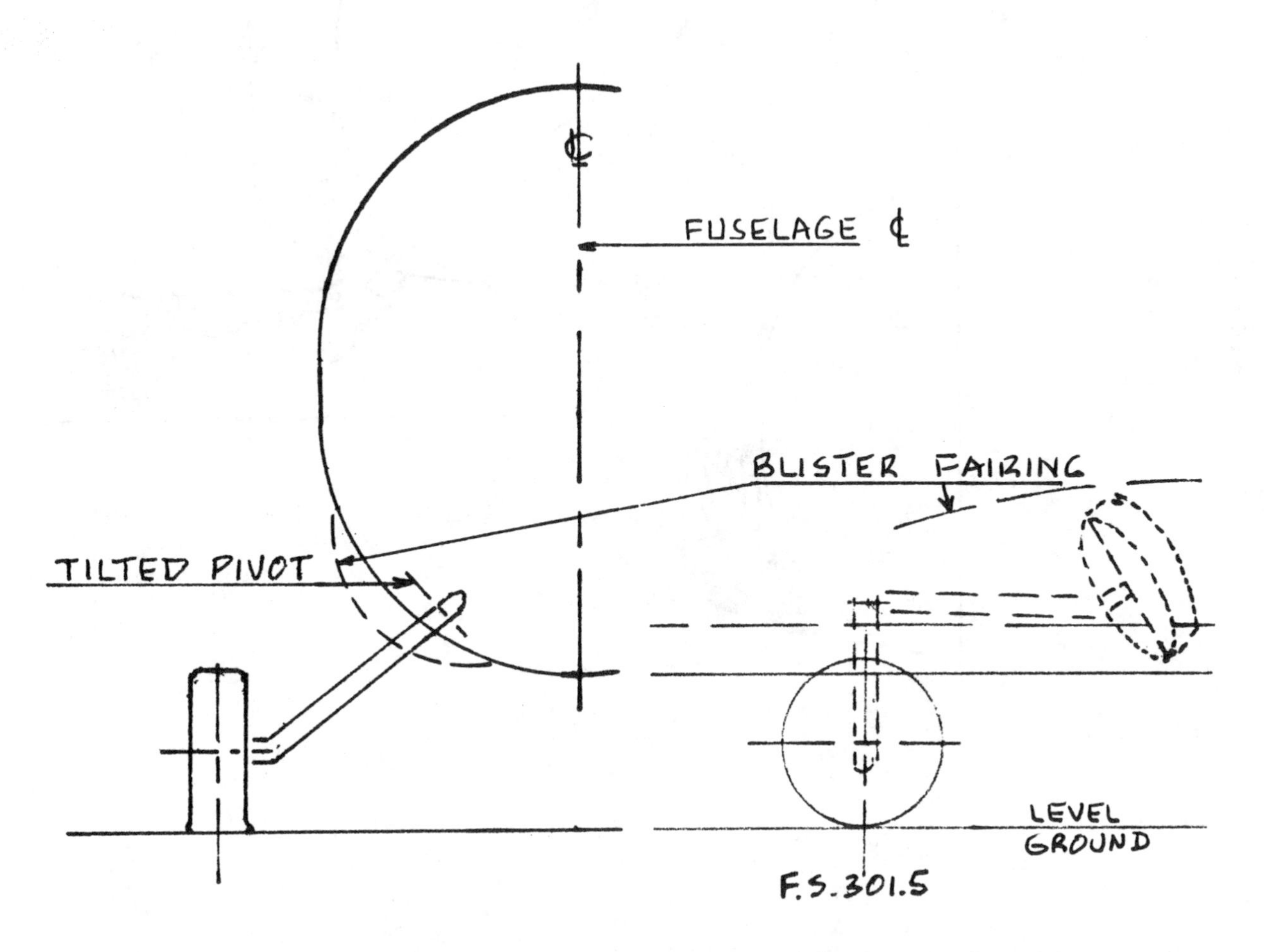

Figure 9.5 Selene: Main Gear Arrangement: Option 2

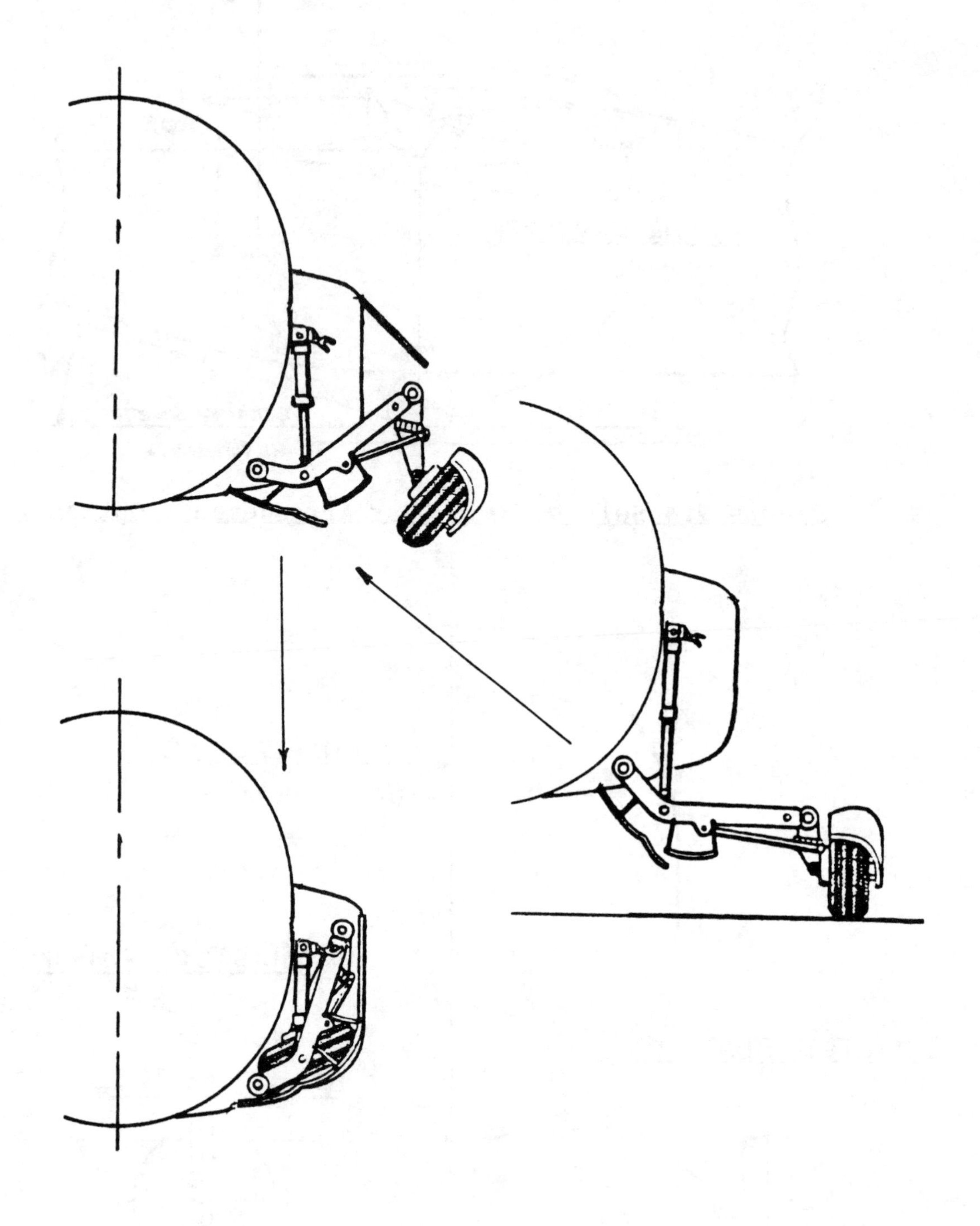

Figure 9.6 Selene: Main Gear Arrangement: Option 3

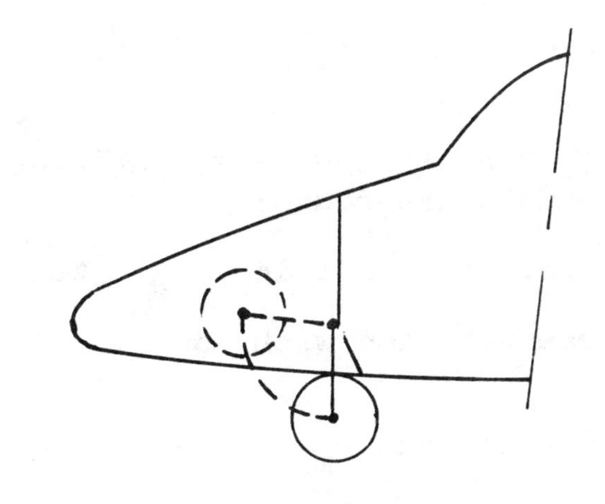

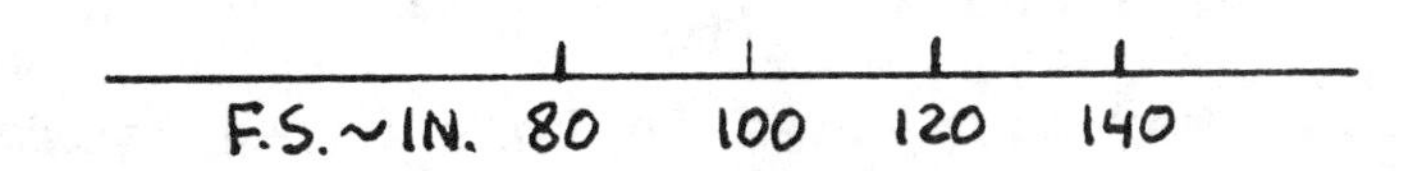

Figure 9.7 Selene: Nose Gear arrangement

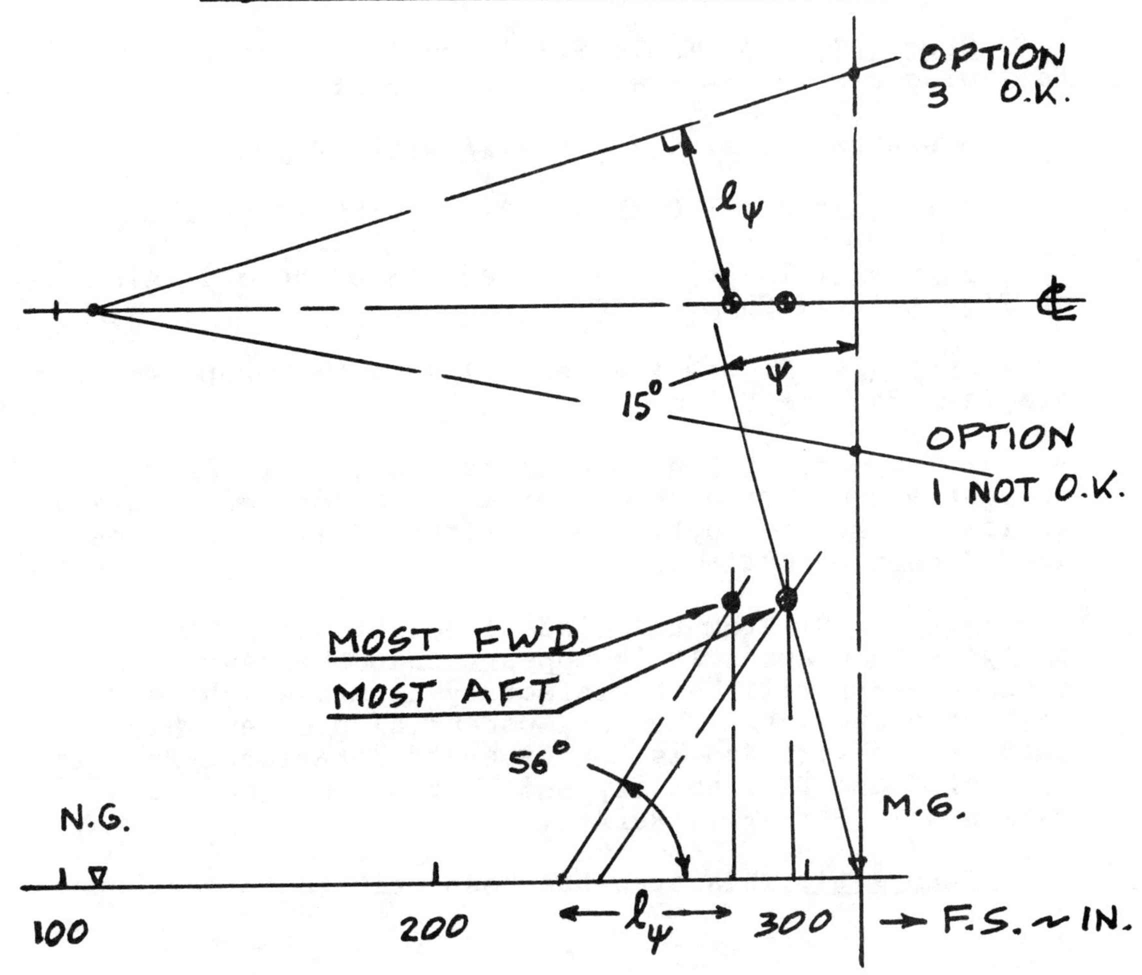

Figure 9.8 Selene: Tip-over Criteria

Step 9.5: From the strut disposition in Figure 10.3 the following data are found:

$l_m = 34$ in., $l_n = 171$ in., $n_s = 2$.

With these data and with Eqns (9.1) and (9.2) it is found that:

$P_n = 1,310$ lbs and $P_m = 3,295$ lbs.

The following gear load ratios are found:

$P_n/W_{TO} = 0.17$ and $2P_m/W_{TO} = 0.83$

Step 9.6: For airplanes in this category Table 9.1 shows that one nose wheel tire and one main gear tire per strut are acceptable choices.

Step 9.7: From Table 9.1 it follows that the following tire sizes are acceptable choices:

Nosewheel tire: $D_t x b_t = 17x6$ with 40 psi.

Main gear tire: $D_t x b_T = 22x6.5$ with 85 psi.

Step 9.8: The tires are drawn into the c.g. sideview of Figure 10.3, Chapter 10.

Step 9.9: Figure 9.6 and 9.7 show the proposed stick diagrams for the Selene.

It appears that nose gear retraction will not present a conflict with any primary structure. Fig.9.7 indicates that for option 3 a blister fairing will be needed on the fuselage.

Step 9.10: From the Class I weight and balance analysis in Chapter 10 it appears that the gear configuration will be satisfactory from a weight and balance viewpoint. The only potential problem which needs to be verified is the take-off rotation. This is part of Class II stability and control analyses as outlined in Part VII (Ref.6).

Step 9.11: This step has been omitted to save space.

9.2.2 Jet Transport

Step 9.1: Because of the high cruise speed requirement of Table 2.18 (Part I) a retractable landing gear will be selected.

Step 9.2: A conventional, tricycle type landing gear will be selected.

Step 9.3: See Sub-section 10.2.2, Chapter 10.

Step 9.4: For the Ourania there appears to be only one option for integrating the main landing gear into the airplane: under the rear spar and retracting into the fuselage. This type of arrangement is very similar to that found on the B737. Figure 9.9 shows the proposed landing gear arrangement. Note that the nosegear retracts forward into the nose.

Figure 9.10 shows the proposed strut layout. It is clear that the Ourania meets the tip-over criteria of Figure 9.1a.

The strut disposition is also shown in the general arrangement drawing of Figure 10.5. It will be seen that the Ourania also meets the geometric ground clearance criteria of Figure 9.1b.

Step 9.5: From the strut disposition in Figure 10.5 the following data are found:

$l_m = 60$ in., $l_n = 520$ in., $n_s = 2$.

The take-off weight is: 127,000 lbs.

With these data and with Eqns (9.1) and (9.2) it is found that:

$P_n = 13{,}138$ lbs and $P_m = 56{,}931$ lbs.

The following gear load ratios are found:

$P_n/W_{TO} = 0.10$ and $2P_m/W_{TO} = 0.90$

Step 9.6: For airplanes in this category Table 9.2 shows that two nose wheel tires and two main gear tires per strut are acceptable choices.

Step 9.7: From Table 9.2 it follows that the following tire sizes are acceptable choices:

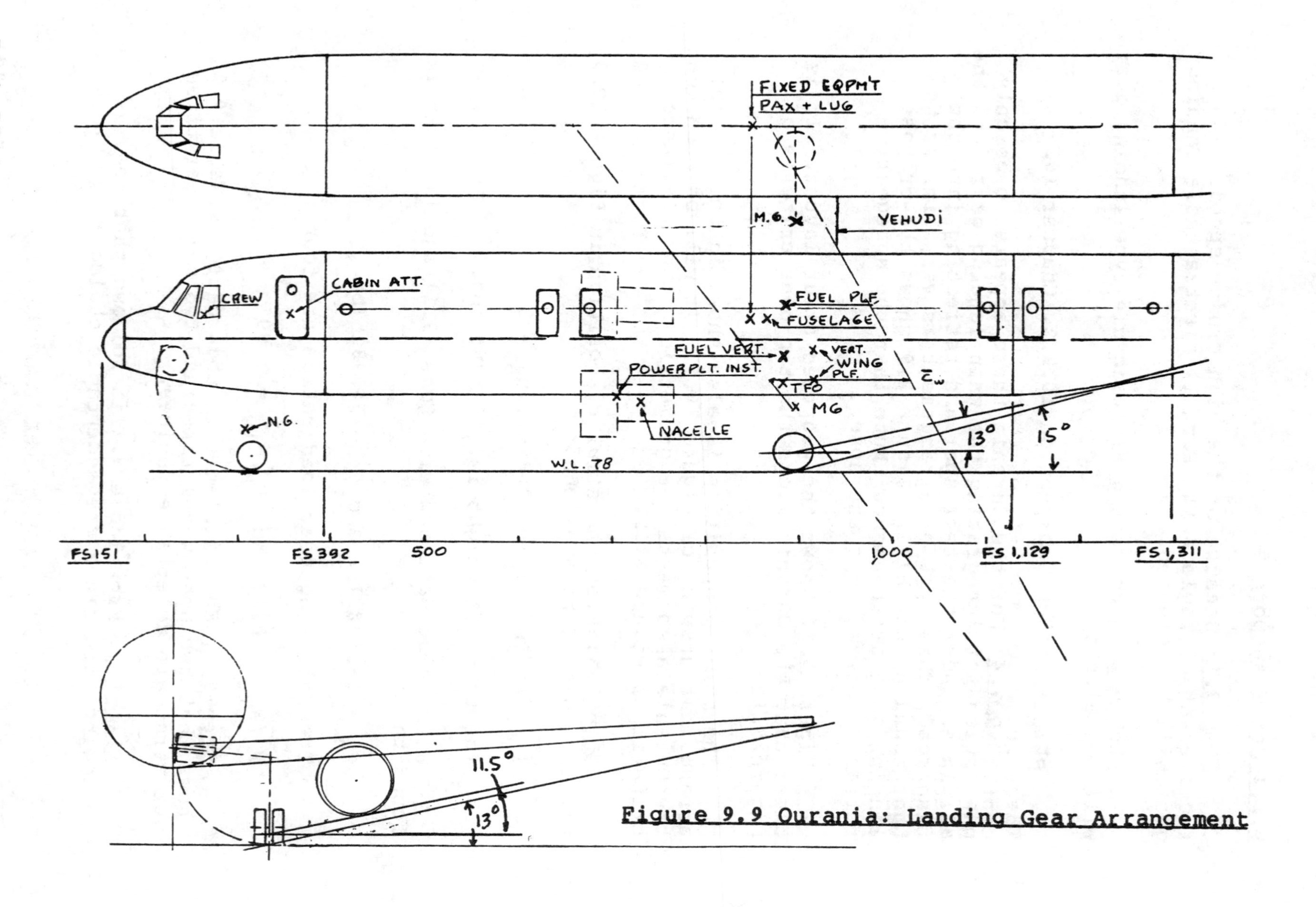

Figure 9.9 Ourania: Landing Gear Arrangement

Nosewheel tire: $D_t x b_t$ = 24x7.7 with 180 psi.

Main gear tire: $D_t x b_T$ = 40x14 with 180 psi.

Step 9.8: The tires are drawn into the c.g. sideview of Figure 10.5 and into the landing gear arrangement of Figure 9.9.

Step 9.9: Figure 9.9 also shows the stick diagrams. These indicate that landing gear retraction does not conflict with any primary structure or with the flaps. Note that to accomodate the main gear a so-called 'yehudi' had to be added to the wing planform. This yehudi carries the inboard flaps. Such an arrangement was pioneered by Boeing on the 707 and is still frequently used in jet transports.

Step 9.10: From the Class I weight and balance analysis in Sub-section 10.2.2 it appears that the gear configuration will be satisfactory from a weight and balance viewpoint. The only potential problem which needs to be verified is the take-off rotation. This is part of Class II stability and control analyses as outlined in Part VII (Ref.6).

Step 9.11: This step has been omitted to save space.

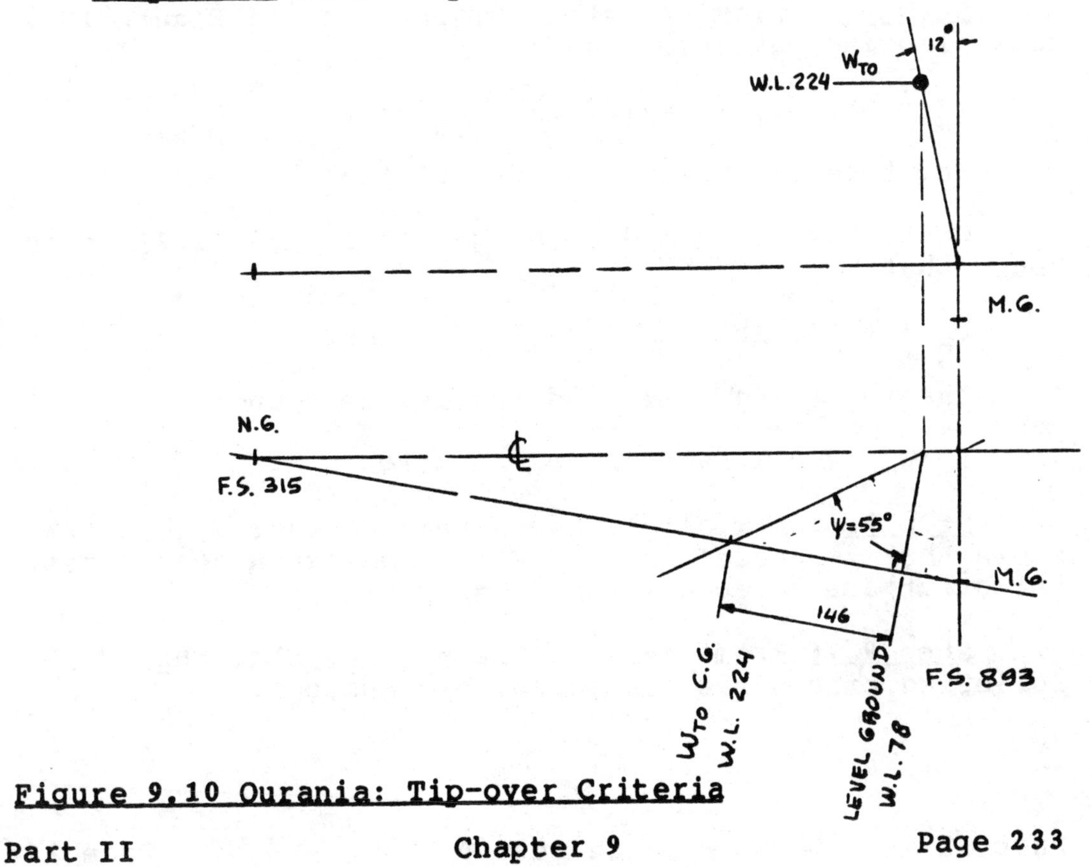

Figure 9.10 Ourania: Tip-over Criteria

9.2.3 Fighter

Step 9.1: Because of the high cruise speed requirement of Table 2.19 (Part I) a retractable landing gear will be selected.

Step 9.2: A conventional, tricycle type landing gear will be selected.

Step 9.3: See Sub-section 10.2.3, Chapter 10.

Step 9.4: For the Eris there appears to be only one option for integrating the main landing gear into the airplane: under the fuselage and retracting into the fuselage underneath the engine bays. This arrangement is fairly typical for modern jet fighters. Figure 9.11 shows the proposed landing gear arrangement.

Figure 9.12 shows the proposed strut layout. It may be seen that the Eris meets the tip-over criteria of Figure 9.1a.

The strut disposition is also indicated in the general arrangement drawing of Figure 10.7. As seen, the Eris also meets the ground clearance criteria of Figure 9.1b.

Step 9.5: From the strut disposition in Figure 10.7 the following data are found:

$l_m = 20$ in., $l_n = 185$ in., $n_s = 2$.

The take-off weight is: 64,905 lbs.

With these data and with Eqns (9.1) and (9.2) it is found that:

$P_n = 6,332$ lbs and $P_m = 29,286$ lbs.

The following gear load ratios are found:

$P_n/W_{TO} = 0.10$ and $2P_m/W_{TO} = 0.90$

Step 9.6: For airplanes in this category Table 9.2 shows that two nose wheel tires and one main gear tires per strut are acceptable choices.

Step 9.7: From Table 9.2 it follows that the following tire sizes are acceptable choices:

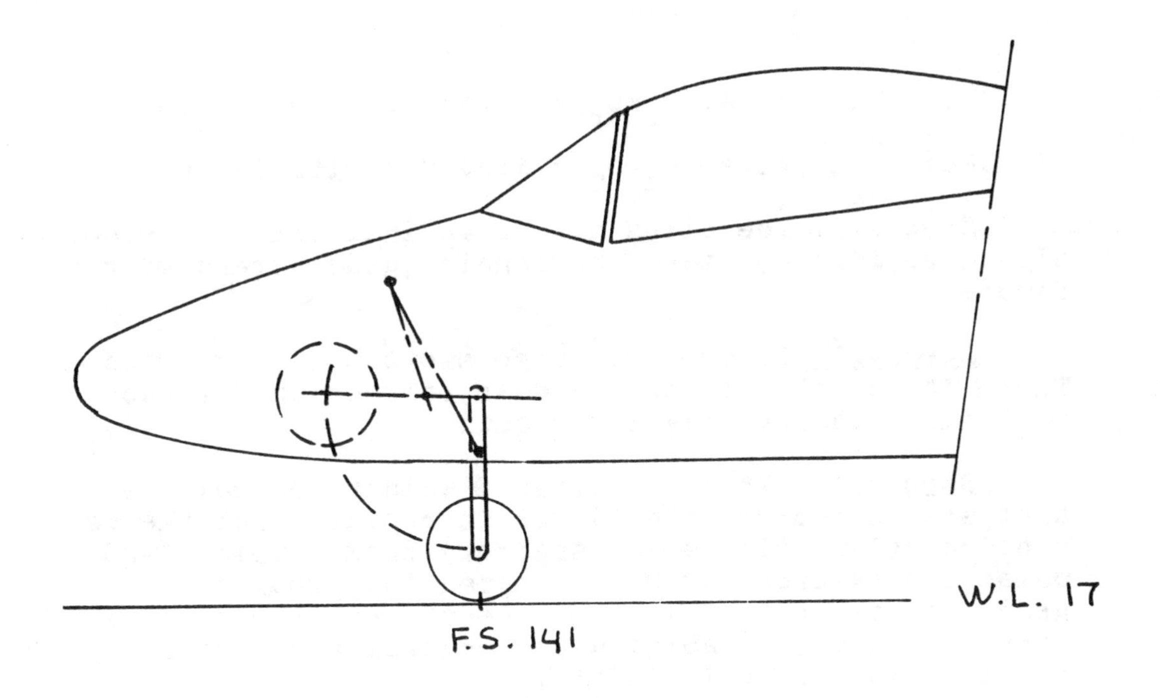

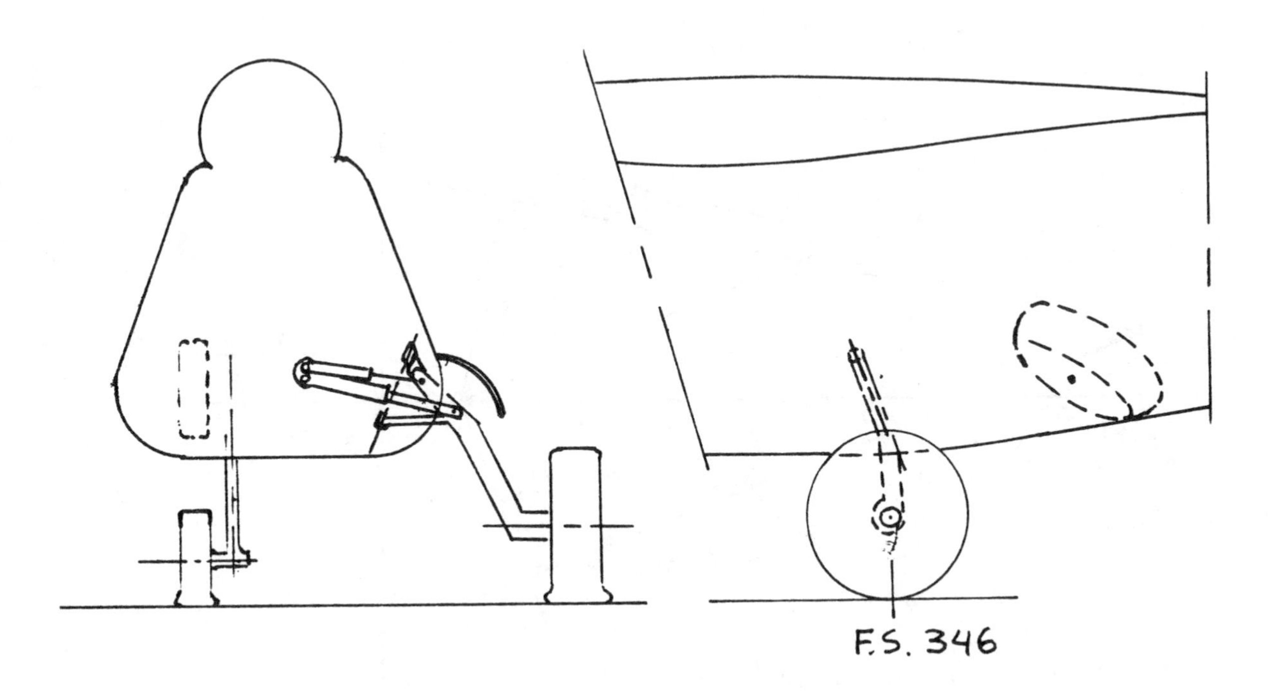

Figure 9.11 Eris: Landing Gear Arrangement

Nosewheel tire: $D_t x b_t$ = 21.6x7.5 with 120 psi.

Main gear tire: $D_t x b_T$ = 35.3x9.3 with 210 psi.

Step 9.8: The tires are drawn into the c.g. sideview of Figure 10.7 and into the landing gear arrangement of Figure 9.11.

Step 9.9: Figure 9.11 also shows the stick diagrams. These indicate that landing gear retraction does not conflict with any primary structure.

Step 9.10: From the Class I weight and balance analysis in Sub-section 10.2.3 it appears that the gear configuration will be satisfactory from a weight and balance viewpoint. The only potential problem which needs to be verified is the take-off rotation. This is part of Class II stability and control analyses as outlined in Part VII (Ref.6).

Step 9.11: This step has been omitted to save space.

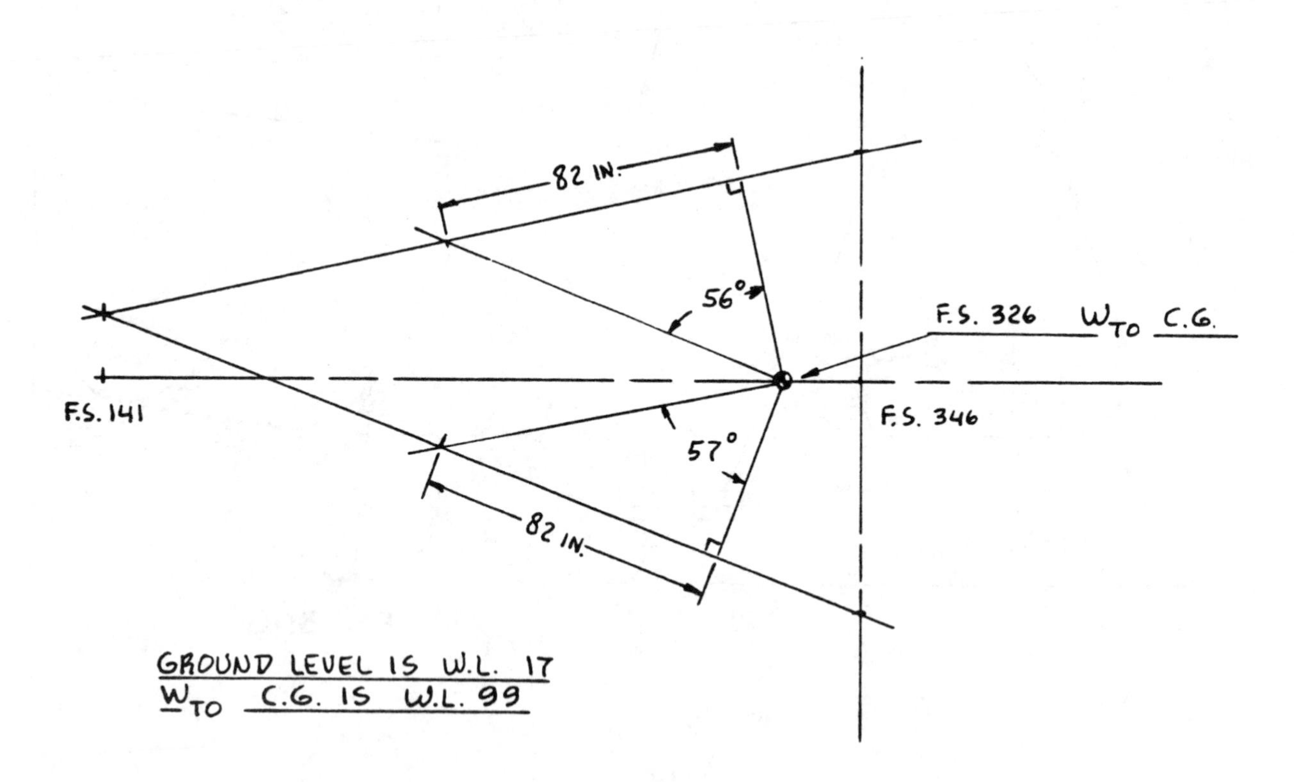

Figure 9.12 Eris: Tip-over Criteria

10. CLASS I WEIGHT AND BALANCE ANALYSIS

The purpose of this chapter is to familiarize the reader with a rapid method to determine whether or not the center of gravity of the proposed airplane design is in 'the right place' for different loading scenarios.

The method is referred to as a Class I weight and balance method and is to be used in conjunction with Step 10 of p.d. sequence I as outlined in Chapter 2.

Section 10.1 presents the method as a 9-step procedure. Example applications are given in Section 10.2.

10.1 CLASS I WEIGHT AND BALANCE METHOD

Step 10.1: Using Class I component weight prediction methods, determine the initial component weight breakdown of the airplane.

Part V (Ref.4), Chapter 2 shows how a Class I component weight breakdown can be prepared. Table 10.1a shows a list of weight components which are typically found in a Class I weight breakdown. Three numerical examples of Class I component weight breakdowns are presented in Section 10.2.

Table 10.1a Typical Class I Component Weight Breakdown

1. Fuselage group
2. Wing group
3. Empennage group
4. Engine group
5. Landing gear group
6. Fixed equipm't group

Empty weight: $W_E = \text{Sum } \sum_{i=1}^{i=6} W_i$

7. Trapped fuel and oil
8. Crew

Operating weight empty: $W_{OE} = \text{Sum } \sum_{i=1}^{i=8} W_i$

9. Fuel
10. Passengers
11. Baggage
12. Cargo
13. Military load

Take-off weight: $W_{TO} = \text{Sum } \sum_{i=1}^{i=13} W_i$

Step 10.2: Prepare a preliminary arrangement drawing of the airplane using the drawings developed in Chapters 5-9.

Figure 10.1 shows a conceptual preliminary arrangement drawing as used in a typical weight and balance analysis. Figure 10.1 is drawn as a threeview because of the asymmetry of that configuration. For many symmetrical airplanes a sideview is sufficient.

Step 10.3: Locate the centers of gravity of all Class I weight components in Figure 10.1.

Note: some airplanes have severe asymmetries in their weight distribution. In that case it will also be necessary to locate the y locations of the component c.g.'s.

At this point, Figure 10.1 is also referred to as a 'c.g. threeview'.

Step 10.4: Enter the appropriate x,y and z coordinates of each component c.g. in a table such as Table 10.1b.

Table 10.2 provides some guidance for locating component c.g.'s of major weight groups. Further guidance to finding the location of component c.g.'s can be found in Chapter 2 of Part V (Ref.4).

CAUTION: Make absolutely certain that the zero reference point as shown in Figures 10.1 is always selected so that all coordinates are positive. To assure that this will be so even for future growth versions of the airplane, 'pick' the zero reference point well to the left and well below the nose of the airplane.

The author has seen both engineers in industry and aeronautical engineering design students make the most awful 'sign' errors as a result of not selecting the zero reference point as suggested here.

The following nomenclature is widely used in the aircraft industry:

x-coordinates as defined in Figure 10.1 are referred to as fuselage stations (F.S.).

y-coordinates as defined in Figure 10.1 are referred to as wing buttock lines (B.L. or W.B.L.).

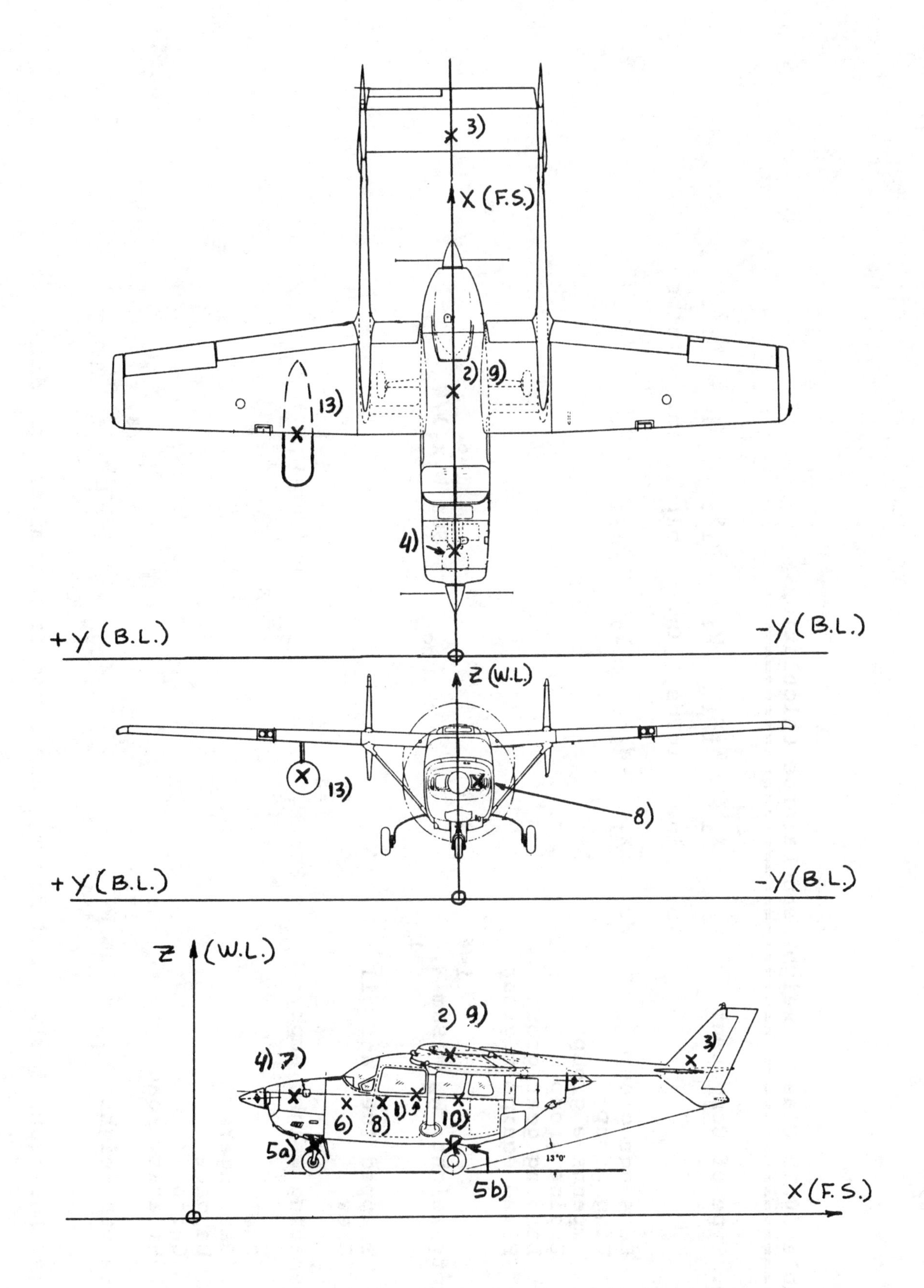

Figure 10.1 Preliminary Configuration Arrangement

Table 10.1b Class I Weight and Balance Calculation

No.	Type of Component	W_i	x_i	$W_i x_i$	y_i	$W_i y_i$	z_i	$W_i z_i$
		lbs	in.	inlbs	in.	inlbs	in.	inlbs
1.	Fuselage group	W_1	x_1	$W_1 x_1$	y_1	$W_1 y_1$	z_1	$W_1 z_1$
2.	Wing group							
3.	Empennage group							
4.	Engine group							
5.	Landing gear group							
6.	Fixed equipm't group							

Empty weight: $W_E = \mathrm{Sum} \sum_{i=1}^{i=6} W_i$ $\qquad x_{cg_{W_E}} = (\mathrm{Sum} \sum_{i=1}^{i=6} W_i x_i)/W_E$

No.	Type of Component
7.	Trapped fuel and oil
8.	Crew

Operating weight empty: $W_{OE} = \mathrm{Sum} \sum_{i=1}^{i=8} W_i$ $\qquad x_{cg_{W_{OE}}} = (\mathrm{Sum} \sum_{i=1}^{i=8} W_i x_i)/W_{OE}$

No.	Type of Component
9.	Fuel
10.	Passengers
11.	Baggage
12.	Cargo
13.	Military load

Take-off weight: $W_{TO} = \mathrm{Sum} \sum_{i=1}^{i=13} W_i$ $\qquad x_{cg_{W_{TO}}} = (\mathrm{Sum} \sum_{i=1}^{i=13} W_i x_i)/W_{TO}$

Note: Locations for y_{cg} and for z_{cg} are found from similar equations.

Table 10.2 Location of C.G.'s of Major Components

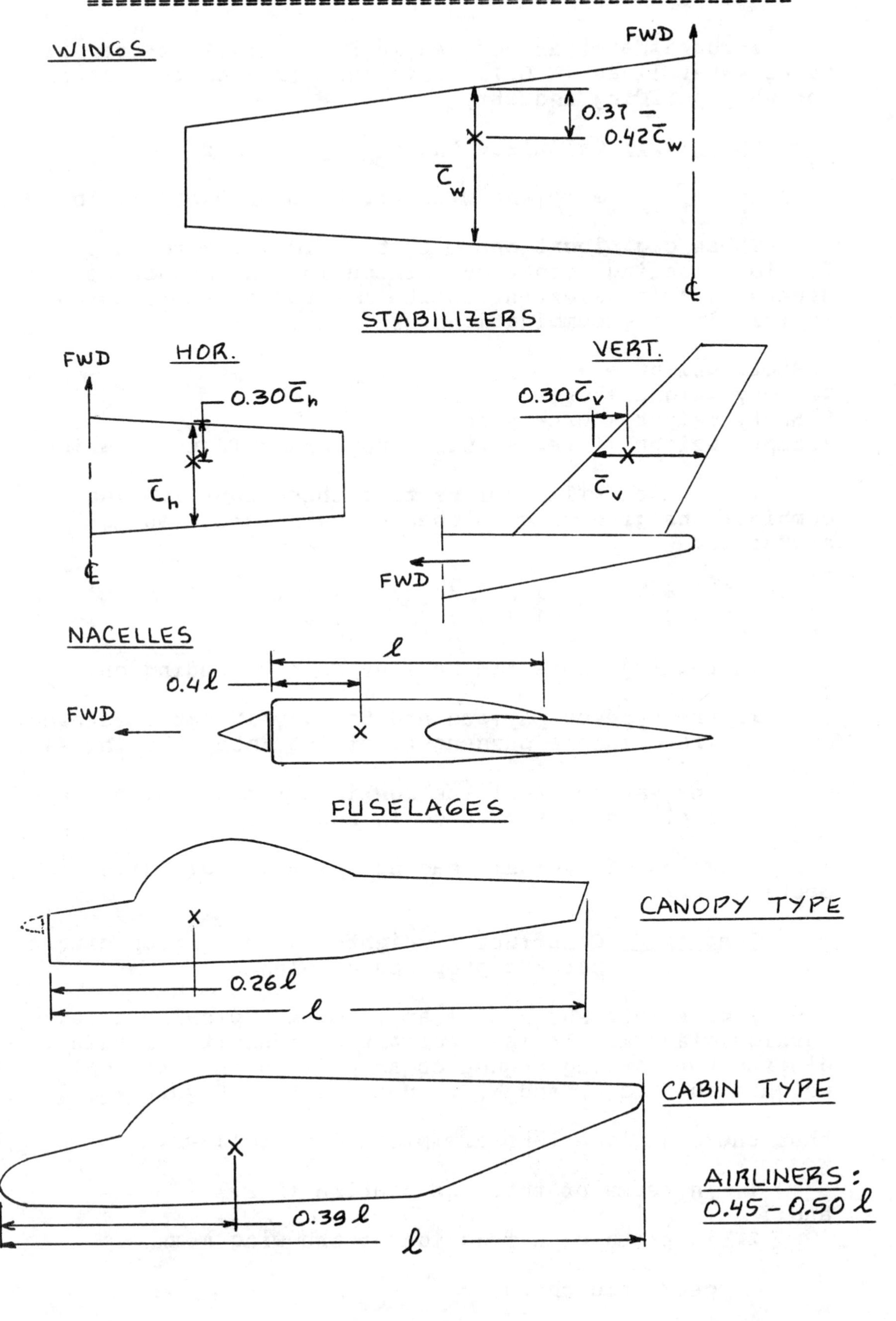

z-coordinates as defined in Figure 10.1 are referred to as water lines (W.L.). This term is a carry-over from the ship building industry.

Step 10.5: Calculate the x_{cg}, y_{cg} and z_{cg} of the airplane with the help of Table 10.1b.

These c.g. locations must be calculated for all feasible loading scenarios. These loading scenarios depend to a large extent on the mission of the airplane. Typical loading combinations are:

1. Empty weight
2. Empty weight + crew
3. Empty weight + crew + fuel
4. Empty weight + crew + fuel + payload = Take-off weight

The reader will realize that these four loading combinations give rise to the following six loading scenarios:

1 2 3 4	1 3 2 4	1 4 2 3
1 2 4 3	1 3 4 2	1 4 3 2

In reality there can be many more depending on:

1. the type of payload and the way it can be stowed: (for example passengers piling into a Boeing 747)

2. the way the fuel tankage is arranged and how the fuel can be sequenced in and out.

Examples of typical loading scenarios are given in Section 10.2.

Step 10.6: Construct a weight-c.g. excursion diagram for the proposed airplane.

Figure 10.2 shows an example of a typical c.g. excursion diagram. It is important to identify in this diagram the loading sequences as well as the critical weights such as W_E and W_{TO}. Note also in Figure 10.2 that the c.g. locations are plotted as follows:

1. in terms of fuselage station (F.S.)

and:

2. in terms of a fraction of the wing mean geometric chord, $\bar{c}_w$.

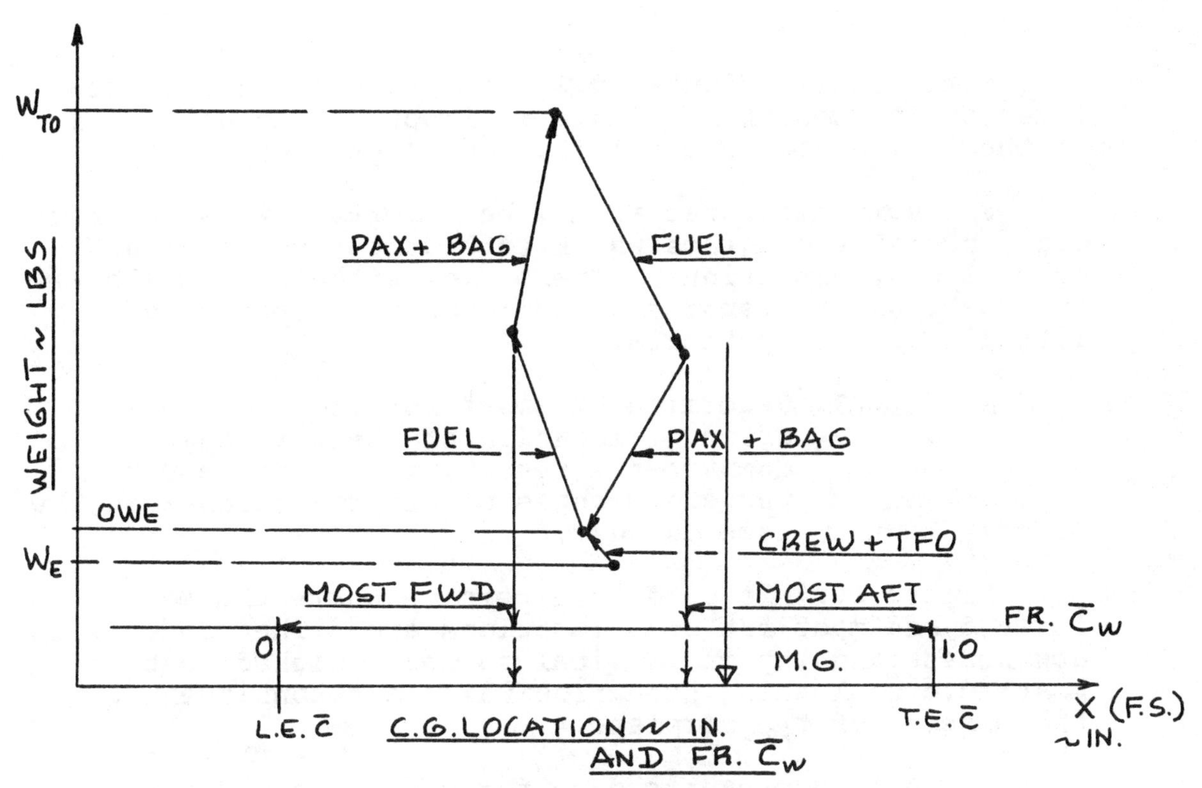

Figure 10.2 Weight-C.G. Excursion Diagram

Table 10.3 Examples of Center of Gravity Ranges

Type	C.G. Range (in.)	C.G. Range fr. $\bar{c}_w$	Type	C.G. Range (in.)	C.G. Range fr. $\bar{c}_w$
Homebuilts	5	0.10	Military Trainers	8	0.10
Single Engine Prop. Driven	7-18	0.06-0.27	Fighters	15	0.20
Twin Engine Prop. Driven	9-15	0.12-0.22	Mil.Patr. Bomb and Transp.	26-90	0.30
Ag. Airpl.	5	0.10			
Business Jets	8-17	0.10-0.21	Fl.Boats, Amph. and Float	7-28	0.25
Regional TBP	12-20	0.14-0.27	Amph. and		
Jet Transp.	26-91	0.12-0.32	Supersonic Cruise	20-100	0.30

Note also in Figure 10.2 that the main landing gear location is identified. This is important to determine if there is a longitudinal 'tip-over' problem.

For some airplanes it may be important to also draw c.g. excursion diagrams which reflect the vertical and lateral c.g. situations. These c.g. situations may have an impact on the landing gear disposition because of lateral tip-over potential.

Step 10.7: Determine the most forward and the most aft c.g. location of the airplane. Compare the resulting c.g. range with the c.g. ranges of other airplanes in the same category.

Figure 10.2 is used to determine where the most forward and most aft c.g. locations are. The reader will now understand why it is vital to have 'smoked' out the most adverse loading scenarios which are consistent with the mission of the airplane.

Table 10.3 presents data for comparing the resulting c.g. range with the c.g. ranges of other airplanes.

Step 10.8: Draw conclusions about the feasibility of the proposed airplane arrangement and if necessary make changes.

In judging the feasibility of the proposed airplane arrangement the following principles must be kept in mind:

Principle 1:

Where possible, the ideal c.g. arrangement is one for which the OWE-c.g., the fuel-c.g. and the payload-c.g. are in the same vertical location.

The reader will find that in most airplane designs it is not possible to reach this ideal situation. One should try to come as close as possible.

Principle 2:

Try to position the landing gear so that no major structural cutouts are needed to retract the gear. Also: make sure that there is a sufficient amount of volume available to retract the gear into.

Principle 3:

Keep in mind that the airplane also has to satisfy certain basic stability and control requirements. Step 12 in p.d. sequence I (Chapter 2) deals with this problem. In this regard there are two types of airplanes:

1. Airplanes which must have inherent static longitudinal and static directional stability. The so-called X-plot method of Step 12 is used in conjunction with the Class I weight and balance analysis to assure inherent static stability. Keep in mind that without minimum static stability levels the proposed airplane design is invalid.

2. Airplanes which can have inherent static longitudinal and/or static directional instability. These airplanes must now have a flight control system which through the correct feedback loops signal control surface actuators to in turn move flight control surfaces in such a way that 'de-facto' stability is insured. This implies a relationship between the 'design' level of inherent instability, control power, feedback gains and actuator rate requirements. A Class I method to account for this during p.d. sequence I is discussed in Chapter 11.

Principle 4:

If an airplane design turns out to have major balance problems it is often possible to 'fix' these problems by moving the wing. If the gear needs to be attached to the wing, the entire wing/gear combination must be moved.

Step 10.9: Document the decisions made under Steps 10.1 - 10.8 in a brief descriptive report including clear, dimensioned drawings.

10.2 EXAMPLE APPLICATIONS

Three examples will now be discussed:

10.2.1 Twin Engine Propeller Driven Airplane: Selene
10.2.2 Jet Transport: Ourania
10.2.3 Fighter: Eris

10.2.1 Twin Engine Propeller Driven Airplane

Step 10.1: Table 10.4 shows the component weight breakdown for the Selene. This breakdown is the result of applying a Class I component weight estimation method to the airplane. This method is discussed in detail in Chapter 2 of Part V (Ref.4).

Step 10.2: Figure 10.3 shows the preliminary arrangement drawing for the Selene. This drawing is the result of combining Figures 4.2, 5.3, 6.3, 8.2 and 9.3. For the Selene only the sideview is important in establishing its weight and balance characteristics.

Step 10.3: Figure 10.3 also shows the component centers of gravity.

Step 10.4: Table 10.4 also lists the x, y and z coordinates of all Selene weight components.

Step 10.5: Table 10.4 also lists the centers of gravity for several important loading configurations.

Step 10.6: Figure 10.4 shows the weight-c.g. excursion diagram for the Selene.

Step 10.7: From Figure 10.4 it follows that the c.g. limits are:

most forward c.g. occurs at W = 7,000 lbs,

F.S.= 280 in. and $0.62\bar{c}_w$

most aft c.g. occurs at W = 5,500 lbs, F.S.= 295 in.

and $0.78\bar{c}_w$

The c.g. range of the Selene is 15 inches or $0.16\bar{c}_w$.

Note that this compares favorably with the data of Table 10.3.

Table 10.4 Component Weight and Coordinate Data: Selene

Component	Weight	x	Wx	y	Wy	z	Wz
	lbs	in.	in.lbs	in.	in.lbs	in.	in.lbs
Wing	738	269	198,522	0	0	118	87,084
Empennage H.T.	120	559	67,080	0	0	189	22,680
V.T.	59	504	29,736	0	0	146	8,614
Fuselage	621	220	136,620	0	0	76	47,196
Nacelles	249	315	78,435	0	0	126	31,374
Landing Gear N.G.	76	110	8,360	0	0	47	3,572
M.G.	304	315	95,760	0	0	55	16,720
Engines + inst.	1,508	331	499,148	0	0	126	190,008
Propellers	200	362	72,400	0	0	129	25,800
Fixed Equipment	1,025	220	225,500	0	0	76	77,900
Empty weight, W_E	4,900	288	1,411,561	0	0	104	510,948
TFO	44	315	13,860	0	0	118	5,192
Fuel	1,706	276	470,856	0	0	118	201,308
2 Pax.	350	184	64,400	0	0	76	26,600
2 Pax.	350	282	98,700	0	0	76	26,600
2 Pax.	350	337	117,950	0	0	76	26,600
Baggage	200	220	44,000	14	2,800	76	15,200
Take-off wht, W_{TO}	7,900	281	2,221,327	0	2,800	103	812,448

Note: other loading conditions shown in Figure 10.4.

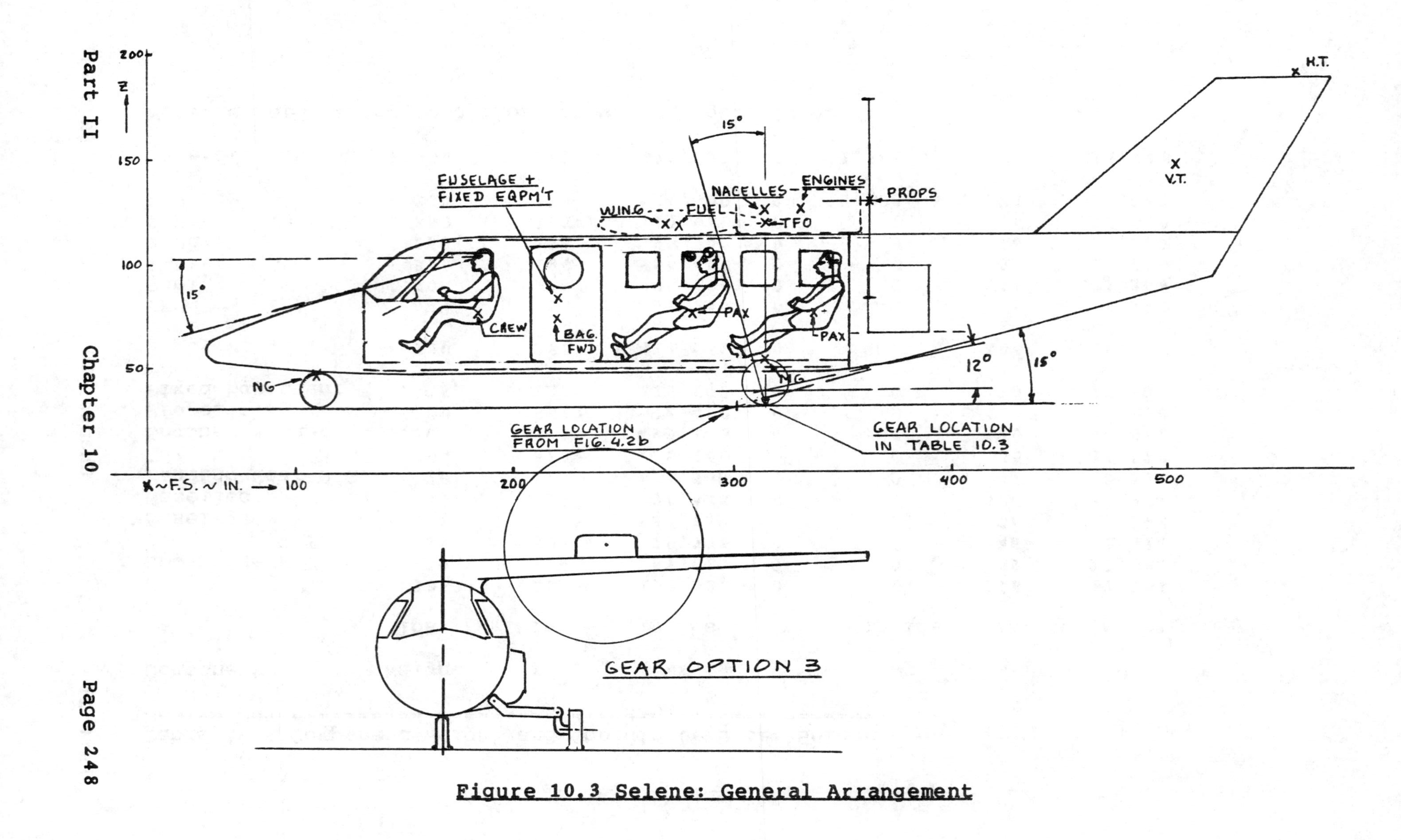

Figure 10.3 Selene: General Arrangement

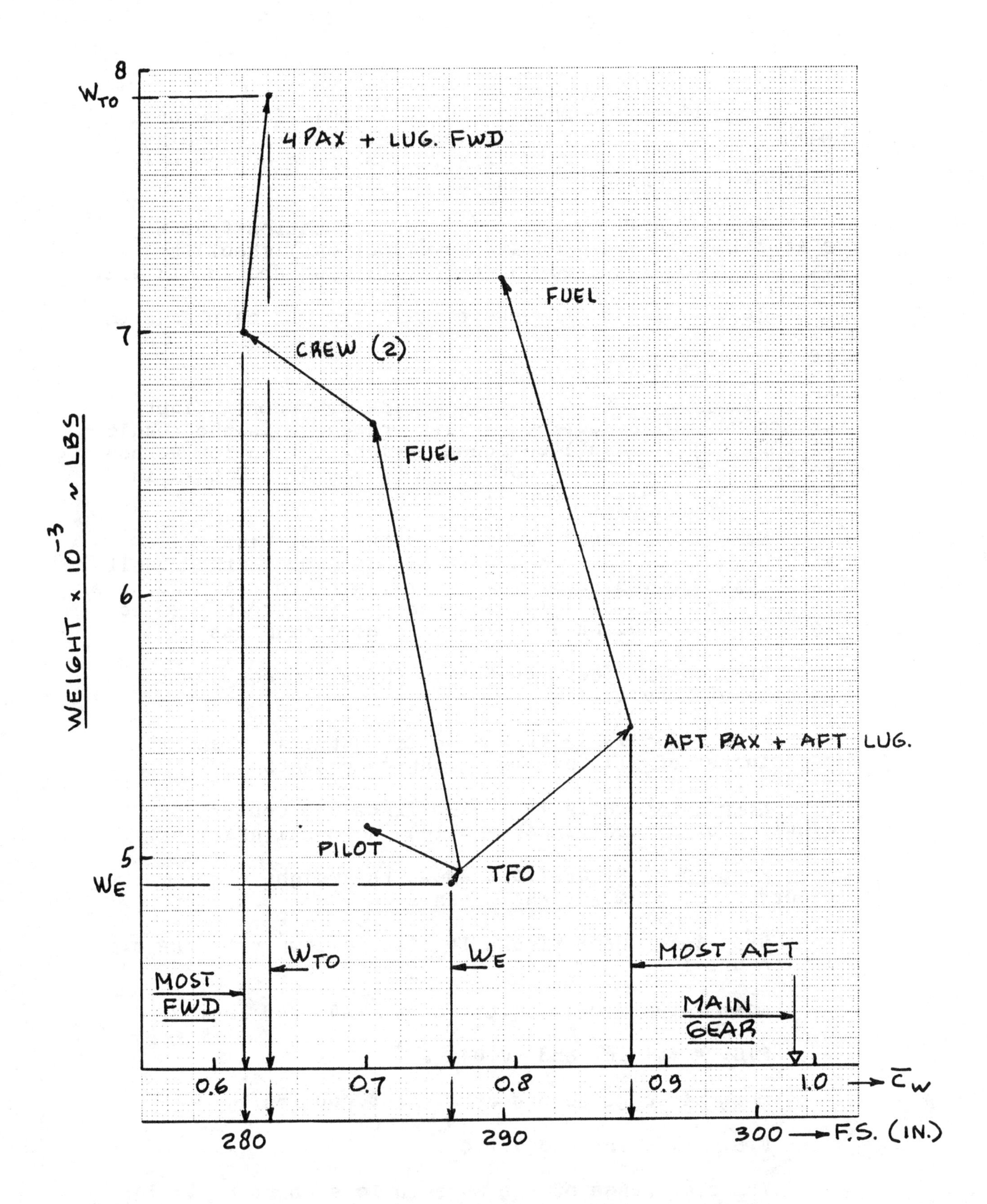

Figure 10.4 Selene: Weight-C.G. Excursion Diagram

Step 10.8: The most aft c.g. is well forward of the main landing gear contact point. The overall landing gear disposition problem relative to the c.g. range is discussed in Chapter 9, Sub-section 9.2.1.

The suitability of the aft c.g. location from a static longitudinal and static directional stability viewpoint is discussed in Chapter 11, Sub-section 11.2.1.

Step 10.9: To save space this step has been omitted.

10.2.2 Jet Transport

Step 10.1: Table 10.5 shows the component weight breakdown for the Ourania. This breakdown is the result of applying a Class I component weight estimation method to the airplane. This method is discused in detail in Chapter 2 of Part V (Ref.4).

Step 10.2: Figure 10.5 shows the preliminary arrangement for the Ourania. This drawing is the result of combining Figures 4.7, 5.5, 6.4, 8.3 and 9.5. For the Ourania only the sideview and the topview are needed to establish its weight and balance characteristics.

Step 10.3: Figure 10.5 also shows the component centers of gravity.

Step 10.4: Table 10.5 also lists the x, y and z coordinates of all Ourania weight components.

Step 10.5: Table 10.5 also lists the centers of gravity for several important loading configurations.

Step 10.6: Figure 10.6 shows the weight-c.g. excursion diagram for the Ourania.

Step 10.7: From Figure 10.6 it follows that the c.g. limits are:

most forward c.g. occurs at W = 100,000 lbs,

F.S. = 861 in. and $-0.04\bar{c}_w$.

most aft c.g. occurs at W = 100,000 lbs,

F.S. = 884 in. and $0.12\bar{c}_w$.

The c.g. range of the Ourania is seen to be 23 in.

This is equivalent to $0.16\bar{c}_w$.

Table 10.5 Component Weight and Coordinate Data: Ourania

Component	Weight	x	Wx	y	Wy	z	Wz
	lbs	in.	in.lbs	in.	in.lbs	in.	in.lbs
Wing	13,664	913	12,475,232	0	0	213	2,910,432
Empennage	3,253	1,535	4,993,355	0	0	343	1,115,779
Fuselage	14,184	866	12,283,344	0	0	248	3,517,632
Nacelles	2,082	728	1,515,696	0	0	150	312,300
Landing Gear N.G.	573	307	175,911	0	0	122	69,906
M.G.	4,632	894	4,141,008	0	0	146	676,272
Powerplant inst.	9,891	705	6,973,155	0	0	157	1,552,887
Fixed Equipment	20,171	846	17,064,666	0	0	248	5,002,408
Empty weight, W_E	68,450	871	59,622,367	0	0	221	15,157,616
TFO	925	882	815,850	0	0	173	160,025
Fuel	25,850	882	22,799,700	0	0	205	5,299,250
Crew flight deck	410	260	106,600	0	0	248	101,680
cabin att.	205	1,339	274,495	0	0	248	50,840
cabin att.	410	354	145,140	0	0	248	101,680
Pax + luggage	30,750	846	26,014,500	0	0	248	7,626,000
Take-off wht, W_{TO}	127,000	864	109,778,652	0	0	224	28,497,091

Note: other loading conditions shown in Figure 10.6.

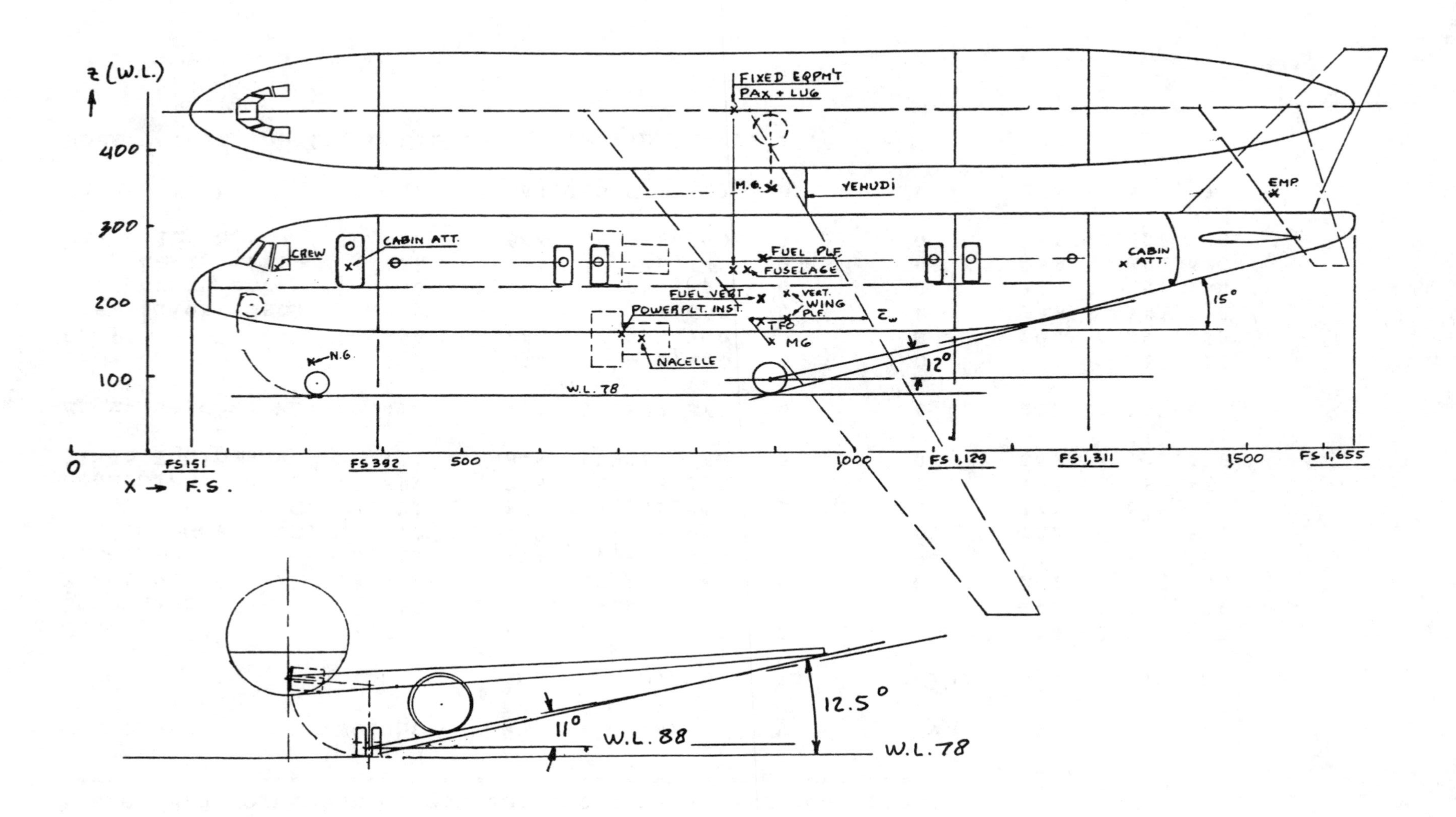

Figure 10.5 Ourania: General Arrangement

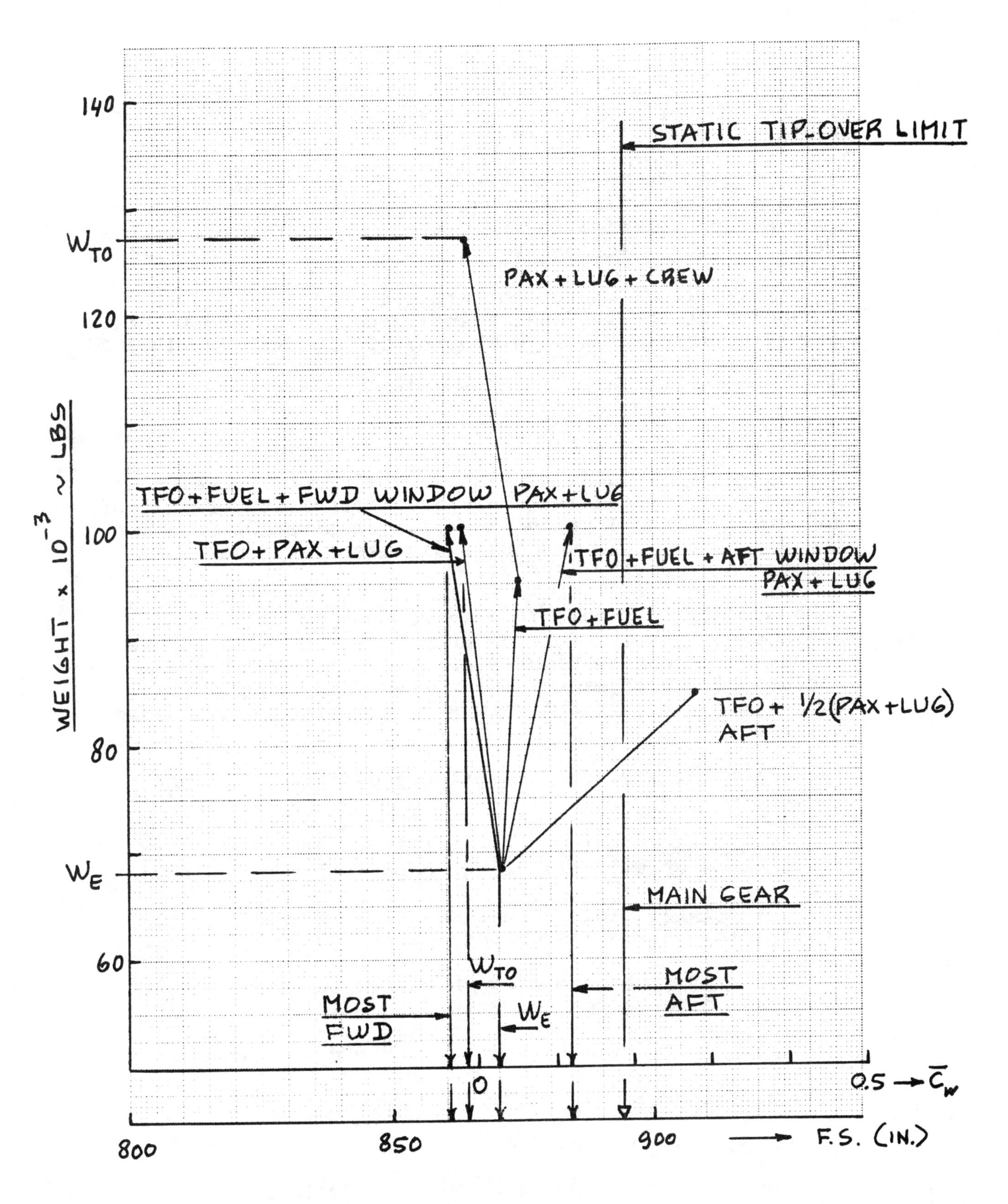

Figure 10.6 Ourania: Weight-C.G. Excursion Diagram

Note that this compares favorably with the data of Table 10.3.

Step 10.8: The most aft c.g. of the Ourania is well forward of the main gear contact point. The overall gear disposition relative to the c.g. range is discussed in Chapter 9, Sub-section 9.2.2.

The suitability of the aft c.g. location from a viewpoint of static longitudinal and static directional stability is discussed in Chapter 11, Sub-section 11.2.2.

Step 10.9: To save space this step has been omitted.

10.2.3 Fighter

Step 10.1: Table 10.6 shows the component weight breakdown for the Eris. This breakdown is the result of applying a Class I component weight estimation method to the airplane. This method is discussed in detail in Chapter 2 of Part V (Ref.4).

Step 10.2: Figure 10.7 shows the preliminary arrangement drawing for the Eris. This drawing is the result of combining Figures 4.9, 6.5, 8.4 and 9.7. Because of the asymmetries involved in the gun and nose gear placement, a front view and a top view are included in Figure 10.7.

Step 10.3: Figure 10.7 also shows the component centers of gravity.

Step 10.4: Table 10.6 also lists the x, y and z coordinates of all Eris weight components.

Step 10.5: Table 10.6 also lists the centers of gravity for several important loading configurations.

Step 10.6: Figure 10.8 shows the weight-c.g. excursion diagram for the Eris.

Step 10.7: From Figure 10.8, the c.g. limits are:

most forward c.g. occurs at W = 46,400 lbs,

F.S.= 324 in. and $0.43\bar{c}_w$.

most aft c.g. occurs at W = 33,500 lbs,

F.S.= 334 in. and $0.50\bar{c}_w$.

Table 10.6 Component Weight and Coordinate Data: Eris

Component	Weight	x	Wx	y	Wy	z	Wz
	lbs	in.	in.lbs	in.	in.lbs	in.	in.lbs
Wing	6,762	331	2,238,222	0	0	118	797,916
Empennage	1,597	614	980,558	0	0	173	276,281
Fuselage + booms	7,347	323	2,373,081	0	0	94	690,618
Engine section	160	417	66,720	0	0	91	14,560
Landing Gear N.G.	554	137	75,898	+16	8,864	44	24,376
M.G.	2,214	350	774,900	0	0	58	128,412
Engines	6,000	417	2,502,000	0	0	91	546,000
Engine inst.	2,834	370	1,048,580	0	0	102	289,068
GAU-8A Gun	2,014	180	362,520	-20	-40,280	60	120,840
Fixed Eq.(- gun)	4,018	189	759,402	0	0	85	341,530
Empty weight, W_E	33,500	334	11,181,881	-1	-31,416	96	3,229,601
TFO	300	370	111,000	0	0	85	25,500
Fuel	18,500	331	6,123,500	0	0	118	2,183,000
Pilot	200	209	41,800	0	0	91	18,200
Ammunition	1,785	283	505,155	0	0	73	130,305
Bombs (fuselage)	4,248	277	1,176,696	0	0	44	186,912
Bombs (wings)	6,372	315	2,007,180	0	0	100	637,200
Take-off wht, W_{TO}	64,905	326	21,147,212	0	-31,416	99	6,410,718

Note: other loading conditions shown in Figure 10.8.

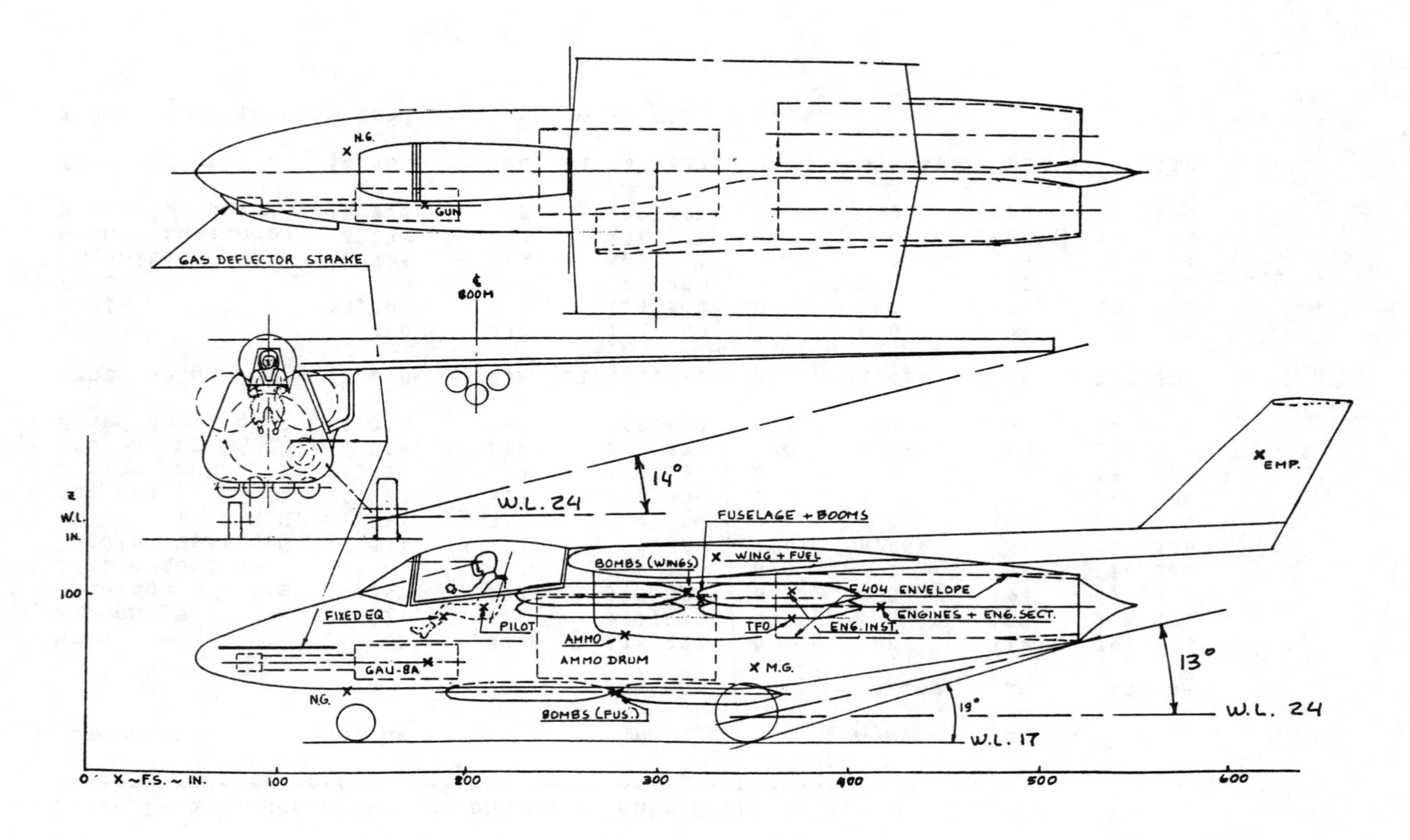

Figure 10.7 Eris: General Arrangement

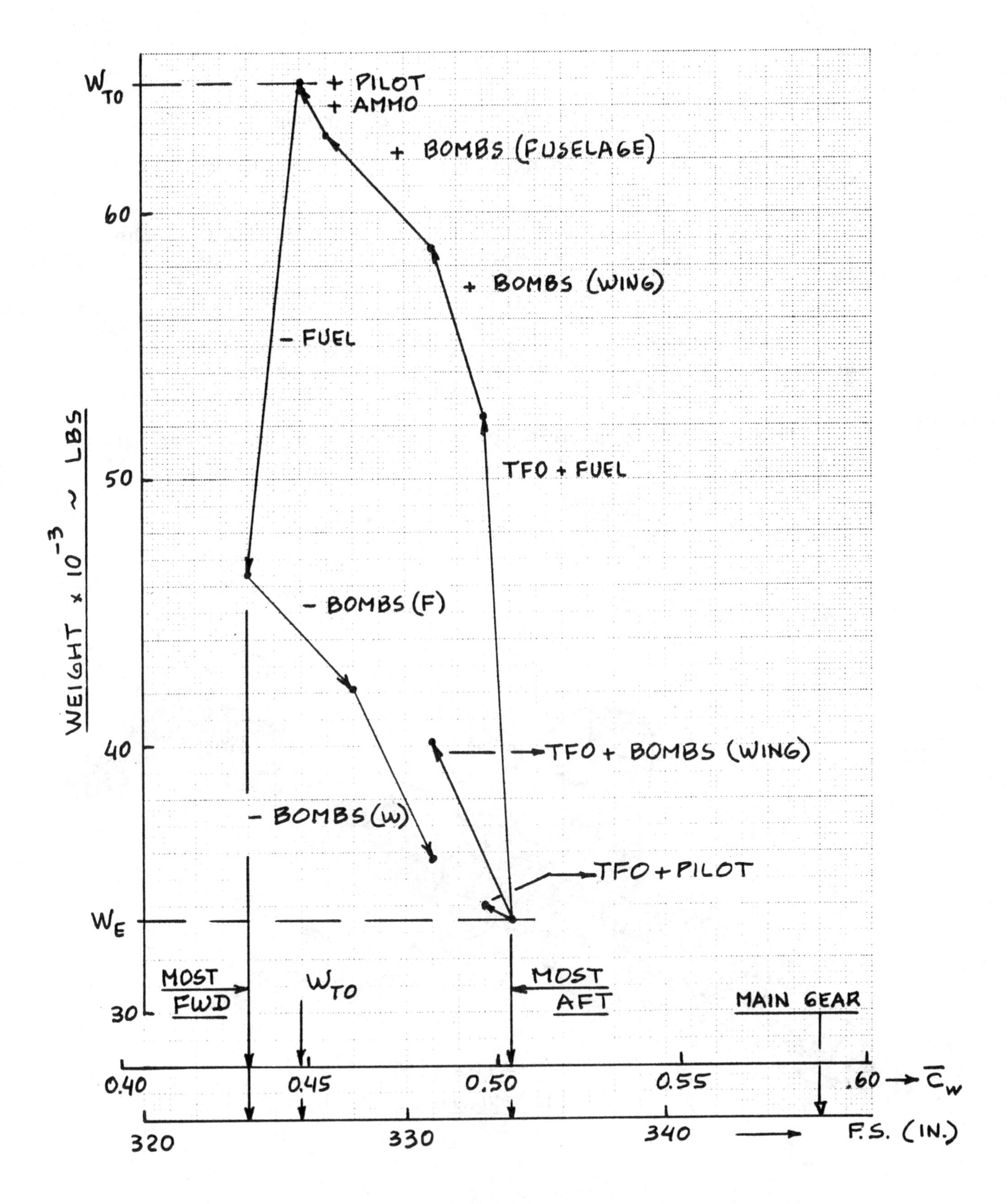

Figure 10.8 Eris: Weight C.G. Excursion Diagram

The c.g. range of the Eris is 10 inches or $0.07\bar{c}_w$.

Note that this compares favorably with the data of Table 10.3.

Step 10.8: The most aft c.g. is well forward of the main landing gear. The overall disposition of the landing gear relative to the c.g. range is discussed in Chapter 9, Sub-section 9.2.3.

The suitability of the aft c.g. location in terms of static longitudinal and static directional stability is discussed in Chapter 11, Sub-section 11.2.3.

Step 10.9: To save space this step has been omitted.

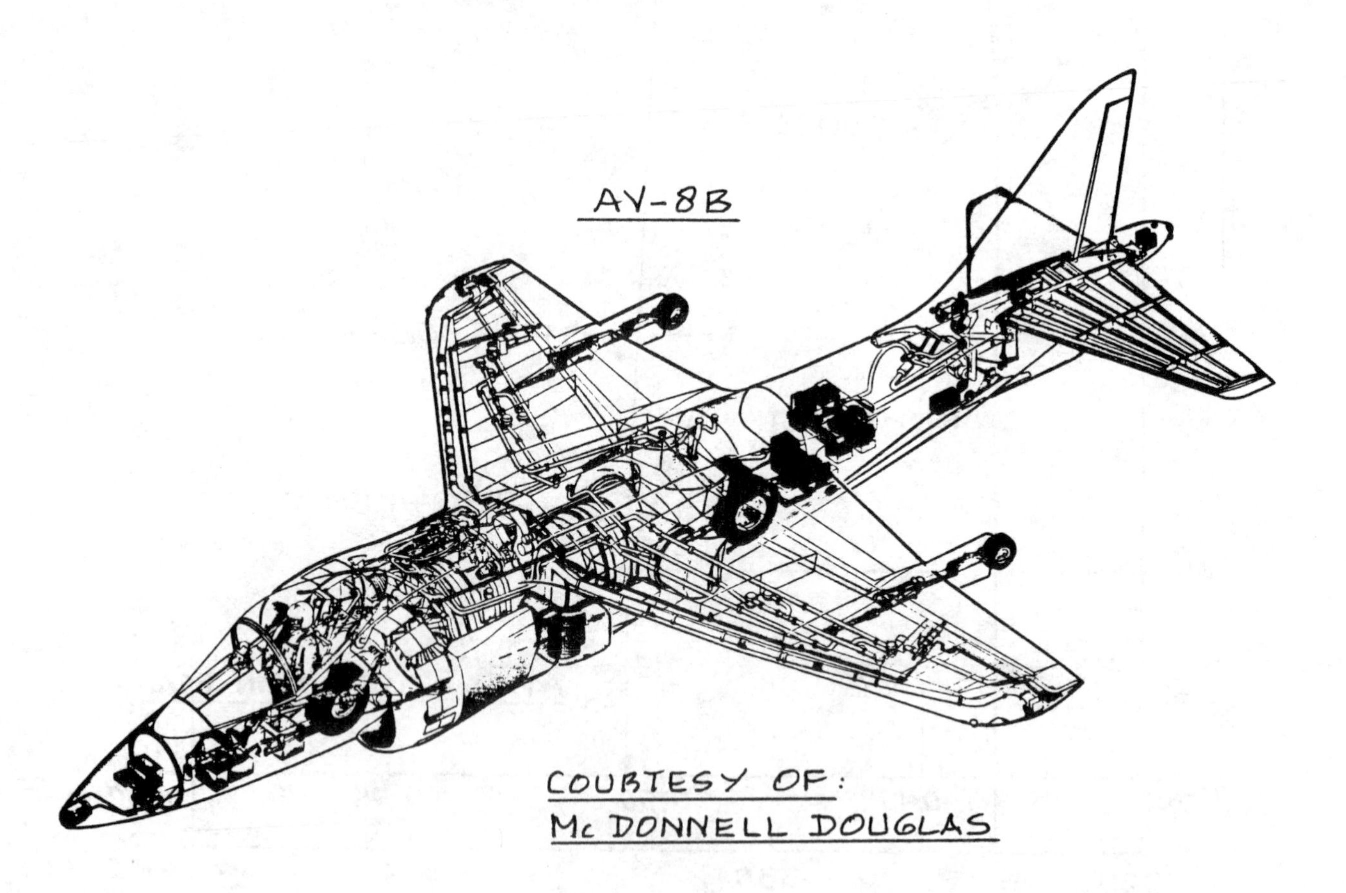

11. CLASS I METHOD FOR STABILITY AND CONTROL ANALYSIS

The purpose of this chapter is to present a method for rapidly determining whether or not the proposed configuration will have satisfactory stability and control characteristics. The method is presented as part of Step 11, p.d. sequence I as outlined in Chapter 2. Because the method is limited in scope as well as in accuracy, it should be used only in conjunction with preliminary design sequence I.

The method consists of 16 steps and deals with the following stability and control characteristics:

1. Static longitudinal stability (Longitudinal X-plot), see steps 11.1 through 11.7 in Section 11.1.

2. Static directional stability (Directional X-plot), see steps 11.8 through 11.11 in Section 11.2.

3. Minimum control speed with one engine out, see steps 11.12 through 11.16 in Section 11.3.

Example applications are given in Section 11.4.

Other important stability and control characteristics such as take-off rotation, cross-wind controllability, trim through the c.g. range and a variety of dynamic stability considerations are not covered by this Class I method. The reader should refer to Part VII (Ref.6) for a detailed discussion of these characteristics.

11.1 STATIC LONGITUDINAL STABILITY (LONGITUDINAL X-PLOT)

Step 11.1: Prepare a longitudinal X-plot for the airplane.

Figure 11.1 presents examples of longitudinal X-plots. Note that the two legs of the X are representative of:

1. The c.g. leg represents the rate at which the c.g. moves aft (fwd) as a function of horizontal tail (canard) area.

2. The a.c. leg represents the rate at which the a.c. moves aft (fwd) as a function of horizontal tail (canard) area.

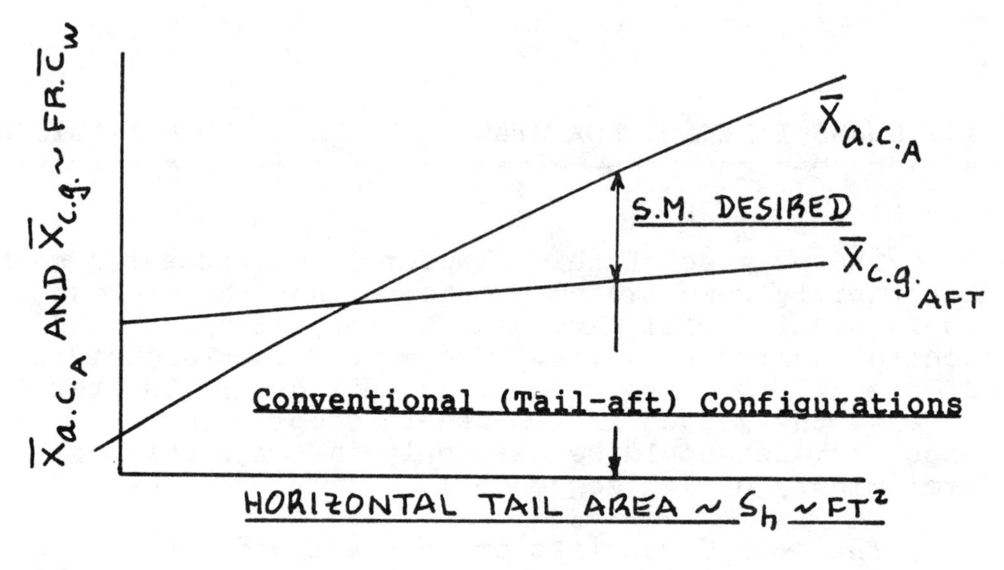

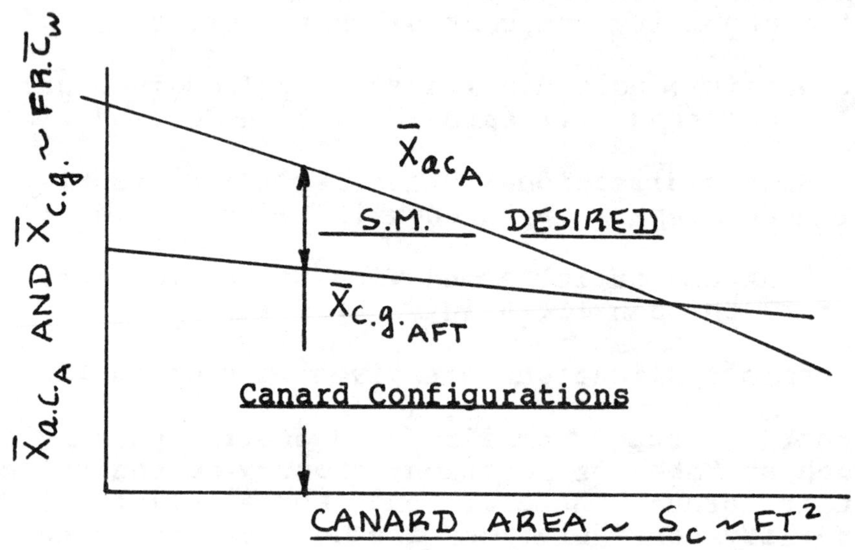

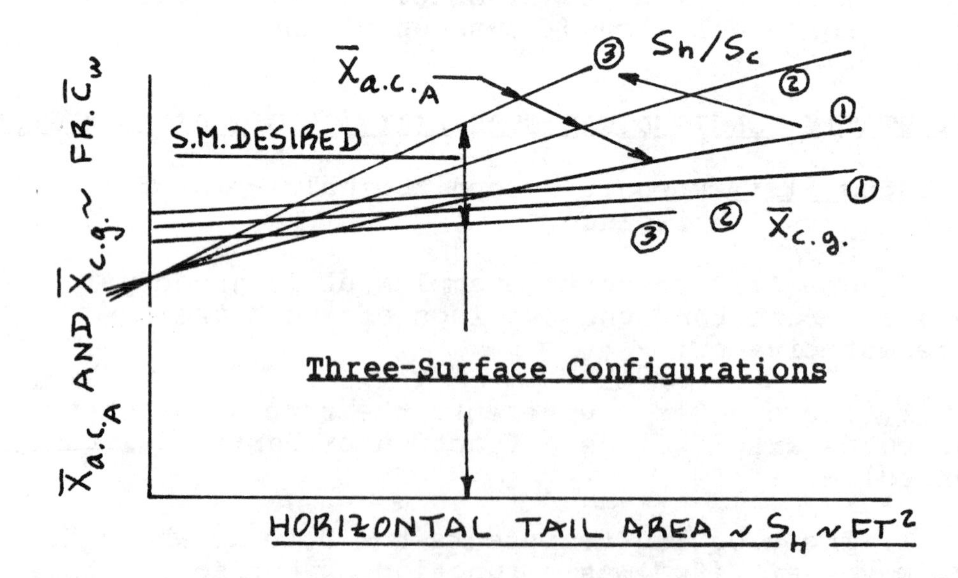

Figure 11.1 Examples of Longitudinal X-Plots

The c.g. leg is easily calculated with the help of the Class I weight and balance analysis of Step 10. From the Class I weight analysis the weight of the horizontal tail (canard) is known on a per ft^2 basis. Assuming this quantity to be independent of surface area, the c.g. can be found for any area of the horizontal tail (or canard).

The a.c. leg is calculated with the following equations:

$$\bar{x}_{ac_A} = [\bar{x}_{ac_{wf}} + \{C_{L_{\alpha_h}}(1 - d\varepsilon_h/d\alpha)(S_h/S)\bar{x}_{ac_h} - C_{L_{\alpha_c}}(1 + d\varepsilon_c/d\alpha)\bar{x}_{ac_c}(S_c/S)\}/C_{L_{\alpha_{wf}}}]/F, \quad (11.1)$$

where:

$$F = [1 + \{C_{L_{\alpha_h}}(1 - d\varepsilon_h/d\alpha)(S_h/S) + C_{L_{\alpha_c}}(1 + d\varepsilon_c/d\alpha)(S_c/S)\}/C_{L_{\alpha_{wf}}}] \quad (11.2)$$

Figure 11.2 defines the required geometric quantities in these equations. The aerodynamic quantities can be computed with methods presented in Part VI (Ref.5).

Note that Eqns.(11.1) and (11.2) apply to three types of airplanes in the following manner:

For a tail-aft airplane: set $S_c = 0$ and consider S_h as the independent variable.

For a canard airplane: set $S_h = 0$ and consider S_c as the independent variable.

For a three-surface airplane: freeze the ratio S_h/S_c and consider S_h as the independent variable.

For a three-surface airplane, the X-plot should be made for different ratios of S_h/S_c.

Both the c.g. leg and the a.c. leg of the 'X' can now be plotted as a function of area (hor.tail or canard). This completes the longitudinal X-plot.

Figure 11.1 presents conceptual X-plots for three types of airplanes.

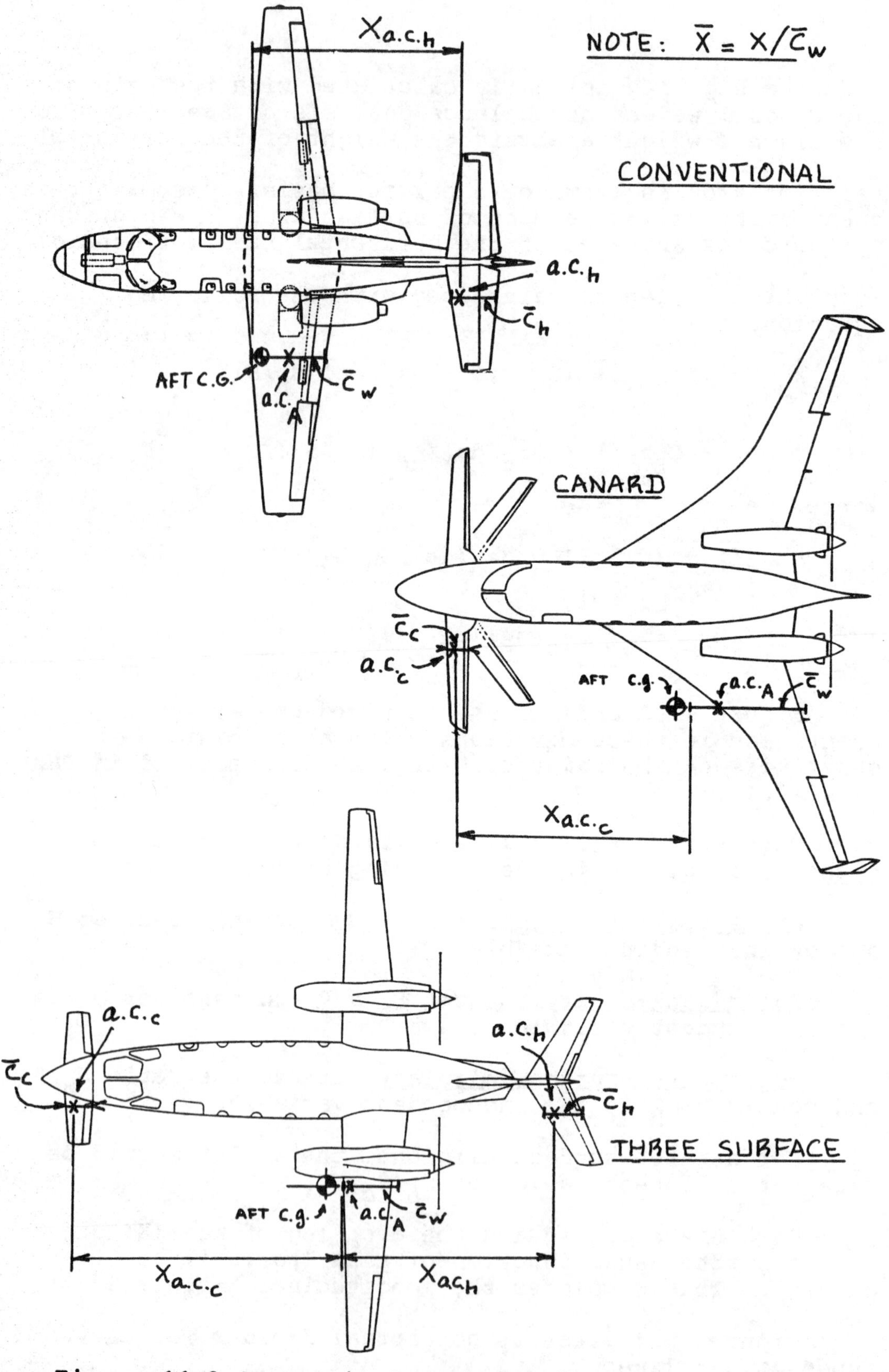

Figure 11.2 Geometric Quantities for A.C. Calculations

Step 11.2: Determine whether or not the airplane being designed needs to be *'inherently stable'* or *'de-facto stable*.

Inherent stability is required of all airplanes which do not rely for their stability on a feedback augmentation system. If the airplane falls in this category proceed to Step 11.3.

De-facto stability is required of all airplanes which are stable only with a feedback augmentation system in place. If the airplane falls in this category proceed to Step 11.6.

Step 11.3: Determine whether the airplane being designed fits in any of the twelve categories listed on p.28 in Chapter 2.

If the airplane fits in categories 1-4, proceed to Step 11.4.

If the airplane fits in categories 5-12, proceed to Step 11.5.

Step 11.4: Using the 'aft' c.g. leg in Figure 11.1 find the empennage area required for a minimum static margin of 10 percent.

Reference 9 (Chapter 5) shows that for a static margin of 10 percent:

$$dC_m/dC_L = \bar{X}_{cg} - \bar{X}_{ac} = -0.10 \qquad (11.3)$$

Figure 11.1 shows how the empennage area follows from this. The required empennage area should be recorded.

Step 11.5: Using the 'aft' c.g. leg in Figure 11.1 find the empennage area required for a minimum static margin of 5 percent.

Reference 9 (Chapter 5) shows that for a static margin of 5 percent:

$$dC_m/dC_L = \bar{X}_{cg} - \bar{X}_{ac} = -0.05 \qquad (11.4)$$

Figure 11.1 shows how the empennage area follows from this. The required empennage area should be recorded.

Step 11.6: Using the 'aft' c.g. leg in Figure 11.1 find the SAS feedback gain required as a function of negative static margin.

This feedback gain is estimated from:

$$k_{\alpha} = (\Delta SM)C_{L_{\alpha}}/C_{m_{\delta_e}} , \qquad (11.5)$$

where:

$$C_{L_{\alpha}} = C_{L_{\alpha_{wf}}} + C_{L_{\alpha_h}}(1 - d\varepsilon/d\alpha)(S_h/S)$$
$$+ C_{L_{\alpha_c}}(1 + d\varepsilon/d\alpha)S_c/S \qquad (11.6)$$

The value of k_{α} thus computed should not exceed 5 deg. of elevator per degree of angle of attack.

Equation (11.5) is 'set up' in terms of angle of attack feedback to the elevator. If angle of attack is fed back to the stabilizer (in some fighters) or to the canard (as in the X29), the limit of 5 deg/deg also applies.

The value of incremental static margin, ΔSM in Eqn.(11.5) itself is obtained from the following 'de-facto' stability requirement:

$$\Delta SM = |\bar{X}_{ac} - \bar{X}_{cg} - 0.05| \qquad (11.7)$$

Values for $\bar{X}_{cg}$ and for $\bar{X}_{ac}$ follow from the X-plot in Figure 11.1 at any value of empennage area.

The highest level of static instability which is practical from a stability augmentation viewpoint is that which drives k_{α} to above 5 deg/deg. The corresponding empennage area is the smallest one allowable. This value should be recorded.

Step 11.7: The empennage area obtained from either Eqn.(11.4), (11.5) or (11.6) is the area to be used instead of that obtained from the $\bar{V}$-method, Eqn.(8.3).

If there is more than 10 percent difference between

the empennage areas predicted from the $\overline{V}$-method and the method just described, the airplane weight and balance calculations of Chapter 10 should be reviewed and any necessary adjustments made.

11.2 STATIC DIRECTIONAL STABILITY (DIRECTIONAL X-PLOT)

Step 11.8: Prepare a directional X-plot for the airplane.

Figure 11.3 shows an example of such an X-plot. The c.g. leg is again determined with the help of the Class I weight analysis of Step 10. The weight per ft^2 of the vertical tail is known from this weight analysis.

The C_{n_β} leg of the X-plot follows from:

$$C_{n_\beta} = C_{n_{\beta_{wf}}} + C_{L_{\alpha_v}}(S_v/S)(x_v/b) \tag{11.8}$$

The geometric quantities in Eqn.(11.8) are defined in Figure 11.4. The aerodynamic quantities on the right hand side of Eqn.(11.8) can be computed with the methods of Part VI (Ref.5).

Step 11.9: Determine whether or not the airplane being designed needs to have *'inherent'* or *'de facto'* directional stability.

If the airplane needs to be 'inherently' directionally stable, proceed to Step 11.10.

If the airplane needs to have 'de facto' directional stability proceed to Step 11.11.

Step 11.10: Assume that the overall level of directional stability must be:

$$C_{n_\beta} = 0.0010 \text{ per deg.} \tag{11.9}$$

Proceed to the X-plot of Figure 11.3 and find the value of S_v which produces this level of directional stability.

Step 11.11: Compute the required sideslip to rudder feedback gain from:

$$k_\beta = (\Delta C_{n_\beta})/C_{n_{\delta_r}} \tag{11.10}$$

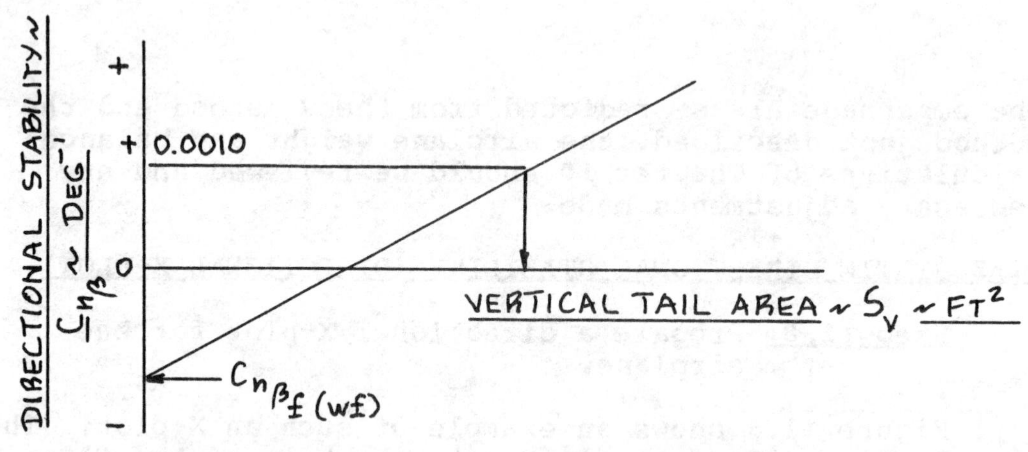

Figure 11.3 Example of Directional X-Plot

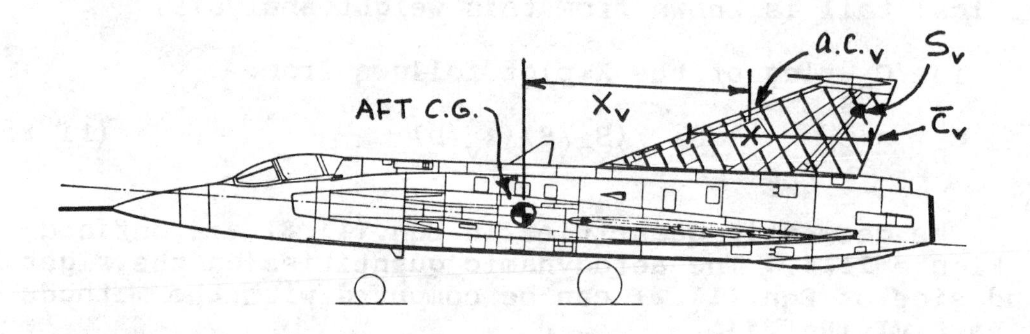

Figure 11.4 Geometric Quantities for Directional X-Plot

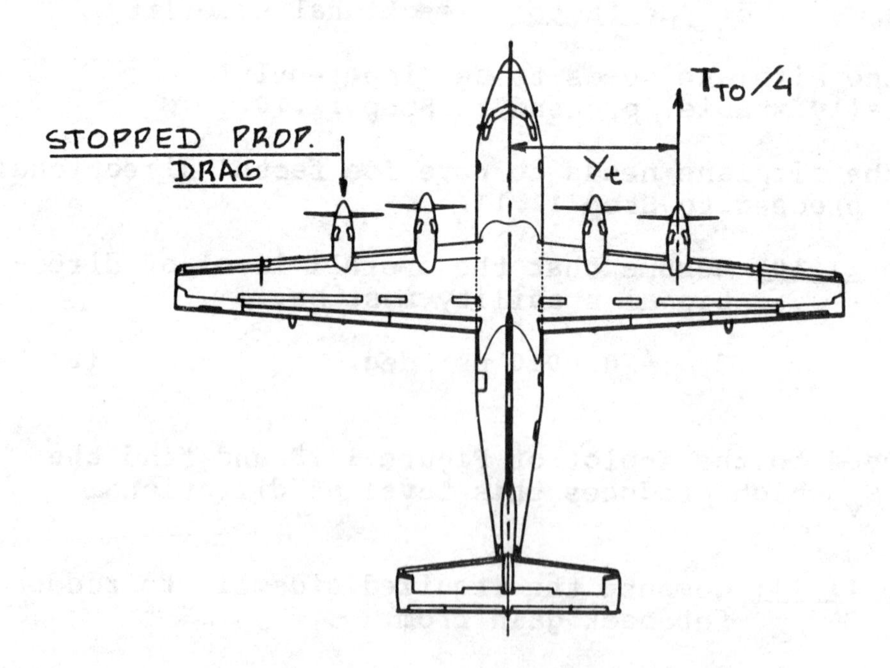

Figure 11.5 Geometry for Engine-out V_{mc} Calculation

The required value of ΔC_{n_β} follows from:

$$\Delta C_{n_\beta} = 0.0010 - C_{n_\beta} \qquad (11.11)$$

The value of k_β thus computed should not exceed 5 deg/deg.

The vertical tail area resulting in the lowest value of inherent C_{n_β} which is consistent with Eqn.(11.11) is the smallest allowable vertical tail area. This empennage area should be recorded.

11.3 MINIMUM CONTROL SPEED WITH ONE ENGINE INOPERATIVE

Step 11.12: Determine the critical engine-out yawing moment from:

$$N_{t_{crit}} = T_{TO_e} y_t \qquad (11.12)$$

The value of y_t corresponds to the lateral thrust moment arm of the most critical engine. Figure 11.5 illustrates y_t.

For a propeller driven airplane the known value of P_{TO} must be changed to the corresponding value of T_{TO}. Figure 3.8 of Part I (p.100) can be used to do this.

Step 11.13: Determine the value of drag induced yawing moment due to the inoperative engine from:

For a propeller driven airplane with fixed pitch propellers:

$$N_D = 0.25 N_{t_{crit}} \qquad (11.13)$$

For a propeller driven airplane with variable pitch propellers:

$$N_D = 0.10 N_{t_{crit}} \qquad (11.14)$$

For a jet driven airplane with a windmilling engine with low b.p.r.:

$$N_D = 0.15 N_{t_{crit}} \tag{11.15}$$

For a jet driven airplane with a wind-milling engine with high b.p.r.:

$$N_D = 0.25 N_{t_{crit}} \tag{11.16}$$

<u>Step 11.14:</u> Calculate the maximum allowable V_{mc} from:

$$V_{mc} = 1.2 V_s, \tag{11.17}$$

where V_s is the lowest stall speed of the airplane. This is usually the landing stall speed.

<u>Step 11.15:</u> Calculate the rudder deflection required to hold the engine out condition at V_{mc} from:

$$\delta_r = (N_D + N_{t_{crit}})/\bar{q}_{mc} S b C_{n_{\delta_r}} \tag{11.18}$$

The value of the control power derivative $C_{n_{\delta_r}}$ may be computed with the methods of Part VI (Ref.5).

The rudder deflection resulting from Eqn.(11.18) should be no more than 25 degrees. If it is more, adjust the rudder size and/or the vertical tail size until this is satisfied. Record this vertical tail area.

<u>Step 11.16:</u> The largest vertical tail area which results from Steps 11.10, 11.11 or 11.15 is the vertical tail area required for the airplane. Determine this area.

If this vertical tail area differs by more than 10 percent from the one computed with the $\bar{V}$-method of Eqn.(8.4) it will be necessary to adjust the weight and balance calculations of Chapter 10.

11.4 EXAMPLE APPLICATIONS

Three example applications will now be discussed:

11.4.1 Twin Engine Propeller Driven Airplane: Selene
11.4.2 Jet Transport: Ourania
11.4.3 Fighter: Eris

11.4.1 Twin Engine Propeller Driven Airplane

Step 11.1: Figure 11.6 presents the longitudinal X-plot for the Selene.

Observe, that for the airplane to be 0.10 stable at its operating weight empty, a horizontal tail area of 58 ft^2 is required. This represents an increase of $58 - 37 = 21 \text{ ft}^2$. This larger horizontal tail has the effect of shifting the aft c.g. to $0.9\bar{c}_w$. This is still forward of the main landing gear. However, it may be necessary to move the main gear aft a bit to accomodate the longitudinal tip-over criterion of Chapter 9.

Note also from the X-plot, that the Selene will have to be restricted from flying at W_{OE} plus two aft passengers plus aft luggage. The airplane would become unstable in this flight condition. This is a rather common occurrence in this type of airplane.

Observe also from the X-plot, that with power-on the stability of the airplane is much better. This is a typical characteristic of pusher-propeller airplanes.

Step 11.2: The Selene must be an inherently stable airplane. Full time stability augmentation in this type of airplane is probably not affordable.

Step 11.3: The Selene fits into category 3: twin engine propeller driven airplanes.

Step 11.4: It was already decided in Step 11.1 that the horizontal tail area needs to be increased from 37 to 58 ft^2.

Steps 11.5 - 11.7: Not applicable.

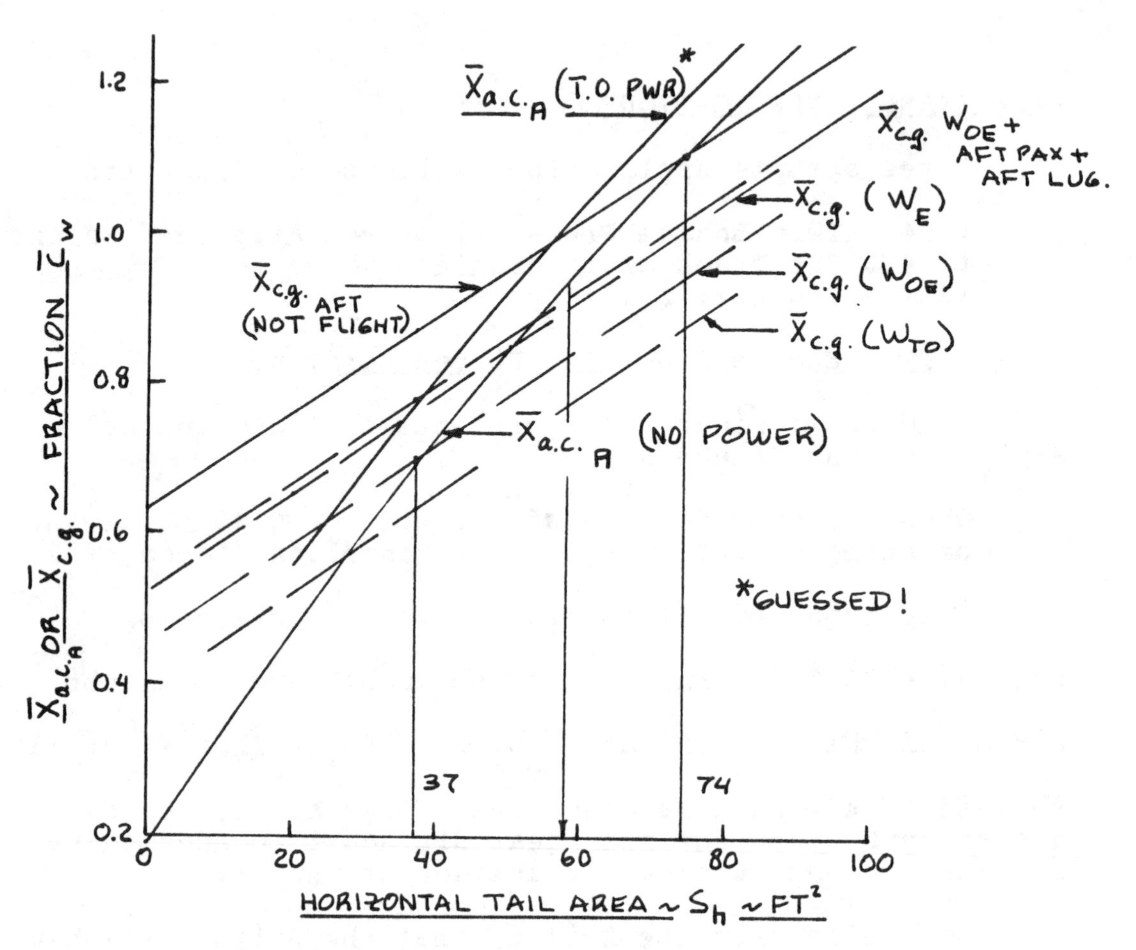

Figure 11.6 Selene: Longitudinal X-Plot

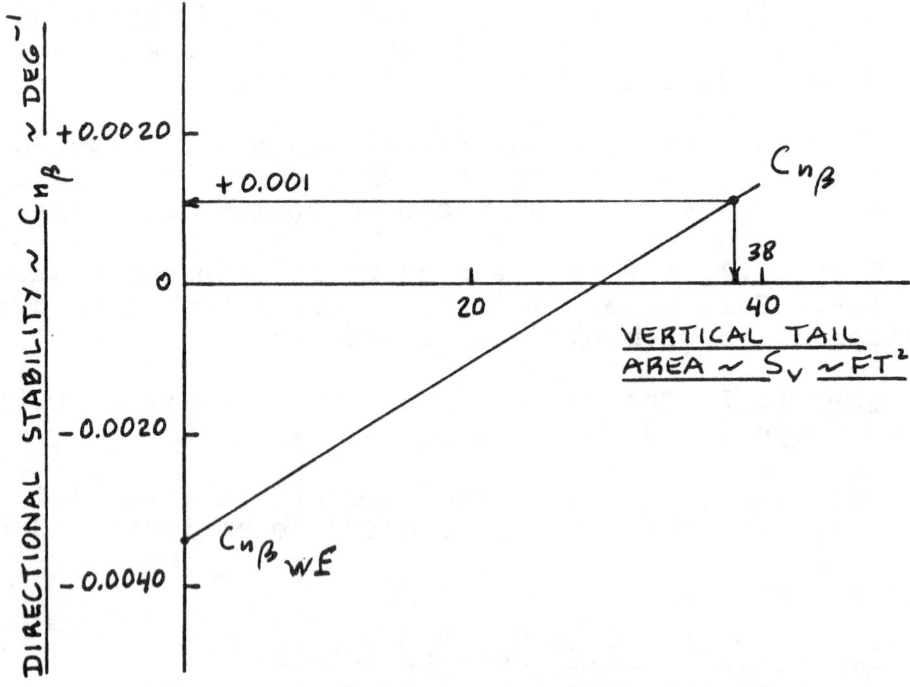

Figure 11.7 Selene: Directional X-Plot

Step 11.8: Figure 11.7 presents the directional X-plot for the Selene.

Step 11.9: The Selene needs to have inherent directional stability: full time stability augmentation in this type of airplane is probably not affordable.

Step 11.10: Note from Figure 11.7 that the vertical tail of the Selene is slightly too large: an area of 36 ft^2 would be sufficient from a directional stability viewpoint.

Step 11.11: Not applicable.

Step 11.12: From the general arrangement drawing of the Selene (Fig.10.3) it follows that y_t= 6.3 ft. The maximum take-off power, P_{TO} was determined in Chapter 5 (p.135) as 449 hp. per engine. From Figure 3.8 in Part I (p.100) it is seen that at this power level, the take-off thrust is: T_{TO}= 1,200 lbs per engine.

The critical engine-out yawing moment it therefore: 1,200x6.3 = 7,560 ftlbs.

Step 11.13: The Selene will have variable pitch propellers. The value for N_D therefore is: 0.25x7,560 = 1,890 ftlbs.

Step 11.14: The landing stall speed is the lowest stall speed for the Selene. At the landing weight this is found to be: 99.3 kts.

The maximum allowable value for V_{mc} is therefore: 1.2x99.3 = 119 kts.

Step 11.15: From the vertical tail and rudder geometry definitions in Chapter 8 (p.210-211) and from the methods of Part VI the following value for rudder control power derivative is computed:

$$C_{n_{\delta_r}} = - 0.0027 \text{ deg}^{-1}$$

With Eqn.(11.18) this yields for the rudder deflection required at V_{mc} a value of 16.4 deg. This is well within the allowable value of 25 deg.

Step 11.16: The vertical tail size of the Selene is thus 'critical' from a directional stability viewpoint.

As seen in Step 11.10 the existing tail size of 38 ft^2 is sufficient.

11.4.2 Jet Transport

Step 11.1: Figure 11.8 presents the longitudinal X-plot for the Ourania.

Observe, that the Ourania is longitudinally stable without a horizontal tail. The cause for this is the too forward position of the wing on the fuselage. By moving the wing, together with the main landing gear 200 inches aft a more reasonable result is obtained. Note that now, at the nominal tail area of 254 ft^2 the Ourania has a level of instability of $0.085\bar{c}_w$. The reader will remember that the Ourania was to be configured as a 'relaxed' stability airplane.

Figure 11.9 shows how 'wing + main gear' movement affects the c.g. location on the mean geometric chord of the wing, $\bar{c}_w$.

Step 11.2: The Ourania must be a 'relaxed stability' airplane. The level of instability at aft c.g. should be the subject of a detailed study of the benefits in 'trimmed lift-to-drag ratio' which this confers on the airplane. For purposes of this p.d. study a level of instability of $0.085\bar{c}_w$ is arbitrarily selected.

Step 11.3: The Selene fits into category 7: jet transports.

Step 11.4: Not applicable.

Step 11.5: Not applicable.

Step 11.6: Using the 'aft' c.g. leg corresponding the 200 in. aft shift of the wing (Figure 11.8) it is found that the longitudinal stability augmentation system must generate a value of incremental static margin of:

$\Delta SM = 0.085 + 0.05 = 0.135.$

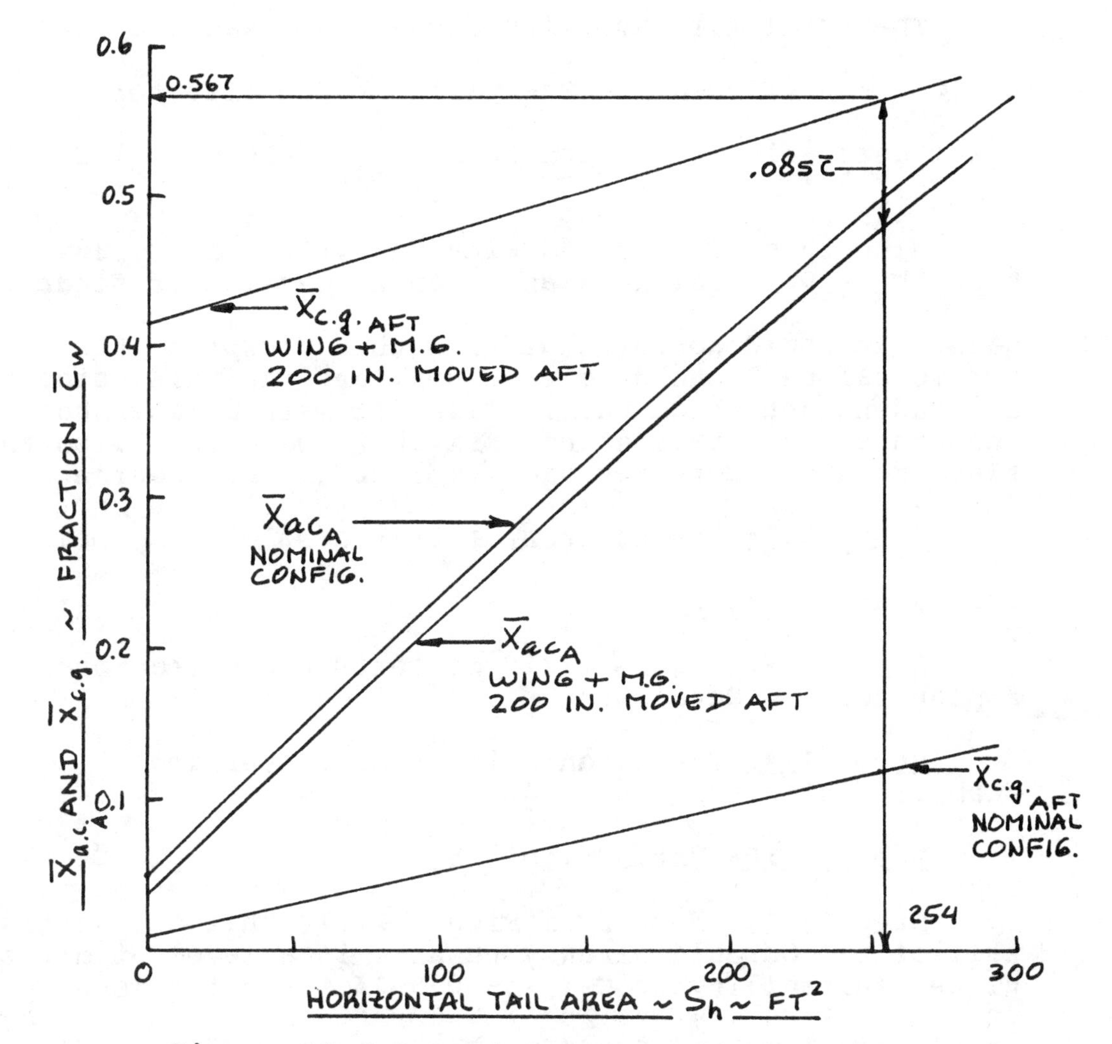

Figure 11.8 Ourania: Longitudinal X-Plot

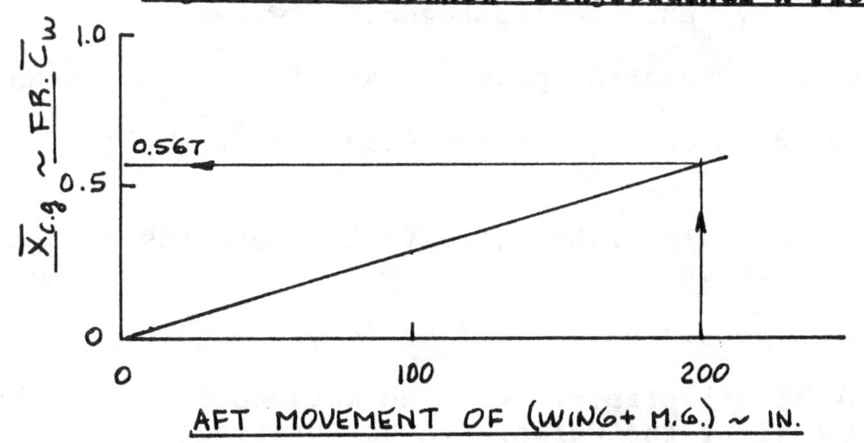

Figure 11.9 Ourania: Effect of 'Wing + Main Gear' Aft Movement on Airplane Center of Gravity

The total airplane lift curve slope was computed to be: $C_{L_\alpha} = 0.081 \text{ deg}^{-1}$. The value of the elevator control power derivative was found to be: $C_{m_{\delta_e}} = -0.0251 \text{ deg}^{-1}$.

With these values and with Eqn.(11.5) it follows that: $k_\alpha = 0.44$ which is an acceptable value of feedback gain. It would appear that from this viewpoint the horizontal tail could be made smaller. At this point it is prudent not to do this. Class II methods may show that take-off rotation and trim at forward c.g. with the flaps down are more restrictive in tailplane design.

Step 11.7: The horizontal tail area will be maintained at 254 ft^2.

Step 11.8: Figure 11.10 presents the directional X-plot for the Ourania.

Step 11.9: The Ourania is to be a 'relaxed' stability airplane.

Step 11.10: Not applicable.

Step 11.11: Note from Figure 11.10 that the vertical tail of the Ourania already results in a level of directional instability of $C_{n_\beta} = -0.0016$. Desired is a 'de-facto' level of 0.0010. The decrement of 0.0026 must be provided by the sideslip feedback system.

The rudder control power derivative of the Ourania was computed to be: $C_{n_{\delta_r}} = -0.0012 \text{ deg}^{-1}$.

With the help of Eqn.(11.10) the feedback gain can be computed to be:

$$k_\beta = 0.0026/0.0012 = 2.2 \text{ deg/deg.}$$

This is acceptable. From this viewpoint then the vertical tail of the Ourania is not critical.

Step 11.12: From the general arrangement drawing of the Ourania (Fig.10.4) it follows that $y_t = 16.7$ ft. The

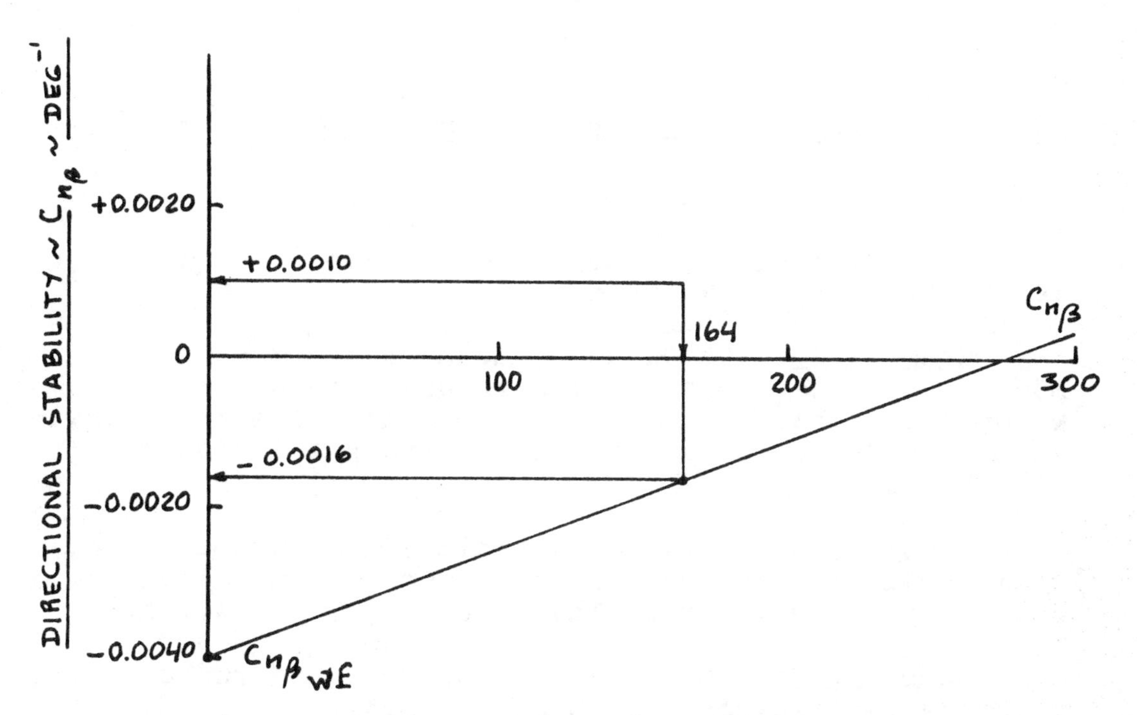

Figure 11.10 Ourania: Directional X-Plot

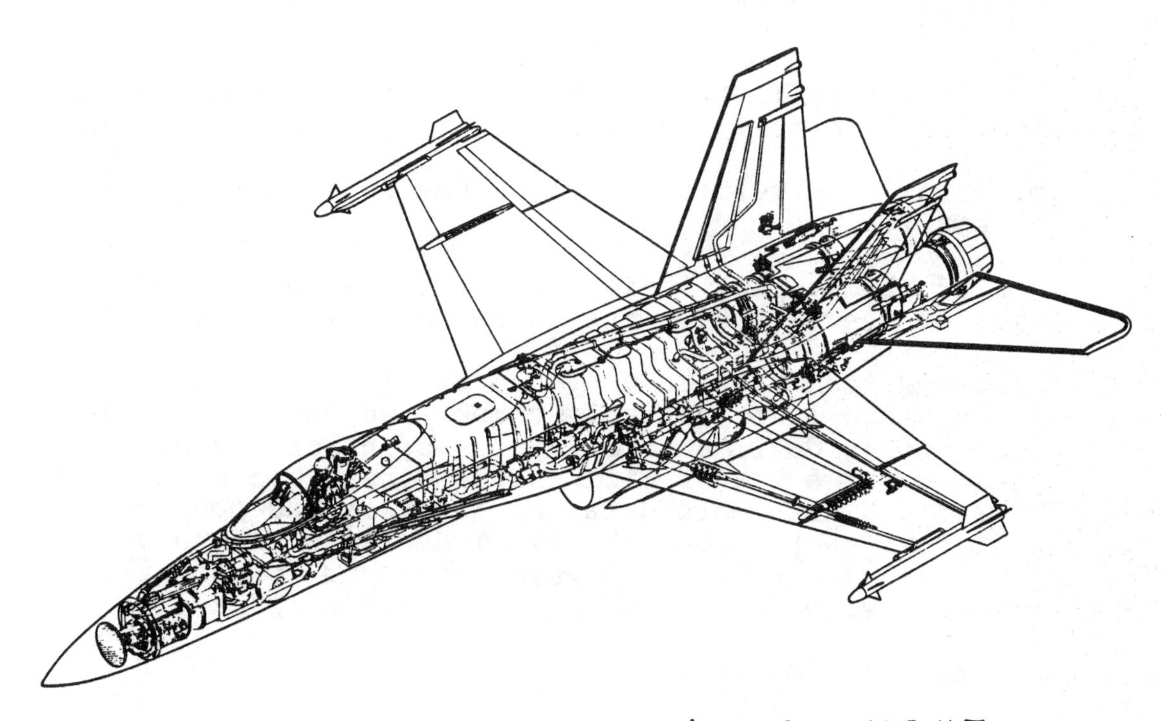

F/A - 18A HORNET
COURTESY OF:
McDONNELL DOUGLAS

maximum take-off thrust, T_{TO} was determined in Chapter 5 (p.138) as 24,000 lbs per engine.

The critical engine-out yawing moment it therefore: 24,000x16.7 = 400,800 ftlbs.

Step 11.13: The Ourania has high b.p.r engines. Eqn.(11.16) therefore applies in determining the windmilling drag induced yawing moment. The total yawing moment to be 'held' at V_{mc} is therefore 1.25x400,800 = 501,000 ftlbs.

Step 11.14: The landing stall speed is the lowest stall speed for the Ourania. At the landing weight it is found that V_{s_L} = 87 kts. This yields a V_{mc} = 105 kts.

Step 11.15: From the vertical tail and rudder geometry definitions in Chapter 8 (p.210-211) and from the methods of Part VI the following value for rudder control power derivative is computed:

$$C_{n_{\delta_r}} = -0.0012 \text{ deg}^{-1}$$

With Eqn.(11.18) this yields for the rudder deflection required at V_{mc} a value of 61 deg. This is clearly too much. The vertical tail of the Ourania is therefore too small.

If the vertical tail size is increased to 200 ft^2 while at the same time the rudder area ratio S_r/S_v is increased from 0.35 to 0.45 and the rudder is given a double hinge line (variable camber) so the rudder can be driven to 40 deg., a satisfactory solution can be obtained. The reader will realize that this will have to be verified with more detailed analyses and possibly a windtunnel test before the final decision on the vertical tail size can be made. However, for p.d. purposes it will be assumed that the vertical tail will have to be increased to 200 ft^2.

Step 11.16: It was already decided in the previous step to increase the vertical tail from 164 to 200 ft^2.

11.4.3 Fighter

Step 11.1: Figure 11.11 presents the longitudinal X-plot for the Eris.

Observe, that the Eris is longitudinally unstable without a horizontal tail. At the horizontal tail area of 93 ft^2 (determined from the V-method in Chapter 8) the level of instability is $0.133\bar{c}_w$. The reader should realize that the X-29 was designed to a level of instability of $0.350\bar{c}_w$ at its aft c.g!

Step 11.2: The Eris must be a negative stability airplane. The level of instability at aft c.g. and at forward c.g. should be the subject of a detailed study of the benefits in 'trimmed lift-to-drag ratio' and maneuvering performance which are conferred upon the airplane. For purposes of this p.d. study a level of instability of $0.133\bar{c}_w$ is arbitrarily selected.

Step 11.3: The Selene fits into category 9: fighters.

Step 11.4: Not applicable.

Step 11.5: Not applicable.

Step 11.6: Using the 'aft' c.g. leg of Figure 11.11 it is found that the longitudinal stability augmentation system must generate a value of incremental static margin of:

$$\Delta SM = 0.133 + 0.05 = 0.185.$$

The total airplane lift curve slope was computed to be: $C_{L_\alpha} = 0.078 \text{ deg}^{-1}$. The value of the elevator control power derivative was found to be: $C_{m_{\delta_e}} = - 0.0182 \text{ deg}^{-1}$.

With these values and with Eqn.(11.5) it follows that: $k_\alpha = 0.80$ which is an acceptable value of feedback gain. It would appear that from this viewpoint the horizontal tail could be made smaller. At this point it

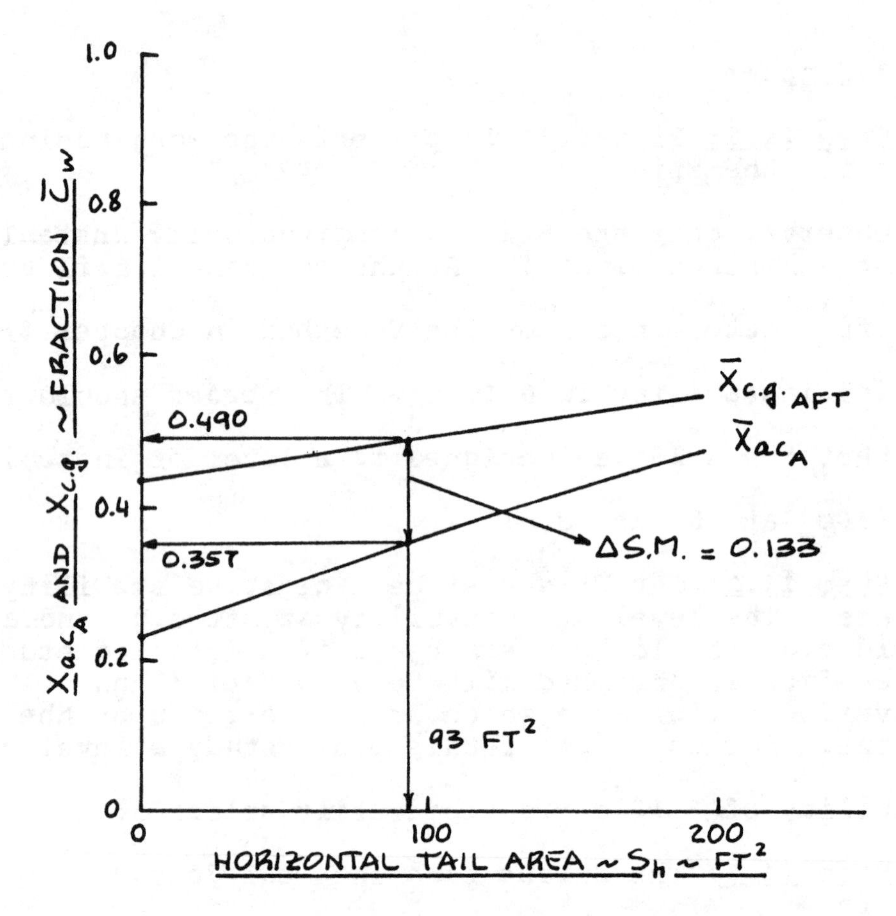

Figure 11.11 Eris: Longitudinal X-Plot

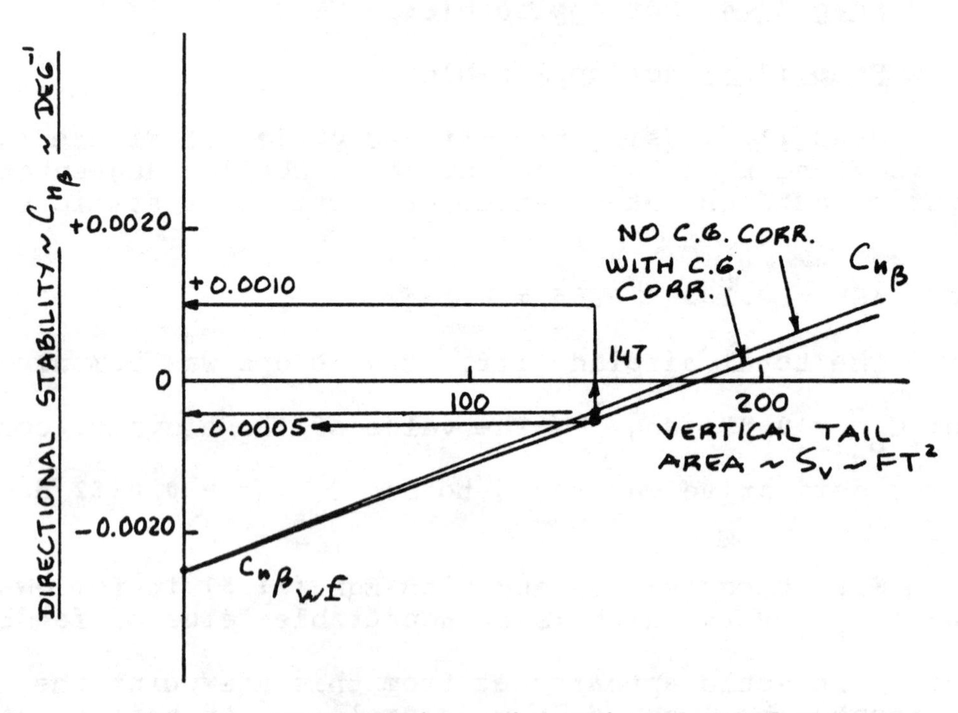

Figure 11.12 Eris: Directional X-Plot

is prudent not to do this. Class II methods may show that take-off rotation and trim at forward c.g. with the flaps down are more restrictive in tailplane design.

Step 11.7: The horizontal tail area of 93 ft^2 will be kept.

Step 11.8: Figure 11.12 presents the directional X-plot for the Eris.

Step 11.9: The Eris is to be a 'negative' stability airplane.

Step 11.10: Not applicable.

Step 11.11: Note from Figure 11.12 that the vertical tail of the Eris renders the airplane directionally unstable at a level of $C_{n_\beta} = -0.0005$. Desired is a 'de-facto' level of 0.0010. The decrement of 0.0015 must be provided by the sideslip feedback system.

The rudder control power derivative of the Eris was computed to be: $C_{n_{\delta_r}} = -0.0007 \text{ deg}^{-1}$.

With the help of Eqn.(11.10) the feedback gain can be computed to be:

$k_\beta = 0.0015/0.0007 = 2.1$ deg/deg.

This is acceptable. From this viewpoint then the vertical tail of the Eris is not critical.

Step 11.12: From the general arrangement drawing of the Eris (Fig.10.5) it follows that $y_t = 1.7$ ft. The maximum take-off thrust, T_{TO} was determined in Chapter 5 (p.140) as 16,000 lbs per engine.

The critical engine-out yawing moment it therefore: 12,000x1.7 = 20,400 ftlbs.

Step 11.13: The Eris has low b.p.r engines. Eqn.(11.16) therefore applies in determining the windmilling drag induced yawing moment. The total yawing moment to be 'held' at V_{mc} is therefore 1.15x20,400 = 23,460 ftlbs.

Step 11.14: The landing stall speed is the lowest stall speed for the Eris. At the landing weight this is 131 kts. This yields a V_{mc} = 158 kts.

Step 11.15: From the vertical tail and rudder geometry definitions in Chapter 8 (p.214-215) and from the methods of Part VI the following value for rudder control power derivative is computed:

$$C_{n_{\delta_r}} = - 0.00074 \text{ deg}^{-1}$$

With Eqn.(11.18) this yields for the rudder deflection required at V_{mc} a value of 9.3 deg. This is acceptable. The vertical tail of the Eris is therefore not critical from a viewpoint of engine-out control.

Step 11.16: It was already decided in the previous step to keep the vertical tail size at 147 ft^2.

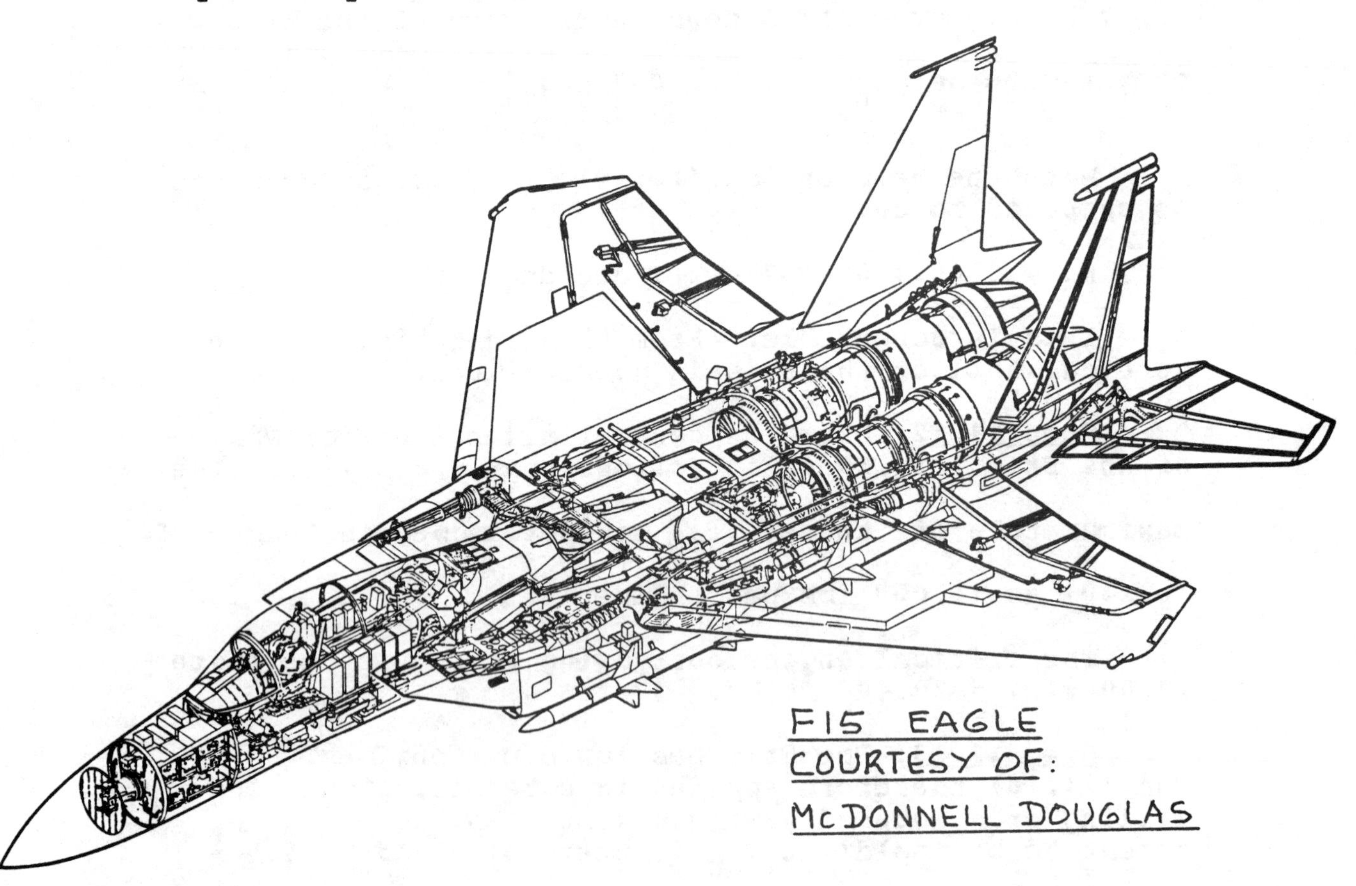

12. CLASS I METHOD FOR DRAG POLAR DETERMINATION

The purpose of this chapter is to present a method for rapidly computing the drag polars for airplanes in the first preliminary design sequence. The method is presented as part of Step 12 in p.d. sequence I as outlined in Chapter 2. Section 12.1 presents the method. Example applications are given in Section 12.2.

12.1 STEP-BY-STEP METHOD FOR DRAG POLAR DETERMINATION

Step 12.1: List all airplane components which contribute to wetted area, compute the wetted area of these components. Find the sum, S_{wet}.

It is assumed here. that a threeview with appropriate cross sections is available for the airplane. Figure 12.1 shows an example threeview.

The wetted area of the airplane is the integral of airplane perimeter versus distance from nose to tail.

A convenient way to find the wetted area is to split the airplane into components such as:

1. fuselage and or tailbooms
2. wing(s)
3. empennage
4. nacelles
5. other components which contribute to wetted area

For fuselages, booms and for nacelles the perimeter method is usually the most efficient way to find the wetted area. Figure 12.2 shows an example of a perimeter plot. Note that the perimeter needs to be known only at certain fuselage stations. Where-ever a significant change in perimeter (or cross section)occurs, there should be a fuselage station defining the local perimeter.

At each fuselage, boom or nacelle station the local perimeter can be determined from:

1. A CAD-program

2. Calculation, provided the cross section has a simple geometry.

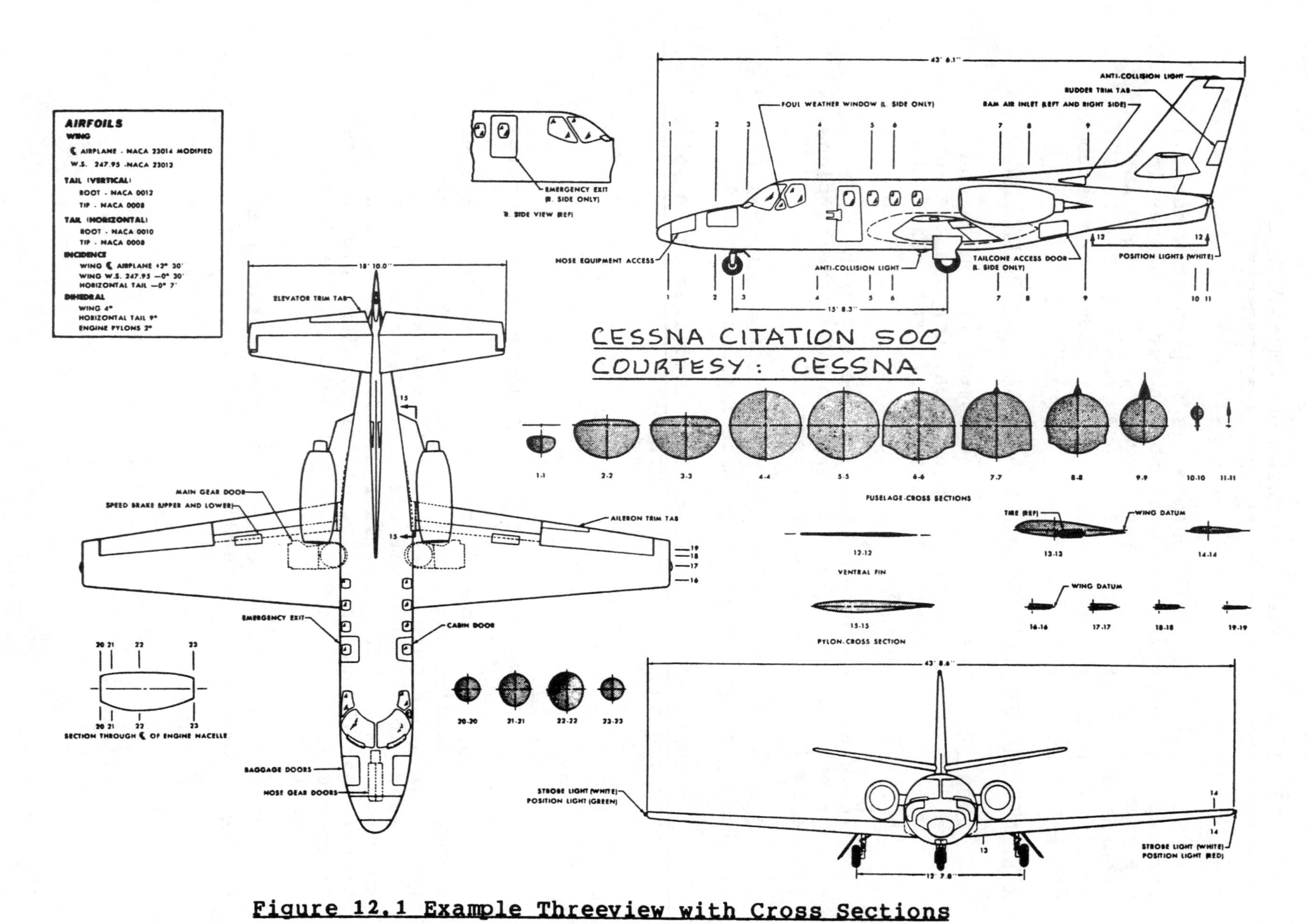

Figure 12.1 Example Threeview with Cross Sections

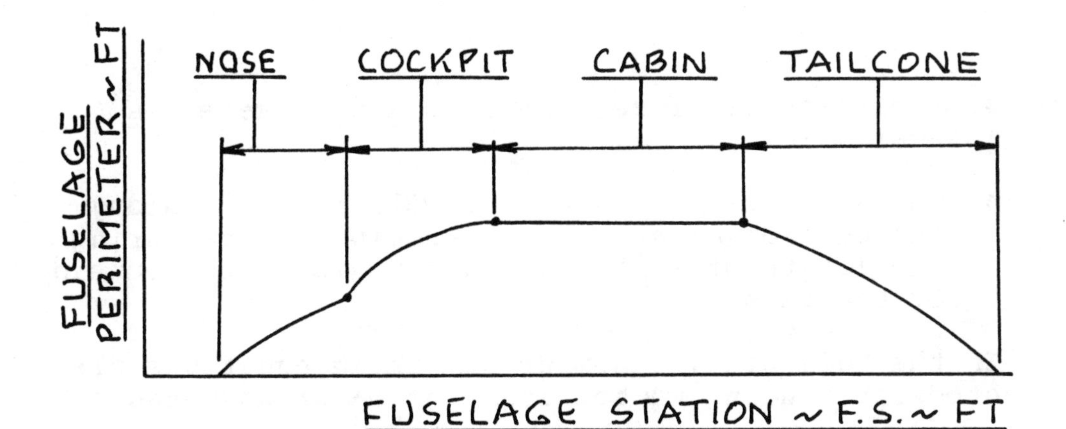

Figure 12.2 Example of a Perimeter Plot

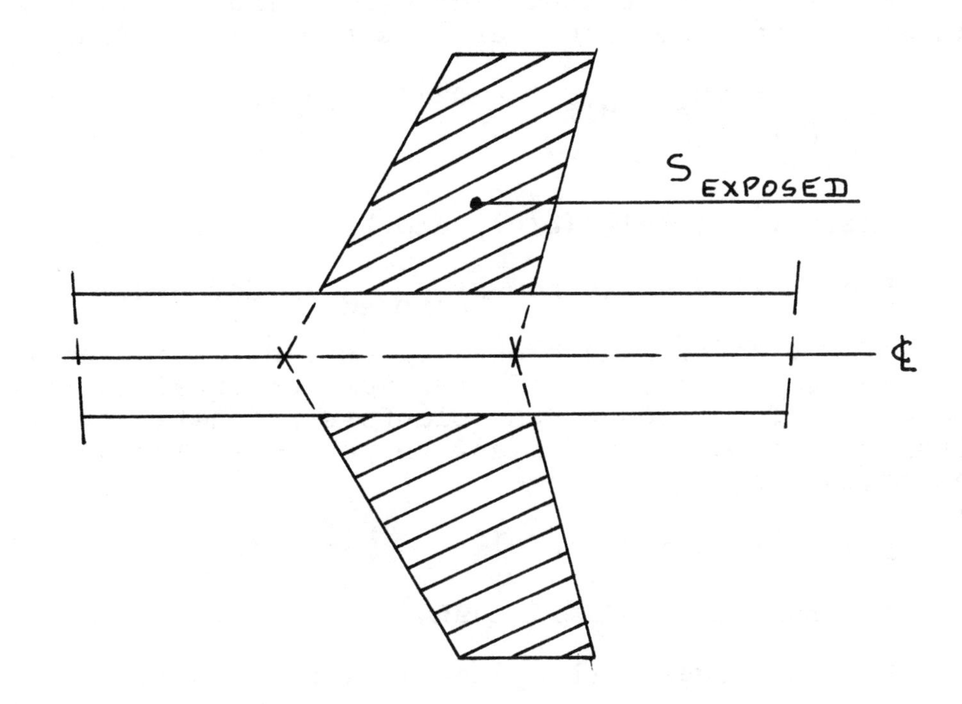

Figure 12.3 Definition of Exposed Planform

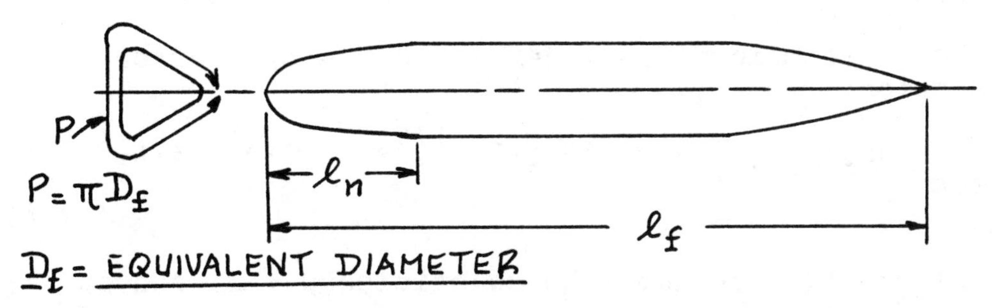

Figure 12.4 Definition of Fuselage Quantities Used in Equation (12.4)

3. A planimeter trace, provided a planimeter is available.

4. The 'pin/string' method: by placing pins along the outside of each cross section and measuring the length of a string wrapped around the outside of the pins.

In the following, a number of simple equations are presented for finding wetted areas of major components.

Wetted Areas for Planforms

For straight tapered planforms (wing, tail, canard, fin and pylon) the wetted area is most easily found from:

$$S_{wet_{plf}} = 2S_{exp.plf}\{1 + 0.25(t/c)_r(1 + \tau\lambda)/(1 + \lambda)\}, \qquad (12.1)$$

where $\tau = (t/c)_r/(t/c)_t$ and $\lambda = c_t/c_r$.

Figure 12.3 shows how $S_{exposed}$ is defined.

If a planform has broken or curved leading and/or trailing edges, the wetted area must be obtained from a spanwise integration of the planform perimeter at each planform station. This planform perimeter may be estimated from:

$$P_{plf} = 2c(1 + 0.25t/c) \qquad (12.2)$$

Wetted Areas for Fuselages

For fuselages with cylindrical mid-sections:

$$S_{wet_{fus}} = \pi D_f l_f (1 - 2/\lambda_f)^{2/3}(1 + 1/\lambda_f^2), \qquad (12.3)$$

where $\lambda_f = l_f/D_f$, the fuselage finess ratio.

For streamlined fuselages without a cylindrical mid-section:

$$S_{wet_{fus}} = \pi D_f l_f (0.50 + 0.135 l_n/l_f)^{2/3}(1.015 + 0.3/\lambda_f^{1.5}) \qquad (12.4)$$

Figure 12.4 defines the quantities D_f, l_n and l_f.

Wetted Areas for Externally Mounted Nacelles

Figure 12.5 shows the geometry of an externally mounted nacelle. The following components of the nacelle contribute to wetted area: fan cowling, gas generator cowling and the plug. For these components, Ref.17, p.449 gives:

$$S_{wet_{fan\ cowl.}} = l_n D_n \{2 + 0.35 l_1/l_n + 0.8 l_1 D_{hl}/l_n D_n + 1.15(1 - l_1/l_n) D_{ef}/D_n\} \quad (12.5)$$

$$S_{wet_{gas\ gen.}} = \pi l_g D_g [1 - (1/3)(1 - D_{eg}/D_g)\{1 - 0.18(D_g/l_g)^{5/3}\}] \quad (12.6)$$

$$S_{wet_{plug}} = 0.7 \pi l_p D_p \quad (12.7)$$

Since wings, empennage and nacelle pylons usually intersect a fuselage or a nacelle it is usually necessary to subtract the areas of intersection from the wetted area of a fuselage or of a nacelle. Figure 12.6 shows some examples of these 'to be subtracted' areas.

Make a list of all wetted area contributions and determine the total wetted area. Compare this number with the statistical correlations of Figures 3.22 in Part I. The difference should not be larger than 10 percent. If the difference is larger, an explanation should be sought.

Step 12.2: Using Figures 3.21 of Part I (pages 119 and 120) find the equivalent parasite area, 'f' of the airplane.

Step 12.3: Determine the 'clean zero lift drag coefficient at low speed from:

$$C_{D_0} = f/S \quad (12.3)$$

Step 12.4: Find the compressibility drag increment of the airplane from Figure 12.7.

Important note 1: The data of Figure 12.7 do not apply to airplanes with cruise Mach numbers above 0.90.

Important note 2: For airplanes with cruise Mach numbers above 0.90 (this includes supersonic cruise airplanes) it will be necessary to prepare a cross sectional area plot. Such a plot is used to determine

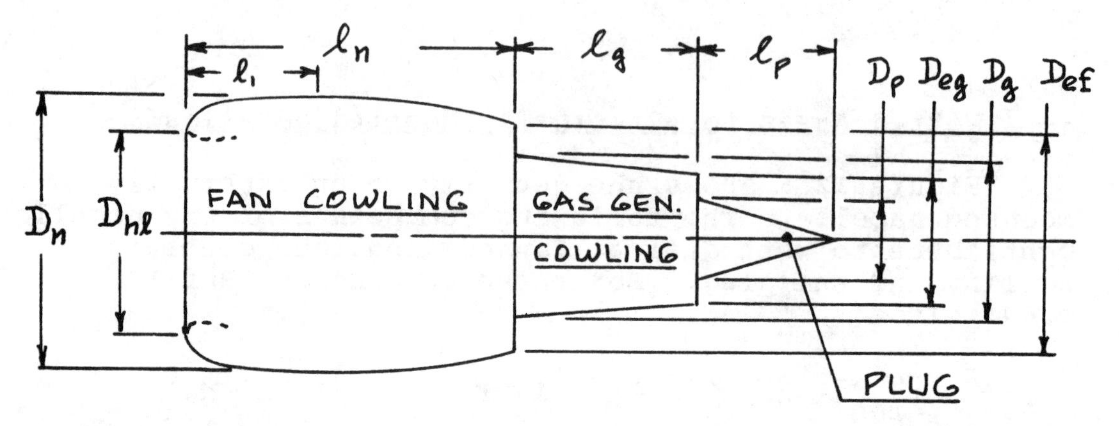

Figure 12.5 Nacelle Geometry for Use in Eqns.(12.5-12.7)

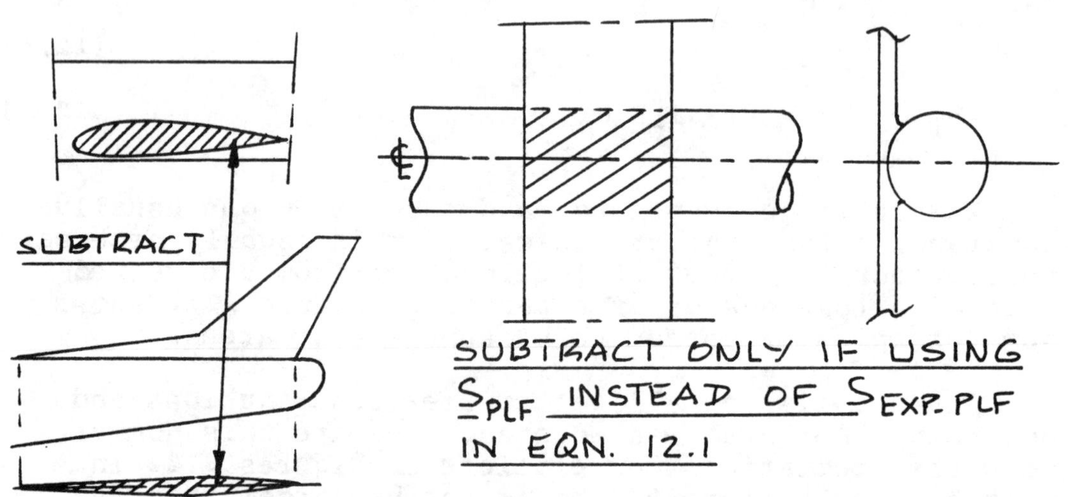

Figure 12.6 Examples of 'Areas to be Subtracted' in a Wetted Area Calculation

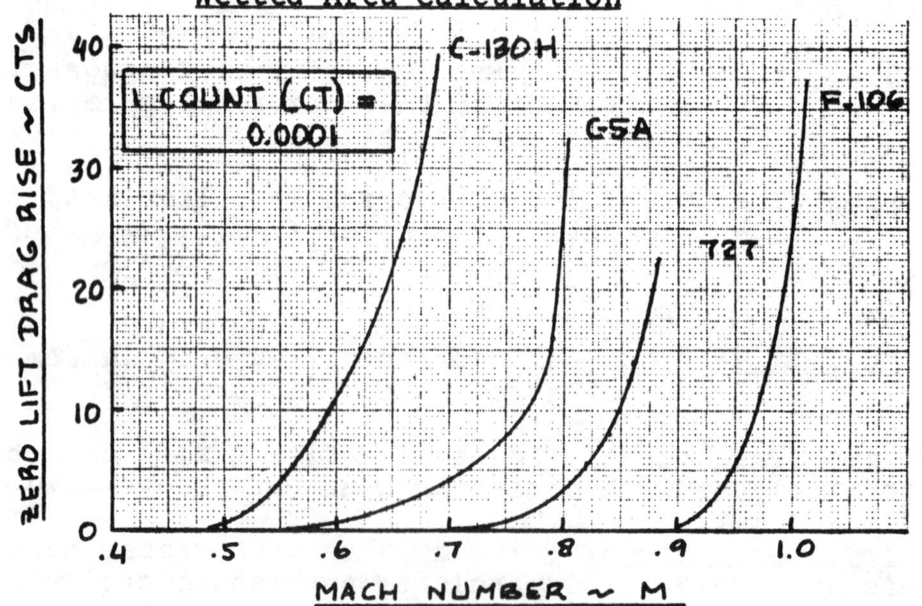

Figure 12.7 Typical Compressibility Drag Behavior

any requirements for area ruling. The area ruling process is described in Part VI (Ref.5).

<u>Step 12.5:</u> Find the flap drag increment(s) from Table 3.6, p.127, Part I.

<u>Step 12.6:</u> Find the landing gear drag increment from Table 3.6, p.127, Part I.

<u>Step 12.7:</u> Construct the cruise, take-off and landing drag polars of the airplane.

<u>Step 12.8:</u> Find the critical L/D values from these drag polars as defined by Step 14 in Chapter 2. Proceed to Step 14 in Ch.2.

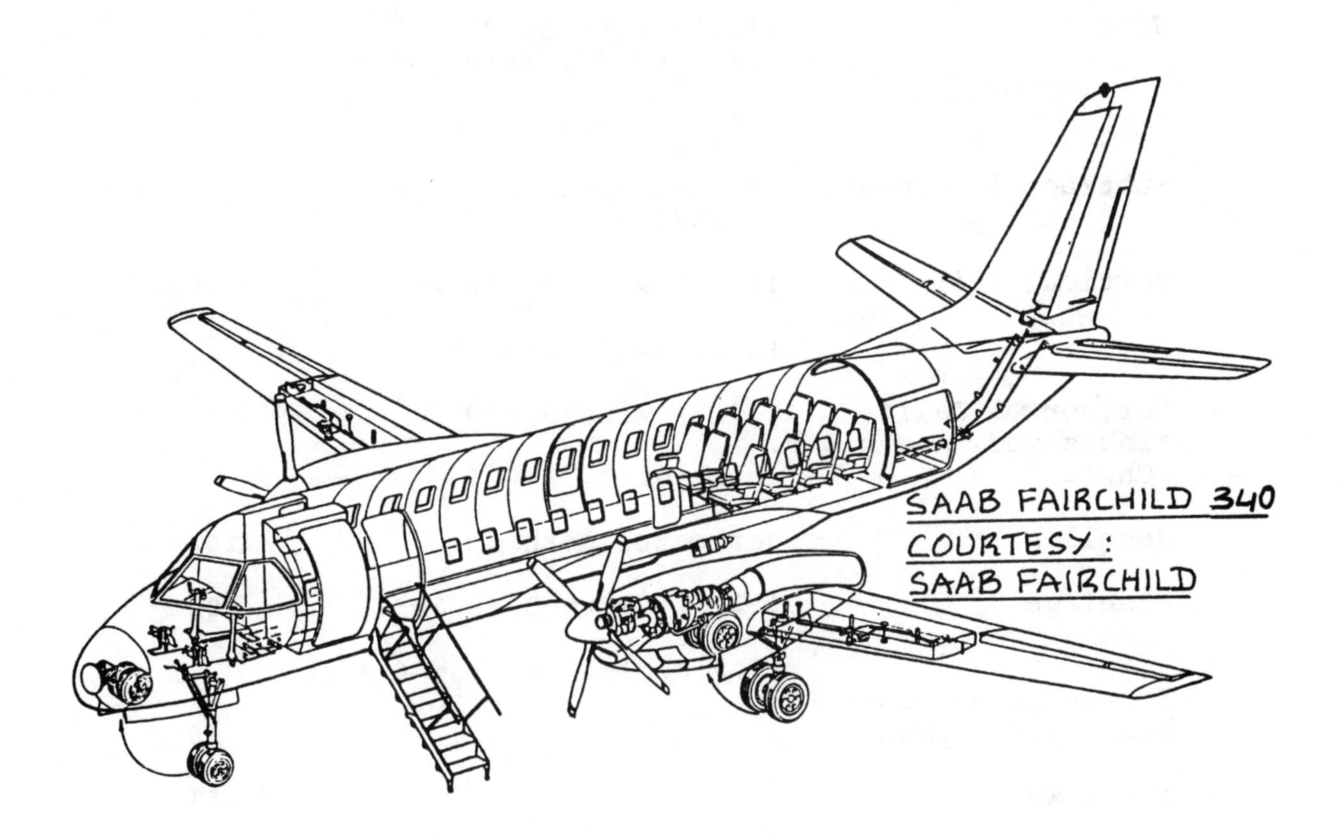

12.2 EXAMPLE APPLICATIONS

Three example applications will be presented:

12.2.1 Twin Engine Propeller Driven Airplane: Selene
12.2.2 Jet Transport: Ourania
12.2.3 Fighter: Eris

12.2.1 Twin Engine Propeller Driven Airplane

Step 12.1: The following tabulation lists all items which contribute to the wetted area of the Selene. Equation numbers used in the calculations are also given.

Component	Equation No.	Wetted Area (ft^2)
Wing	(12.1) with $S=172\ ft^2$, $(t/c)_r=0.17$, $(t/c)_t=0.13$, $\tau=1.3$, $\lambda=0.4$	360
Subtract intersection of wing and fuselage:	$-6.62x4.5=$	-30
Vertical Tail	(12.1) with $S_v=38\ ft^2$, $(t/c)=0.15$, $\lambda=0.56$	79
Horizontal Tail* *increased, see p.269, Ch.11.	(12.1) with $S_h=58\ ft^2$, $(t/c)=0.12$, $\lambda=0.4$	119
Nacelles	perimeter method	105
Fuselage	(12.3), with $D_f=0.5x(4.5+5.5)=5$ ft, $l_f=38.3$ ft	500
Increment due to blister fairings		20

Total wetted area		1,153

Comparison with Figure 3.22a, (Pt.I) shows that for twins with a take-off gross weight of 7,900 lbs the wetted area is predicted to be 1,130 ft^2. This compares very well with the 1,153 ft^2 value computed from the actual configuration!

Steps 12.2-12.8: Because of the excellent agreement in wetted areas just noted there is no need to recompute the Selene drag polars. Those of Part I, Sub-section 3.7.2 should still be valid.

12.2.2 Jet Transport

Step 12.1: The following tabulation lists all items which contribute to the wetted area of the Ourania. Equation numbers used in the calculations are also given.

Component	Equation No.	Wetted Area (ft^2)
Wing	(12.1) with $S=1,296\ ft^2$, $(t/c)_r=0.13$, $(t/c)_t=0.11$, $\tau=1.18$, $\lambda=0.32$	2,795
Subtract intersection of wing and fuselage:	$-12.9 \times 17.5=$	-226
Vertical Tail* *increased, see p.276, Ch.8.	(12.1) with $S_v=200\ ft^2$, $(t/c)=0.15$, $\lambda=0.32$	415
Horizontal Tail	(12.1) with $S_h= 254\ ft^2$, $(t/c)=0.12$, $\lambda=0.32$	523
Nacelles	perimeter method	455
Fuselage	(12.3), with $D_f= 12.9$ ft, $l_f= 123.3$ ft	4,320

Total wetted area		8,282

Comparison with Figure 3.22b, (Pt.I) shows that for transport jets with a take-off gross weight, W_{TO} of 127,000 the wetted area is predicted to be $7,400\ ft^2$. This is within the 10 percent expected in the wetted area correlations. However, since it is a significant increase, the impact of any change in cruise L/D needs to be evaluated.

Step 12.2: From Figure 3.21b, p.120, Part I it is seen that for an advanced jet transport a value of

c_f = 0.0030 should be attainable. With the wetted area of 8,282 ft^2 this implies a value of $f = 25\ ft^2$.

Step 12.3: The zero lift drag coefficient of the Ourania at low subsonic speed now follows from Eqn.(12.3): $C_{D_0} = 25/1,296 = 0.0193$.

Step 12.4: The compressibility drag increment for the Ourania is seen from Figure 12.7 to be roughly 0.0005.

Steps 12.5 - 12.6: Because the slight change in cruise drag has a negligible effect on the take-off and landing polars, these do not have to be re-evaluated.

Step 12.7 and 12.8: The cruise value of zero lift drag coefficient is now:

$$C_{D_0} = 0.0005 + 0.0193 = 0.0198$$

In Part I, p.182 it was determined that:

$$C_{D_0} = 0.0005 + 0.0184 = 0.0189$$

The maximum value of lift-to-drag ratio, $(L/D)_{max}$ is the critical measure of cruise fuel consumption in any comparative study of jet transports, assuming all other factors stay constant. For the Ourania it is found that:

Before: $(L/D)_{max} = (\pi x10x0.85/4x0.0189)^{1/2} = 18.8$

Now: $(L/D)_{max} = (\pi x10x0.85/4x0.0198)^{1/2} = 18.4$

From the sensitivity analysis data in Part I, p.78 it can be found that:

$$\partial W_{TO}/\partial (L/D) = -2287 \text{ lbs.}$$

This means that because of the effectice decrease in L/D from 18.8 to 18.4 the take-off weight of the Ourania needs to be increased by 2287x0.4 = 915 lbs.

This weight increase will not result in any drastic changes to the airplane. In fact, it is quite possible to absorb this by the use of more advanced structural materials. The structural weight of the Ourania can be computed from Table 10.5 (Ch.10) as $W_{struct.}$ = 33,183 lbs.

The 915 lbs represents only 2.8 percent of this structural weight. Structural weight savings of up to 10 percent are probably 'in the cards'.

It is concluded that the Ourania design is now 'ready' for preliminary design sequence II.

12.2.3 Fighter

Step 12.1: The following tabulation lists all items which contribute to the wetted area of the Eris. Equation numbers used in the calculations are also given.

Component	Equation No.	Wetted Area (ft^2)
Wing	(12.1) with $S=787ft^2$, $(t/c)_r=0.10$, $(t/c)_t=0.08$, $\tau=1.25$, $\lambda=0.50$	1,617
Subtract intersection of wing and fuselage:	$-15x7.7=$	-115
Vertical Tail	(12.1) with $S_v=147\ ft^2$, $(t/c)=0.15$, $\lambda=0.55$	305
Horizontal Tail	(12.1) with $S_h= 93\ ft^2$, $(t/c)=0.10$, $\lambda=1.0$	191
Penalty for inlet bulges	perimeter method	50
Fuselage	(12.3), with $D_f= 5.5$ ft, $l_f= 38.3$ ft	540
Tail booms	assume cylinder shape	229
Total wetted area		2,817

Comparison with Figure 3.22c,(Pt.I) shows that for fighters with a take-off gross weight of 64,905 lbs the wetted area is predicted to be 3,500 ft^2. This number is obtained from Fig.3.22c (Pt.I) by accounting for the fact that a number of high weight fighters have wetted areas actually aboven the correlation line.

The Eris appears to have an actual wetted area which is significantly below that of fighters with similar gross weights. This does not seem reasonable. One reason is the fact that the 'base-drag' due to the Eris engine configuration is not accounted for in this 'wetted area' method. This base drag is estimated from the general arrangement drawing of Figure 10.7 (Ch.10) to result in an additional parasite area of 2 ft^2.

<u>Step 12.2:</u> From Figure 3.21b, p.120, Part I it is seen that for a fighter a value of c_f = 0.0030 should be attainable. With the wetted area of 2,817 ft^2 this implies a value of f = 8.7 ft^2.

Add to this the estimated base drag value of 2 ft^2 results in a total f = 10.7 ft^2.

<u>Step 12.3:</u> The zero lift drag coefficient of the Eris at low subsonic speed now follows from Eqn.(12.3): C_{D_0} = 10.7/787 = 0.0135.

<u>Step 12.4:</u> The compressibility drag increment for the Eris is seen from Figure 12.7 to be roughly 0.0020 at M=0.80 and 0.0030 at M=0.85.

<u>Steps 12.5 - 12.6:</u> Because the change in cruise drag has a negligible effect on the take-off and landing polars, these do not have to be re-evaluated.

<u>Step 12.7:</u> The following tabulation summarizes the drag polars of the Eris and compares them with those obtained in Part I (p.188 and 189) on the basis of very rough estimates.

Flight Condition	Part I	Part II
	A = 4, e = 0.8	A = 5, e = 0.75
Low speed, clean	$0.0096 + 0.0995C_L^2$	$0.0135 + 0.0707C_L^2$
Low speed, stores	0.0126 + ''	0.0165 + ''
M = 0.8, stores	0.0146 + ''	0.0185 + ''
M = 0.85, clean	0.0126 + ''	0.0165 + ''

Step 12.8: The following tabulation lists the lift and drag coefficients for the critical mission legs of the Eris. The resulting values of L/D are also shown.

The data are shown for both Part I and Part II drag polars

Part I				Part II			
W lbs	C_L	C_D	L/D	W lbs	C_L	C_D	L/D
sealevel, 400 kts, stores							
64,500	0.101	0.0136	7.4	64,905	0.152	0.0181	8.4
sealevel, 450 kts, clean							
54,500	0.068	0.0101	6.7	54,905	0.102	0.0142	7.2
40,000 ft, M=0.8, stores							
64,500	0.312	0.0243	12.8	64,905	0.469	0.0341	13.8
40,000 ft, M=0.85, clean							
54,500	0.235	0.0181	13.0	54,905	0.352	0.0253	13.9

These data indicate that the Eris has slightly better L/D values than predicted during the performance sizing in Part I. However, when comparing these values of L/D with those used in the preliminary weight sizing of Sub-section 2.6.3 in Part I considerably larger differences are seen to exist:

Mission Leg	Preliminary Weight Sizing Part I, Sub-section 2.6.3 L/D	P.D. Sequence I Step 12.8, Part II L/D
s.l., 400 kts, stores	4.5	8.4
s.l., 450 kts, clean	5.5	7.2
40,000 ft, M=0.8, stores	7.0	13.8
40,000 ft, M=0.85, clean	7.5	13.9

What this implies is that the weight sizing process should be repeated at this point. The reader is encouraged to do this. Actual engine sfc data should be used in this process. Preliminary data indicate that the engine sfs values are significantly higher than those assumed in Part I. The overall effect on the weight of the Eris is therefore expected to be rather minor.

Caution: The reader should not attempt to use the 'sensitivity slopes' of Part I, p.84. These slopes apply only for weight extrapolations dus to small changes in the independent parameters. The L/D changes which have occurred here are too large for the sensitivity slopes to be valid!

To summarize, it is expected that, after doing the weight resizing the Eris will come out relatively unchanged. It can then be taken into the design process of p.d. sequence II.

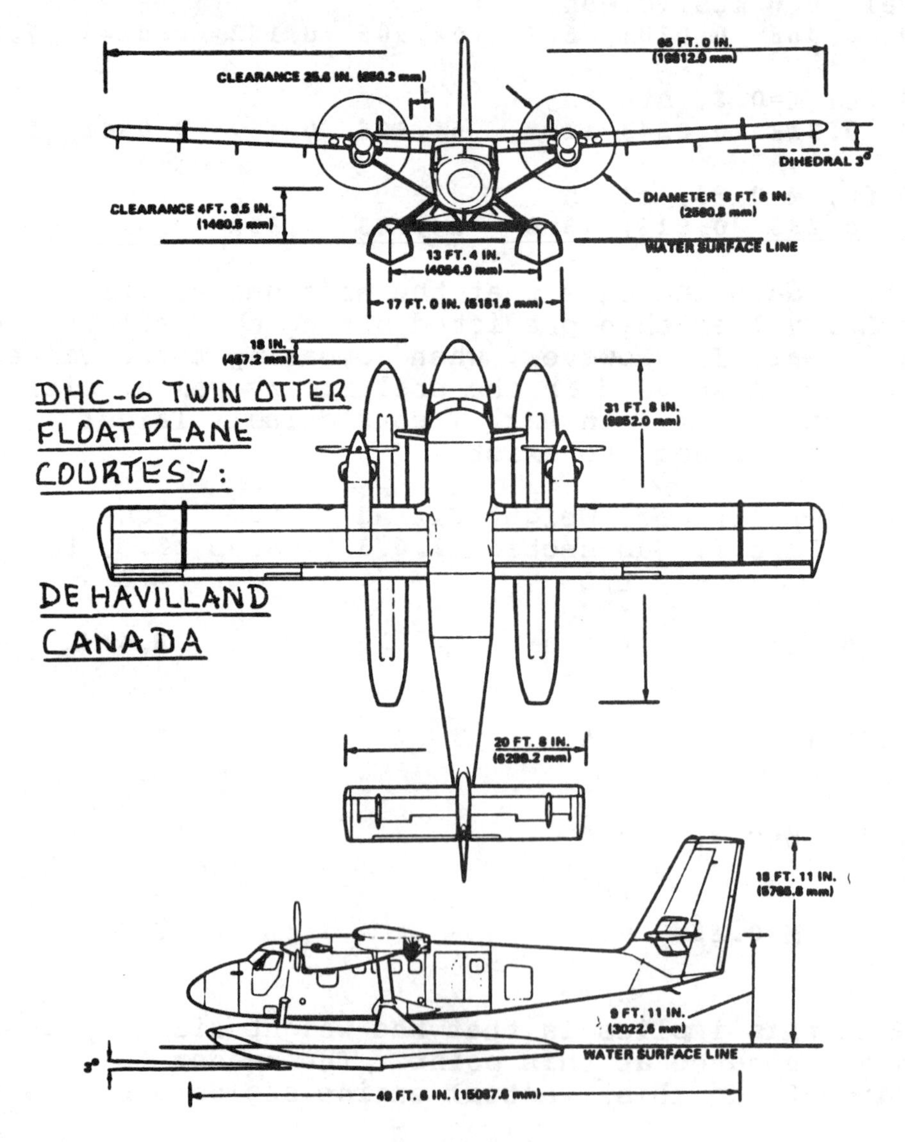

13. THE RESULT OF PRELIMINARY DESIGN SEQUENCE I: THE PRELIMINARY THREEVIEW

The purpose of this chapter is to combine the work done in Chapters 3 - 12 into a preliminary threeview of the configuration. The reader must understand the fact that such a preliminary threeview (also called Class I threeview) is just that: PRELIMINARY. This threeview combines all necessary corrections to the configuration which needed to be made as a result of the work outlined in Chapters 3 - 12. It forms the basis for the work which needs to be done in p.d. sequence II. That work starts with Step 17 in Chapter 2.

During p.d. sequence II the reader will have to use more sophisticated approaches to further configuration development. These approaches form the subject of Parts III through VIII.

The remaining part of this chapter presents the Class I threeviews for three example airplanes. The geometric characteristics of these airplanes are all summarized in tables.

13.1 CLASS I THREEVIEW AND GEOMETRIC SUMMARY FOR A TWIN ENGINE PROPELLER DRIVEN AIRPLANE

Figure 13.1 presents the Class I threeview for the Selene. The geometric characteristics are contained in Table 13.1.

13.2 CLASS I THREEVIEW AND GEOMETRIC SUMMARY FOR A JET TRANSPORT

Figure 13.2 presents the Class I threeview for the Ourania. The geometric characteristics are given in Table 13.2.

13.3 CLASS I THREEVIEW AND GEOMETRIC SUMMARY FOR A FIGHTER

Figure 13.3 presents the Class I threeview for the Eris. The geometric characteristics are contained in Table 13.3.

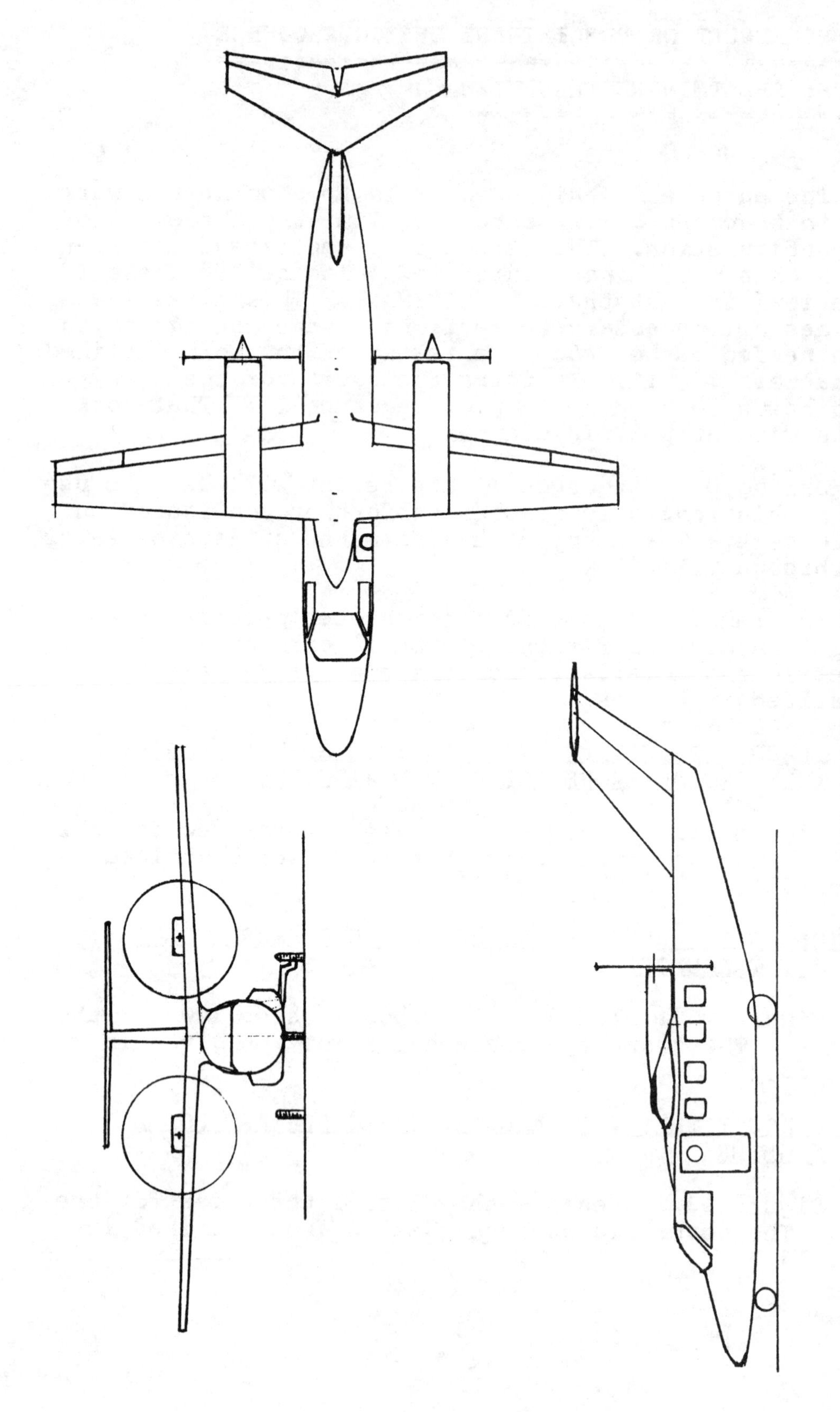

Figure 13.1 Selene: Class I Threeview

Table 13.1 Selene: Geometric Characteristics

	Wing	Horizontal Tail	Vertical Tail
Area	172 ft^2	58 ft^2	38 ft^2
Span	37.1 ft	14.9 ft	6.16 ft
MGC	4.92 ft	4.12 ft	6.31 ft
MGC L.E.: F.S.	20.3 ft	45.1 ft	40.0 ft
Aspect Ratio	8	3.85	1.0
Sweep Angle	0 deg.(c/4)	30 deg.(L.E.)	50 deg.(L.E.)
Taper ratio	0.4	0.4	0.56
Thickness Ratio	0.17 root 0.13 tip	0.12	0.15
Airfoil: root	NASA(1)-0317	NACA0012	NACA 0015
tip	NASA(1)-0313		
Dihedral angle	2 deg.	0 deg.	not appl.
Incidence angle	+2.5 deg. root -0.5 deg. tip	variable	0 deg.
Aileron chord ratio	0.25	Elevator chord ratio 0.32	Rudder chord ratio 0.43
Aileron span ratio	0.76 - 1.00		
Flap chord ratio	0.25		
Flap span ratio	0.12 - 0.76		

	Fuselage	Cabin Interior	Overall
Length	39.3 ft	18.5 ft	43.0 ft
Maximum height	5.5 ft	4.4 ft	12.8 ft
Maximum width	4.5 ft	4.25 ft	37.1 ft

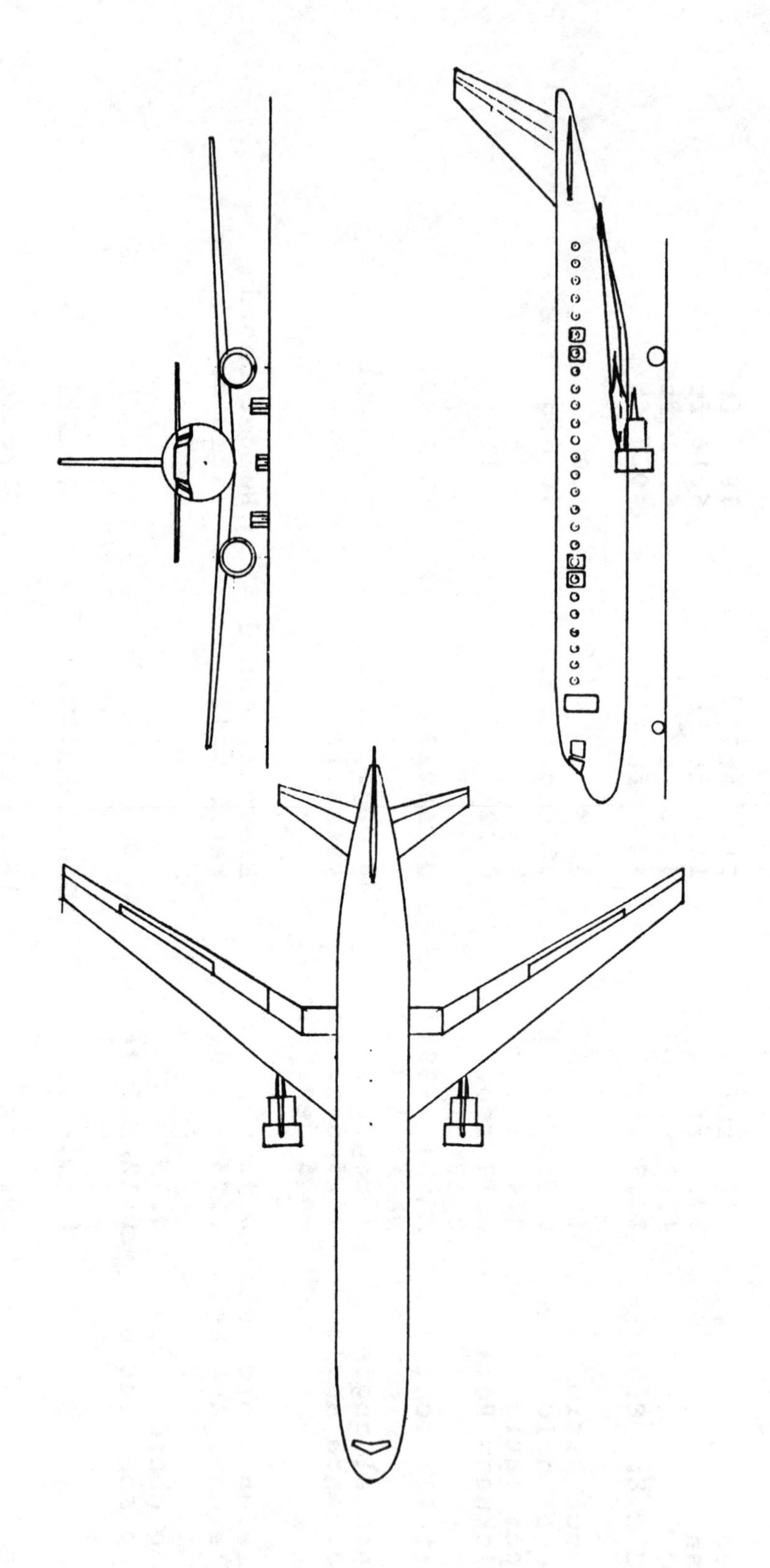

Figure 13.2 Ourania: Class I Threeview

Table 13.2 Ourania: Geometric Characteristics

	Wing	Horizontal Tail	Vertical Tail
Area	1,296 ft^2	254 ft^2	200 ft^2
Span	113.8 ft	35.6 ft	19.0 ft
MGC	12.5 ft	7.75 ft	11.5 ft
MGC L.E.: F.S.	88.8 ft	124.9 ft	123.5 ft
Aspect Ratio	10	5	1.8
Sweep Angle	35 deg.(c/4)	35 deg.(L.E.)	45 deg.(L.E.)
Taper ratio	0.32	0.32	0.32
Thickness Ratio	0.13 root 0.11 tip	0.12	0.15
Airfoil: root	NACA 64A413(mod.)	NACA0012	NACA 0015
tip	NACA 64A411(mod.)		
Dihedral angle	3 deg.	0 deg.	not appl.
Incidence angle	+1.5 deg. root -0.5 deg. tip	variable	0 deg.
Aileron chord ratio	0.30	Elevator chord	Rudder chord
Aileron span ratio	0.23 - 0.34	ratio 0.30	ratio 0.45
Spoiler chord ratio	0.20 hinge line at 0.70c		(Double hinge rudder)
Spoiler span ratio	0.50 - 0.80		
Flap chord ratio	0.30		
Flap span ratio	0.11 - 0.23 and 0.34 - 1.00		

	Fuselage	Cabin Interior	Overall
Length	1243 ft	90.8 ft	1270 ft
Maximum height	13.2 ft	7.5 ft	38.3 ft
Maximum width	13.2 ft	12.4 ft	113.8 ft

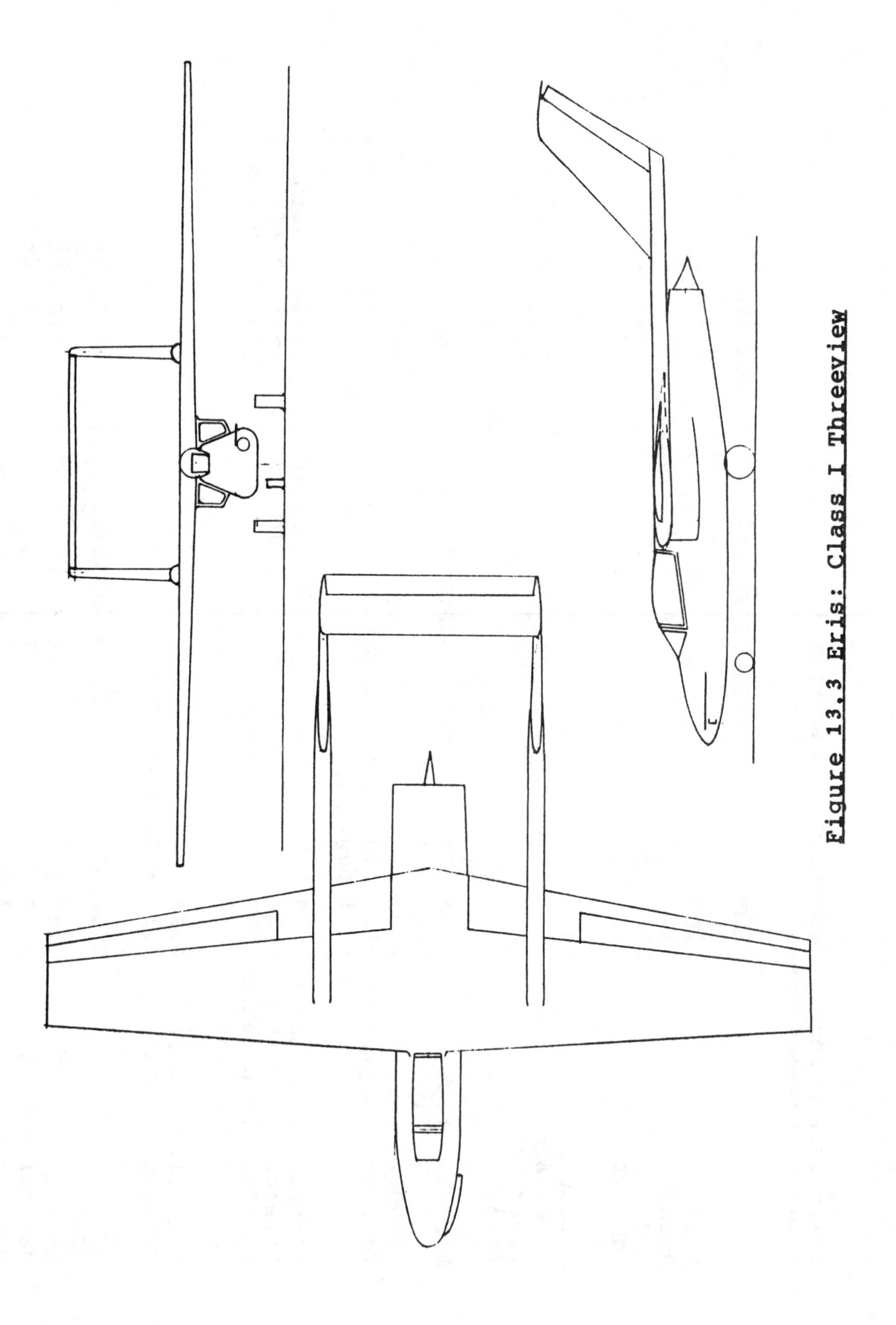

Figure 13.3 Eris: Class I Threeview

Table 13.3 Eris: Geometric Characteristics

	Wing	Horizontal Tail	Vertical Tail
Area	787 ft^2	93 ft^2	147 ft^2
Span	68.7 ft	18.3 ft	10.3 ft
MGC	11.9 ft	5.08 ft	7.4 ft
MGC L.E.: F.S.	21.8 ft	51.7 ft	46.4 ft
Aspect Ratio	6	3.6	1.2
Sweep Angle	0 deg.(c/4)	0 deg.(L.E.)	45 deg.(L.E.)
Taper ratio	0.5	1.0	0.55
Thickness Ratio	0.10 root 0.08 tip	0.10	0.15
Airfoil: root tip	NACA 64A210(mod.) NACA 64A208(mod.)	NACA0010	NACA 0015
Dihedral angle	0 deg.	0 deg.	not appl.
Incidence angle	0 deg. root -2 deg. tip	variable	0 deg.
Spoiler chord ratio	0.20	Elevator chord ratio 0.31	Rudder chord ratio 0.22
Spoiler span ratio	0.40 - 1.00		
Spoiler hinge line at 0.70c			
Flap chord ratio	0.30		
Flap span ratio	0.12 - 1.0		

	Fuselage	Overall
Length	41.3 ft	50.7 ft
Maximum height	6.83 ft	15.7 ft
Maximum width	7.47 ft	68.7 ft

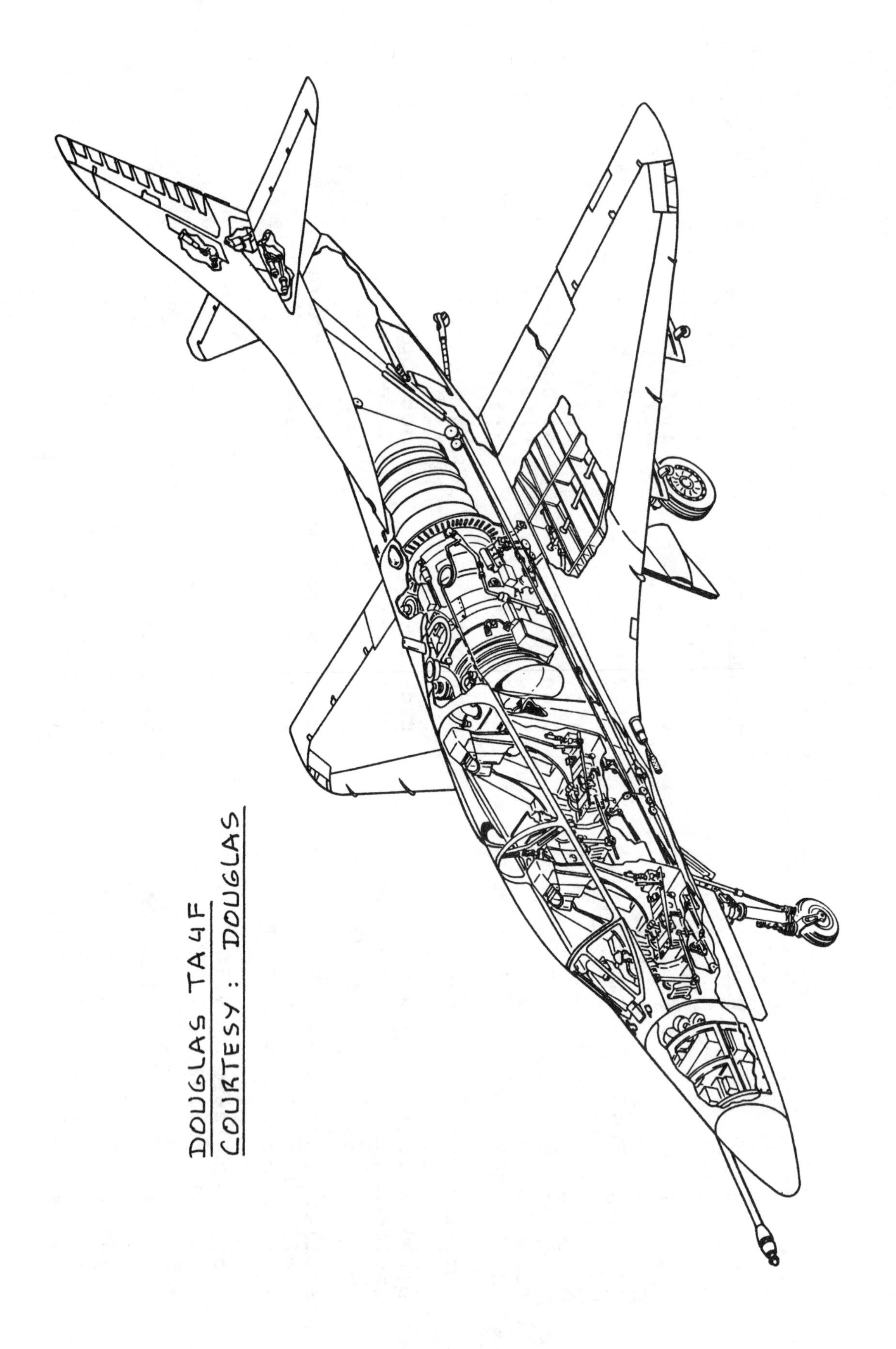
DOUGLAS TA4F
COURTESY : DOUGLAS

14. REFERENCES

14.1 TECHNICAL REFERENCES CITED IN THIS TEXT

1. Roskam, J., Airplane Design: Part I, Preliminary Sizing of Airplanes.

2. Roskam, J., Airplane Design: Part III, Layout Design of Cockpit, Fuselage, Wing and Empennage: Cutaways and Inboard Profiles.

3. Roskam, J., Airplane Design: Part IV, Layout Design of Landing Gear and Systems.

4. Roskam, J., Airplane Design: Part V, Component Weight Estimation.

5. Roskam, J., Airplane Design: Part VI, Preliminary Calculation of Aerodynamic, Thrust and Power Characteristics.

6. Roskam, J., Airplane Design: Part VII, Determination of Stability, Control and Performance Characteristics: FAR and Military Requirements.

7. Roskam, J., Airplane Design: Part VIII, Airplane Cost Estimation: Design, Development, Manufacturing and Operating.

Note: These books are all published by: Design, Analysis and Research Corporation, 1440 Wakarusa Drive, Suite 500, Lawrence, KS 66049-3879, Tel. 785-832-0434.

8. Taylor, J.W.R., Jane's All The World Aircraft, Published Annually by: Jane's Publishing Company, 238 City Road, London EC1V 2PU, England. (Issues used: 1945/46, 1968/84)

9. Roskam, J., Airplane Flight Dynamics and Automatic Flight Controls, Part I, Fourth Printing, 1984. For publisher see note after ref.7.

10. Chambers, J.R. and Yip, L.P., Wind-Tunnel Investigation of an Advanced General Aviation Canard Configuration, NASA TM 85760, April 1984.

11. Anderson, S.B., Handling Qualities of Canards, Tandem Wings, and Other Unconventional Configurations, SAE Paper 830763, April 12-15, 1983.

12. Wolkovitch, J., Principles of the Joined Wing, Engel Engineering Report No. 80-1, 28603 Trailriders Drive, Rancho Palos Verdes, CA, 90274.

13. Clyde, J.A., Bonner, E., Goebel, T.P. and Spacht, L., Joined Wing Transonic Test Validation, NA-84-1434, Rockwell International, North American Aircraft Ops., P.O. Box 92098, L.A., CA, 90009.

14. Adams, F.D., Aeronautical Dictionary, NASA, US Government Printing Office, Washington D.C., 1959.

15. Kohlman, D.L. and Hammer, J., Design Study of Technology Requirements for High Performance Single-Propeller-Driven Business Airplanes, NASA Contractor Report 3863, January, 1985.

16. Nicolai, L.M., Fundamentals of Aircraft Design, METS, Inc., 6520 Kingsland Court, CA, 95120.

17. Torenbeek, E., Synthesis of Subsonic Airplane Design, Kluwer Boston Inc., Hingham, Maine, 1982.

18. Stinton, D., The Design of the Aeroplane, Granada Publishing, London, England, 1983.

19. Küchemann, F.R.S., The Aerodynamic Design of Aircraft, Pergamon Press, London, England, 1978.

20. Abbott, I.H. and Von Doenhoff, A.E., Theory of Wing Sections, Dover Publications, Inc., N.Y., 1959.

21. Shevell, R.S., Fundamentals of Flight, Prentice Hall, Englewood Cliffs, N.J., 1983.

22. McGhee, R.J. and Beasley, W.D., Low-Speed Aerodynamic Characteristics of a 17-Percent-Thick Medium-Speed Airfoil Designed for General Aviation Applications, NASA Technical Paper 1786, December 1980.

23. Hoerner, S.F. and Borst, H.V., Fluid Dynamic Lift, Hoerner Fluid Dynamics, P.O. Box 342, Brick Town, N.J., 08723, 1975.

24. Hoak, D.E., Ellison, D.E. et al., USAF Datcom, Air Force Flight Dynamics Laboratory, WPAFB, Ohio.

14.2 HISTORICAL REFERENCES

1. Mansfield, H., Vision, A Saga of the Sky, Duell, Sloan and Pierce, N.Y., 1956.

2. Mansfield, H., Billion Dollar Battle, David McKay Company, Inc., N.Y., 1965.

3. James, D.N., Gloster Aircraft Since 1917, Putnam, London, 1971.

4. Bowers, P.M., Boeing Aircraft Since 1916, Putnam, London, 1966.

5. Jackson, A.J., Blackburn Aircraft Since 1909, Putnam, London, 1968.

6. Barnes, C.H., Bristol Aircraft Since 1910, Putnam, London, 1970.

7. Mason, F.K., Hawker Aircraft Since 1920, Putnam, London, 1961.

8. Andrews, C.F., Vickers Aircraft Since 1908, Putnam, London, 1969.

9. Taylor, H.A., Fairey Aircraft Since 1915, Putnam, London, 1974.

10. Francillon, R.J., McDonnell Douglas Aircraft Since 1920, Putnam, London, 1979.

11. Francillon, R.J., Lockheed Aircraft Since 1913, Putnam, London, 1982.

12. Barnes, C.H., Handley Page Aircraft Since 1907, Putnam, London, 1976.

13. Tapper, O., Armstrong Whitworth Aircraft Since 1913, Putnam, London, 1973.

14. Taylor, H.A., Airspeed Aircraft Since 1931, Putnam, London, 1970.

15. Andrews, C.F. and Morgan, E.B., Supermarine Aircraft Since 1914, Putnam, 1981.

16. Bowers, P.M., Curtiss Aircraft 1907-1947, Putnam, London, 1979.

17. Jackson, A.J., De Havilland Aircraft Since 1909, Putnam, London, 1962.

18. Brown, D.L., Miles Aircraft Since 1925, Putnam, London, 1970.

19. AIAA Professional Study Series, Case Study in Aircraft Design: The Boeing 727, September 14, 1978.

20. Duval, G.R., British Flying Boats and Amphibians, 1909-1952, Putnam, London, 1966.

21. Lippisch, A., The Delta Wing, Iowa State University Press, Ames, Iowa, 1961.

22. Knott, R.C., The American Flying Boat, U.S. Naval Institute, 1979.

23. Heinemann, E.H. and Rausa, R., Ed Heinemann: Combat Aircraft Designer, U.S. Naval Institute, 1980.

24. Hegener, H., Fokker: The Man and the Aircraft, Aero Publishers, Inc., Fallbrook, CA, 1961.

25. Van Ishoven, A., Messerschmitt: Aircraft Designer, Gentry Books Ltd., London, 1975.

26. Ingells, D.J., L-1011 Tristar and The Lockheed Story, Aero Publishers, Inc, Fallbrook, CA, 1973.

27. Anderson, F., Northrop, an Aeronautical History, Published by Northrop Corporation, Century City, CA, 90067, 1976.

28. Jones, L.S., U.S. Bombers, Aero Publishers, L.A., CA, 1962.

29. Angelucci, E., The Rand McNally Encyclopedia of Military Aircraft 1914-1980, The Military Press, NY, '83.

15. INDEX

Notes

Notes

Notes

Notes

Notes

Notes

Notes

Notes

Notes

Notes

Notes

Notes

Airplane Design & Analysis Book Descriptions

All books can be ordered from our on-line store at www.darcorp.com.

Airplane Aerodynamics & Performance
C.T. Lan & Jan Roskam

The atmosphere • basic aerodynamic principles and applications • airfoil theory • wing theory • airplane drag • airplane propulsion systems • propeller theory • fundamentals of flight mechanics for steady symmetrical flight • climb performance and speed • take-off and landing performance • range and endurance • maneuvers and flight

Airplane Flight Dynamics & Automatic Flight Controls Part I
Jan Roskam

General steady and perturbed state equations of motion for a rigid airplane • concepts and use of stability & control derivatives • physical and mathematical explanations of stability & control derivatives • solutions and applications of the steady state equations of motion from a viewpoint of airplane analysis and design • emphasis on airplane trim, take-off rotation and engine-out control • open loop transfer functions • analysis of fundamental dynamic modes: phugoid, short period, roll, spiral and dutch roll • equivalent stability derivatives and the relation to automatic control of unstable airplanes • flying qualities and the Cooper-Harper scale: civil and military regulations • extensive numerical data on stability, control and hingemoment derivatives

Airplane Flight Dynamics & Automatic Flight Controls Part II
Jan Roskam

Elastic airplane stability and control coefficients and derivatives • method for determining the equilibrium and manufacturing shape of an elastic airplane • subsonic and supersonic numerical examples of aeroelasticity effects on stability & control derivatives • bode and root-locus plots with open and closed loop airplane applications, and coverage of inverse applications • stability augmentation systems: pitch dampers, yaw dampers and roll dampers • synthesis concepts of automatic flight control modes: control-stick steering, auto-pilot hold, speed control, navigation and automatic landing • digital control systems using classical control theory applications with Z-transforms • applications of classical control theory • human pilot transfer functions

Airplane Design Part I
Preliminary Sizing of Airplanes
Jan Roskam

Estimating take-off gross weight, empty weight and mission fuel weight • sensitivity studies and growth factors • estimating wing area • take-off thrust and maximum clean, take-off and landing lift • sizing to stall speed, take-off distance, landing distance, climb, maneuvering and cruise speed requirements • matching of all performance requirements via performance matching diagrams

Airplane Design Part II
Preliminary Configuration Design and Integration of the Propulsion System
Jan Roskam

Selection of the overall configuration • design of cockpit and fuselage layouts • selection and integration of the propulsion system • Class I method for wing planform design • Class I method for verifying clean airplane maximum lift coefficient and for sizing high lift devices • Class I method for empennage sizing and disposition, control surface sizing and disposition, landing gear sizing and disposition, weight and balance analysis, stability and control analysis and drag polar determination

Airplane Design & Analysis Book Descriptions

Airplane Design Part III
Layout Design of Cockpit, Fuselage, Wing and Empennage: Cutaways and Inboard Profiles Jan Roskam

Cockpit (or flight deck) layout design • aerodynamic design considerations for the fuselage layout • interior layout design of the fuselage • fuselage structural design considerations • wing aerodynamic and operational design considerations • wing structural design considerations • empennage aerodynamic and operational design considerations • empennage structural and integration design consideration • integration of propulsion system • preliminary structural arrangement, material selection and manufacturing breakdown

Airplane Design Part IV
Layout Design of Landing Gear and Systems
Jan Roskam

Landing gear layout design • weapons integration and weapons data • flight control system layout data • fuel system layout design • hydraulic system design • electrical system layout design • environmental control system layout design • cockpit instrumentation, flight management and avionics system layout design • de-icing and anti-icing system layout design • escape system layout design • water and waste systems layout design • safety and survivability considerations

Airplane Design Part V
Component Weight Estimation
Jan Roskam

Class I methods for estimating airplane component weights and airplane inertias • Class II methods for estimating airplane component weights, structure weight, powerplant weight, fixed equipment weight and airplane inertias • methods for constructing v-n diagrams • Class II weight and balance analysis • locating component centers of gravity

Airplane Design Part VI
Preliminary Calculation of Aerodynamic, Thrust, and Power Characteristics
Jan Roskam

Summary of drag causes and drag modeling • Class II drag polar prediction methods •airplane drag data • installed power and thrust prediction methods • installed power and thrust data • lift and pitching moment prediction methods • airplane high lift data • methods for estimating stability, control and hingemoment derivatives • stability and control derivative data

Airplane Design Part VII
Determination of Stability, Control, and Performance Characteristics: FAR and Military Requirements
Jan Roskam

Controllability, maneuverability and trim • static and dynamic stability • ride and comfort characteristics • performance prediction methods • civil and military airworthiness regulations for airplane performance and stability and control • the airworthiness code and the relationship between failure states, levels of performance and levels of flying qualities

Airplane Design Part VIII
Airplane Cost Estimation: Design, Development, Manufacturing, and Operating
Jan Roskam

Cost definitions and concepts • method for estimating research, development, test and evaluation cost • method for estimating prototyping cost • method for estimating manufacturing and acquisition cost • method for estimating operating cost • example of life cycle cost calculation for a military airplane • airplane design optimization and design-to-cost considerations • factors in airplane program decision making

Design • Analysis • Research
1440 Wakarusa Drive, Suite 500, Lawrence, Kansas 66049, USA - Tel: (785) 832-0434 - Fax: (785) 832-0524
info@darcorp.com – www.darcorp.com